FROM CUSTODIAL TO THERAPEUTIC PATIENT CARE IN MENTAL HOSPITALS

Explorations in Social Treatment

By

Milton Greenblatt, M.D.
Richard H. York, Ph.D.
Esther Lucile Brown, Ph.D.

In collaboration with

Robert W. Hyde, M.D.

Russell Sage Foundation

New York ، ، ، 1955

Contents

v

7011

PART III

MOTIVATING PATIENTS ON CHRONIC WARDS AT METROPOLITAN STATE HOSPITAL
by Richard H. York

CONCLUSION
by Esther Lucile Brown and Milton Greenblatt

Tables and Charts

Introduction

HOSPITALS MADE THEIR APPEARANCE in this country prior to the Revolutionary War, but only in the past few decades have they become numerous, large, complex, and generally considered necessities. The frequency with which a prospective purchaser of real estate is today informed of the distance to hospitals as as well as schools is an indication of current attitudes. Since World War I and particularly World War II new, more functionally designed, and better-equipped hospital buildings have been dotted across the United States. Simultaneously, enlarged staffs of more competently prepared and diversified personnel have been introduced, together with better methods of administration. So pronounced has been the interest in and the success of this movement toward improved, well-distributed hospitals that vast numbers of lay persons and private organizations, as well as representatives of governments and of the health services, have labored to provide the resources needed.

But, strangely enough, more than half of the hospital world has not shared to anything like an equal degree in the phenomenal gains made. Those hospitals whose function it is to minister to the sick minds of nearly three-quarters of a million patients rather than to sick bodies continue to struggle with buildings of which some are firetraps and almost all are much overcrowded. More significantly, they struggle with inadequacies in number and preparation of staff so marked that almost no general hospital would consider operation possible under the circumstances.

There are so few physicians that each of them generally carries responsibility for several hundred patients. And there are proportionately still fewer qualified psychiatrists. Although graduate nurses are increasing appreciably in numbers, only about 12,000, less than 5 per cent of those in active practice, are employed by all hospitals for the mentally ill. Hence, care is largely in the hands of attendants of whom there are supposedly from 80,000 to 90,000. Thousands of budgeted positions for attendants remain unfilled, or are held by men and women who have neither the needed aptitude nor experience.

In recent years state governments and the federal Veterans Administration, that together care for 95 per cent of all hospitalized mental patients, have attempted amelioration and occasionally drastic improvement of conditions. However, a large proportion, particularly of the state institutions, continue to be so far behind the standards of general hospitals in the same area that progress cannot be measured comparatively.

So far as the public is concerned, treatment centers for the mentally ill have remained largely outside the great upsurge of nationwide interest in providing for the institutional care of illness. Although the actual number of individual persons and organizations concerned with the plight of these hospitals has probably increased somewhat, much of the energy spent by the press, investigating commissions, and self-appointed committees still goes only into exposés of evils rather than carefully considered, positive steps designed to make mental institutions more nearly comparable to general hospitals. Fortunately, several contributors to widely read magazines are beginning to focus attention upon the assets of and improvements in psychiatric centers, and upon reasoned interpretation to a still frightened public of the nature of mental illness.

If such efforts are vastly expanded and include specific suggestions of constructive action that can be taken by clubs, churches, colleges, and other large community organizations, the tide of public opinion may indeed be turned toward finding solutions for this problem. Certain it is that hundreds of thousands of Americans are needed who will interest themselves in every facet of improvement of mental institutions, particularly in breaking the political stranglehold over state hospitals that still widely exists, and in demanding provision of far more adequate public funds.

FUNCTION OF PSYCHIATRIC HOSPITALS

The purpose of this Introduction is not to dwell upon the sorry history of psychiatric hospitals or to attribute blame for sins of omission and commission. Enough of the consequences of economic impoverishment and community neglect and their concomitant intellectual, emotional, and spiritual impoverishment will emerge from this report, which necessarily refers to past practices in patient care as the backdrop against which various programs of improvement are now at least in rehearsal. Nothing more need be noted here than that mental hospitals are so beset with exceedingly difficult problems of financing, administration, and staffing that trustees and personnel alike often find it almost impossible to shake off the deadening sense of frustration or even defeat sufficiently to give positive consideration to practical solutions. We believe, however, that a first step can be taken in the reduction of confusion and discouragement if attention is shifted from the multifarious aspects of "running" hospitals and is centered squarely upon the *function* for which they are run. In the very act of trying to operate these institutions their *raison d'être* has often been neglected or forgotten.

We would state, therefore, as the first working hypothesis, which cannot be too frequently reiterated, that the basic function of hospitals for the mentally ill is the same as the basic function of general hospitals, provided that the latter accept responsibility for the long-term care of some patients. *That function is the utilization of every form of treatment available for restoring patients to health or helping them improve sufficiently to be able to leave the hospital at the earliest possible moment; and, short of such success, it is aiding them to live as nearly normal lives as possible within the institutional setting.*

Some readers will suggest that this definition of function presupposes too high a level of expectation and, therefore, does not constitute a good working principle. Developments in psychiatry during recent years have demonstrated, however, how favorable are the various forms of somatic treatment including chemotherapy, and of individual and group psychotherapy in helping acutely ill psychotic patients make relatively quick and successful recoveries. To persons unacquainted with present-day rates of discharge from active treatment hospitals, statistical data such as those appearing in this report may seem almost unbelievable. In addition, there are other developments which, although less clear-cut, make the function of the mental hospital as a custodial institution truly outmoded, even when that concept is applied only to chronically ill patients.

We have been learning of late that when chronic patients, whose clinical prognosis has been regarded as hopeless, are provided with psychiatric therapy, or an enriched and more permissive social environment, considerable numbers show marked improvement. Experiments, like those recently conducted at Stockton State Hospital in California, Topeka State Hospital in Kansas, and those reported in this study, indicate that some patients who had been hospitalized for five to twenty years have improved sufficiently during the relatively brief period of the experiment to be able to return to the community. A vastly larger proportion have been unable in the same space of time to reach a comparable level of "social efficiency," to quote Dr. P. Stefan Kraus's perceptive use of that term. But their improvement in engaging in social interaction with patients, staff, and relatives, and in taking responsibility at least for their own social behavior has been sufficient to demonstrate a broad swing toward more normal living. Where this improvement has occurred, the utterly depressing atmosphere of the "back wards," which has long stigmatized large mental hospitals, has almost ceased to exist.

In the face of these developments we believe that the foregoing hypothesis of the basic function of the psychiatric hospital is expressed in terms of an expectation that can be progressively realized, and with ever-increasing efficiency and comprehensiveness.[1] This is a dynamic positive approach that permits us to *move away from* frustration and that fosters "that

---

[1] It should be said, however, that many of the persons now living in mental hospitals probably belong elsewhere. The large state hospitals, particularly, are burdened with vast numbers of elderly persons and long "burned-out" psychotic patients who are rarely dangerous either to themselves or others but are confused, apprehensive, infirm, or otherwise unable to adjust themselves to the

renewal of spirit" whereby it is easier to view squarely further steps to be taken in *moving toward* the functional goal.

USE OF THE SOCIAL ENVIRONMENT OF THE HOSPITAL
FOR THERAPEUTIC PURPOSES

During the past two or three decades, while marked progress has been made in the variety and use of psychiatric therapy, the profession of psychiatry has devoted itself primarily to attempting to understand the nature of psychopathology and how it could be altered through some process of somatic or psychological treatment. Thus, laboratory research tended to be concerned with physiological problems, while psychoanalytical studies focused upon reduction of intrapsychic conflict. Therapy was generally viewed either as intervention in the form of insulin or electric shock, and more recently of new drugs, or as psychological intervention by the psychiatrist who sought to establish a supporting interpersonal relationship with his patient. So fixedly was attention riveted upon these forms of treatment and/so conditioned were psychiatrists to view the medical profession as the exclusive purveyors of "therapy" that as a group they failed to comprehend the extent of the potential usefulness to the healing process of other categories of personnel (and even of patients), as well as of the physical environment of the hospital in which patients lived. Equally they failed to comprehend or obtain preparation for another role that they might assume, namely, that of leader of a therapeutic team./

Interestingly enough, it was not the psychopathology of the individual patient but his social adjustment that was used in most hospitals as the criterion for determining whether he should be transferred from one type of ward to another, given "ground privileges," or permitted to go home. An occasional

exigencies of contemporary life. They need a comfortable, friendly environment that provides them with protection, medical care, and the essentials of living, including those social activities in which they can participate. They do not need hospitalization, and to keep them in mental institutions does them a disservice, confuses the fundamental purpose of a hospital, and compounds its difficulties in becoming an active treatment center.

small institution working with gravely ill patients, as does Chestnut Lodge Sanitarium for example, places its essential emphasis on resolution of deep psychological conflict. But the measuring stick for discharge in practically every public hospital that cares for large numbers of patients was, and still remains, ability to handle one's self in a manner acceptable to the mores of the family and community from which the patient comes.

Viewed in retrospect, it seems strange that reliance upon the criterion of social adjustment did not lead psychiatrists to raise the question sooner and with more discernment of whether patients might be helped in that adjustment through *planned and directed* social means, as well as through psychiatric intervention. Perhaps the failure lay in the fact that although psychiatrists used the standard of social adjustment, they did not use the specific phrase nor was their terminology sufficiently precise to serve as a broadly applicable tool. Their thinking was influenced more by individual than by social psychology, and particularly by formulations growing out of psychoanalysis. They spoke of "behavior," of whether the patient was "ready to go home," could "get along" with his family, and so on. Had they been acquainted with the body of conceptualization that sociologists had built around the term "social adjustment" and that is now being built around the more dynamic words "social efficiency" and "interpersonal competence," it is possible that the social environment of the hospital—*consisting both of persons and physical resources*—might have been envisaged earlier as a facility to be used therapeutically. Especially enlightening is Dr. Milton Greenblatt's subsequent account of how Boston Psychopathic Hospital worked consistently for several years to create an environment which would be humanitarian and more homelike. Only then was it in a position to borrow ideas and concepts whereby it could utilize that environment consciously and systematically to allay anxiety, to permit patient leadership to emerge, or to increase social interaction among withdrawn psychotic persons.

No one should conclude from the foregoing that the social

environment of the hospital has never before served therapeutic purposes. Nothing could be farther from the truth. It has served such purposes ever since hospitals made their appearance, but the service rendered has at best been fortuitous, limited to a small proportion of the patients and to a few specific places within the hospital, or has rested on some premise, such as that of the value of work, which however excellent in itself did not provide a principle of generic applicability. And it must be said categorically that although the social environment has at times fostered therapeutic ends, it has more often been so economically and emotionally impoverished as to accomplish the reverse.

In the doctrine of "moral treatment," expounded by the forefathers of state hospitals, solicitous suggestions were given for warm and kindly attention to patients by staff and for the creation of a friendly, pleasant physical setting. In those days when current forms of psychiatric therapy were unknown, a few physicians at least believed that the mentally ill could recover if the virtues of humanitarianism were practiced. Most unfortunately, the teachings of moral treatment were lost to sight in the great flood of seriously disturbed patients whom an overrapid, urban industrialization and unrestricted immigration dumped into the lap of the states. Thus, fertile beginnings in the use of interpersonal relationships and a pleasing physical environment were replaced by custodial attendants, by prisonlike wards devoid of any appurtenances either of comfort or culture, and often by provision for the use of physical restraints.

Use of Physical Resources for Therapeutic Work and Play

Within these forbidding institutions, nevertheless, there was always present the belief that work and, to a lesser degree, play "were good for patients." The belief may have rested on no other foundation than that normal persons worked and played. The fact that many hospitals relied heavily upon patient labor as the only means for remaining in operation probably reinforced belief in the value of work. However that may have been, the existence of an "occupational therapy" room, of sewing-rooms, and of ward, farm, and kitchen detail, as well as of the occasional dance, motion picture, or game evening had many assets—and also liabilities.

One asset was that varying numbers of patients who could behave with sufficient social acceptability were given an opportunity to participate in activities that bore some resemblance to their former work and play life. In the majority of instances they engaged in these activities outside the drab monotony of the wards, sometimes out-of-doors, sometimes in rooms brightened with curtains and plants. Chiefly in the course of the less frequent "play" periods, some men and women had a chance to see and talk to each other, although under sharp observation.

Another asset, of a very different kind but extremely important within the framework of this report, was that the existence of such activities led finally to their scrutiny by trained occupational and recreational therapists, psychiatrists, psychiatric nurses, and now initially by social scientists. This scrutiny has already resulted in introducing more numerous and diversified forms of work and play; in utilizing activities, for example, for purposes of quieting disturbed patients, improving the concentration of wandering minds, increasing social interaction, or teaching new skills and giving new interests to persons occupationally and emotionally bankrupt. The outcome in the more favored hospitals has been greater individualization of work and recreation according to the background, interests, and overt needs of the various patients. In recent years some psychiatrists with psychoanalytic orientation have carried individualization even farther, and have sought to make the activities they have carefully prescribed serve the unconscious needs of their patients. In the very act of individualizing work and play, hospital staffs have obviously begun to make systematic use of the physical environment, with full awareness of their intent, if not always of what the therapeutic outcome may be.

But the deficiencies that have accompanied this important evolution have not been inconsiderable. The actual proportion of patients participating more or less regularly in some form of activity is generally small. In hospitals where selection is still based, not upon individual patient needs, but upon institutional needs for a work force, those patients tend to be chosen who are best fitted to get work done. Through this practice not only are hundreds of patients deprived of the therapeutic opportunity they should have, but those who are chosen do not necessarily derive any benefit from it. Some workshops are staffed with persons who have performed the same duties for years. That such a practice can be regressive rather than progressive in nature is evidenced, for example, by those occasional patients who seek to make themselves indispensable on the job in order to avoid the alarming possibility of being transferred to a ward demanding greater personal responsibility or of being discharged from the hospital.

The reason generally given for not extending activities, particularly of the play variety, to more persons is insufficiency of staff. Although this statement is generally valid, the following report will seek to demonstrate that when attendants are cast primarily in the role of assistant occupational and recreational therapists rather than custodial officers and housekeepers,[1] and when patients who exhibit skill in engaging the interest of other patients are thus used, the range and amount of recreational activity can be greatly enlarged.

This brings us to the second shortcoming and one that again is of major importance to this study. The very development of programs of work and play—so desirable in themselves—has been achieved at the expense of that focal point of patient life, the ward. Except for daily cleaning and bedmaking, all other activities are provided for in large measure elsewhere than on the ward. The occupational therapy and other workrooms, recreation hall, library, and canteen are perhaps the most pleasant and cheerful spots in the hospital and are used by the more socially amenable patients. As a consequence, they

---

[1] In its simplest definition as used in the social sciences, role is the appropriate or culturally expected behavior that goes with the position a person occupies in a group.

are the places most readily seen by visitors, and where the staff are most likely to receive warm commendation from guests and administrative personnel alike. They are the places that receive gifts of equipment, food, flowers, and books from persons in the community and where volunteer ladies can most often be found presiding over a coffee hour, a card game, or a sewing-room.

But on the wards, where even the patients who go regularly to activities generally spend the larger part of their time and where that vast number who have no such privileges spend almost the entire time, the picture is often one of degrading poverty. The number of attendants on duty is minimal, and most of them have been taught to view their role as that of watching patients, taking care of the latter's basic physical needs, and either supervising or doing the daily ward housekeeping. Consequently, there is neither much time for, nor interest in, sitting down and talking with patients or playing games, should the necessary equipment be at hand. Rounds by physicians and nurses or supervisory attendants are generally infrequent and hurried and visitors are rare. Hence, there is a lack of professional assistance, little relief to tedium, and few words of praise for those attendants who attempt to give something of themselves to their charges. Under such circumstances, neither physical facilities nor positive interpersonal relations are available for therapeutic purposes.

Many persons will perhaps consider the foregoing paragraph unduly pessimistic in tone. They will point rightfully to those small teaching and research institutes, a few distinguished private sanatoria, the psychiatric service of general hospitals, and the admission or acute service of some large hospitals to which such characterization is not applicable. They will note the vigorous gains made since 1945 by the Veterans Administration neuropsychiatric hospitals (hereafter designated V.A. hospitals) and to a lesser degree by state hospitals in the more progressive and prosperous jurisdictions. But the bitter fact cannot be sidestepped that in the majority of large institutions, the ward remains less studied, less developed, and less considered an aid in the healing process than any other part of the hospital. It was realization of this fact, and a conviction that truly marked changes must be made in *ward care* if the psychiatric hospital is *to fulfill its function of utilizing all forms of possible treatment,* that resulted in the experimental undertaking reported in this book.

Therapeutic Use of Interpersonal Relations and Group Processes

At the same time that hospital staffs have been coming to recognize the desirability of individualized assignments of work and recreation and of better utilization of much of the physical environment, recognition has been slowly growing of how therapeutically important is that other part of the social environment, namely, the persons who comprise it. An increasing number of psychiatrists, psychiatric nurses, social workers, clinical psychologists, and occupational and recreational therapists are beginning to testify to a belief that perhaps almost unlimited latent possibilities exist for helping patients if interpersonal relations and group processes could be handled with competence.

Recognition of the inherent influence upon patients of every person who comes in contact with them, including the influence of patients upon one another, opens the door to an enormous broadening of the therapeutic potential over the almost exclusive reliance that has been placed upon somatic treatment and psychotherapy by psychiatrists. Since enough psychiatrists will not be available in the foreseeable future to furnish individual or even group treatment for all patients in public hospitals, this recent acknowledgment that roles having therapeutic value may be taken by other members of the staff and by patients can scarcely be overestimated as a promise of greatly enlarged and improved patient care. Lest we seem more optimistic than realistic, however, we immediately add as a footnote that the nature of interpersonal relations and group processes is as yet but little understood, and hence continued penetrating study will be required before they can be utilized to anything like their maximum effectiveness.

This emerging point of view has resulted from a number of sometimes unrelated developments within several professions whose members are concerned with human behavior either as practitioners or as research workers. Hypotheses and techniques growing out of these developments are now in the process of converging and of reinforcing each other. For example, as psychiatrists have increasingly joined the staffs of federal and state hospitals and found themselves charged with responsibility for large wards of psychotic patients, they have been forced to discover other therapeutic means to supplement their own. As long as they remained in private practice, private sanatoria, or outpatient departments, where they saw chiefly psychoneurotic patients, they could more easily cling to their image of the psychiatrist as *the* therapist. Work with schizophrenic patients particularly has influenced their thinking. These patients are generally so "desocialized" and therefore progress so slowly that, if the process is to be accelerated, concentrated and continuing efforts must be made to induce social interaction. Hence, as Dr. Elvin V. Semrad once remarked to the writer, any psychiatrist interested in the treatment of schizophrenia can scarcely fail to welcome assistance from ward and other hospital personnel, when such personnel have the ability to inspire confidence and to transmit a feeling of warm understanding and sympathetic support.

The very fact, moreover, that the psychiatrist is frequently unable to determine what factors are responsible for improvement in hospitalized patients, particularly in those receiving no psychiatric therapy as such, has opened the door to exploring the roles taken by nurses, attendants, and other types of personnel. Dr. Karl Menninger has said that even the person who swept the floor might be the very one who was able to give to a particular patient the kind of psychological help needed. The Menninger Foundation considered every individual who came in contact with patients, as well as every aspect of the physical environment, so potentially important that it instituted what is designated "milieu therapy."[1] It seeks

[1] Because "milieu therapy" as developed by the Menninger Foundation is more sharply psychoanalytic in orientation than is the generally held concept of

to instruct all personnel in how to interact with patients, depending upon the kind of interaction prescribed by the diagnostic team.

Simultaneously with the attempt to recruit more psychiatrists for institutional positions has gone the attempt greatly to enlarge the number of graduate nurses and wherever possible to obtain specialized psychiatric nurses. In many hospitals there were formerly so few nurses that large areas of the institution were left entirely in the hands of attendants. Thanks to the relatively generous salary scale, improved working conditions, and provision for advanced study introduced after World War II, not only have the V.A. hospitals succeeded in expanding their nursing personnel, but a considerable nucleus has enrolled in academic or professional courses, many of which relate to psychological and sociological aspects of patient care.

Most of the state hospitals have not been able to make comparable gains, although the record of a few jurisdictions is impressive. However, the requirement by some of the state boards of nurse examiners that all students in basic schools of nursing receive a period of orientation in psychiatric hospitals has proved helpful to those institutions selected for affiliation. The effect of the better-equipped wards necessary for teaching purposes, and of the presence of even a small faculty and a continuous flow of students, is often reflected in improved standards throughout much of the hospital.

The significance of the introduction of nurses in any psychiatric hospital that seeks to make therapeutic use of its social environment can scarcely be overstated. Like that of the patient, the focal point of the nurse's life while on duty is the ward. She has worked in, and administered, wards for so long that she is remarkably adept in molding them to the needs of patient care. Because she has not had to take major responsibility for diagnosis and medical treatment, she has had opportunity to emphasize other goals. Hence, the philosophy has evolved that it is the nurse's responsibility "to make the patient

---

therapy stemming from utilization of the social milieu, this Introduction has employed the cumbersome phrase "use of the social environment of the hospital for therapeutic purposes."

comfortable" and to represent his interests and welfare when she thinks they are being endangered. These are goals of inestimable value in the improvement of ward care.

It is true that many graduate nurses, particularly those who did not have the now generally required orientation in psychiatric nursing, experience difficulties upon entering mental hospitals. They discover that competence does not rest to any large degree upon the carrying out of procedures used in nursing the physically ill, and that the acquisition of new skills, including psychological ability to "reach" withdrawn or excited patients, may be a slow and painful process. Moreover, because attendants of necessity have assumed responsibility and been given sanctions out of all proportion to those of aides and orderlies in general hospitals, many nurses consider themselves in an ambiguous position regarding questions of authority and status. How they, as well as other categories of personnel, are being helped to overcome such difficulties will be described later.

Of scarcely less import than the introduction of the graduate nurse to the ward is the current reevaluation of the position of attendant—or psychiatric aide or psychiatric technician, as he is coming to be called in some places that have desired to upgrade this position. Although superintendents and staff physicians have repeatedly said that the attendant is truly *important* in the lives of patients, lack of provision for proper selection of applicants or adequate orientation to the job; poor salary, living, and working conditions; and lack of recognition by hospital personnel generally have caused the attendant to regard such a statement as hypocritical. In the hierarchical system of the large hospital he was the "low man," and although he had probably never heard of the concept of expectation, he illustrated its validity by tending to act as was expected of him. The ward work done by Quakers and other conscientious objectors during World War II, and the opportunity provided psychiatrists and nurses in the armed forces to see the quality of care given by corpsmen were no inconsiderable factors in raising the sights of administrators. They began to seek means for attracting more able and interested attendants and for creating more favorable work conditions whereby a higher level of expectation might be realized.

By extending their liberalized policies to attendant personnel, the V.A. hospitals achieved greater success in recruiting than formerly. The introduction of four weeks of in-service training proved so valuable that it was gradually lengthened to fourteen, and plans are now being made for experimenting on a selective basis with advanced training. In a few states better recruitment procedures, higher wages, improved orientation courses, and a new title for attendants were introduced simultaneously in their mental hospitals. One state even initiated a full year of in-service preparation for psychiatric technicians who, it was hoped, would gradually replace attendants. Such efforts have received encouragement and advisory assistance from the National Association for Mental Health, which gives particular attention to this category of hospital staff. Because no national association existed to represent the interests of attendants, it has for several years operated a department devoted exclusively to their welfare. More recently, the American Psychiatric Association, the National League for Nursing, and the American Nurses' Association have committed themselves to larger examination of the ward needs of mental hospitals, to helping with recruitment both of nurses and attendants, and to development of standards for attendant selection and duties to be performed.

There have been local advances of a more radical nature looking toward the discovery of persons with better education and with emotional commitment to the task of caring for the mentally ill; toward formulating individualized roles for some attendants or a new generic role for all attendants; or toward creating less formalized but more intensive methods for the development of latent aptitudes among ward personnel.[1] Here

[1] One of the freshest, most productive approaches to recruitment and use of staff, particularly "nurses," as well as to fostering socialization and greater individual responsibility among patients, appears in Dr. Maxwell Jones's *The Therapeutic Community*, Basic Books, New York, 1953. Certainly everyone interested in the care of the mentally ill will want to read this report of an exceptionally encouraging English experiment.

and there a particular appeal is made to premedical, theology, social science, and other students concerned with human behavior to work in mental hospitals. It was found that they, and also "volunteers" and affiliate nursing students, could do much to change the social climate of wards. The school for psychiatric aides, recently operated experimentally for three years in conjunction with the Menninger Foundation and the Topeka State Hospital, with some financial aid from the Rockefeller Foundation, sought to demonstrate how high could be the level of patient care resulting from a dynamic one-year curriculum offered warmly motivated students with at least complete high-school education. The interest stirred by this school and its report, *Psychiatric Aide Education,* published in 1952,[1] created a widespread, healthy ferment even in those psychiatric hospitals and medical and nursing organizations that were sharply critical of teaching basic principles of psychoanalytic theory to persons not prospective physicians or nurses.

Diversification of attendant roles, although in an initial stage, offers promise of giving work satisfaction and recognition to those men and women who show particular interest and some skill in patient care. It represents individualization and specialization of function, and used imaginatively is capable of wider application than has yet been tried. Early experiments have resulted in taking selected attendants from their custodial and housekeeping positions on the ward, and putting them in charge, for example, of the warm water pool or some occupational or recreational unit. Thus, patients who were formerly not permitted to leave the ward unless close supervision were available, have been able to spend time in a more wholesome physical and social environment, under the guidance of a person who gains gratification from his ability and initiative in working with them. More basic, however, than this kind of individualization of tasks is the effort being made in some places to create a different role for all ward attendants. Em-

[1] See Hall, Bernard H., and others, *Psychiatric Aide Education,* Grune and Stratton, New York.

phasis is placed upon social interaction of attendant with patients in such a manner that the custodial role can be minimized, and even housekeeping can be made more specifically a tool for social interaction and for rebuilding responsibility in patients. Thus, motivation and prestige of attendants are improved, to the great benefit of the ill under their care. Further reference to this significant development appears in the subsequent reports.

Of even greater importance than the introduction of in-service training or revision of roles is the effort, through informal but continuous means, to help attendants—as well as all other categories of staff—develop latent aptitudes. Such an effort is usually a concomitant of a broad attempt to remake the hospital as a social institution: to replace autocratic administration, inflexible departmentalism, and reliance upon considerations of status, salary, and power by more democratic procedures, greater general permissiveness and delegation of responsibility, reduction of departmental and status barriers, greater encouragement of initiative, and utilization of the concept of the therapeutic *team*. In such institutions the belief is held, however expressed, that the best way to assure good patient care is to provide ample opportunity for the staff to grow and develop intellectually, emotionally, and in degree of responsibility assumed. It is believed, furthermore, that for persons employed in positions that are psychologically threatening, growth is possible only if support, sympathetic understanding, and recognition are generously supplied by the administration and by one staff member to another; if supervision is used for counseling purposes rather than for checking on employees and "handing down" orders; and if opportunities abound for discussion (and perhaps also psychodrama) groups uninhibited enough to permit release of tensions, and for considerable informality in working and playing together. Wherever conditions such as these obtain, even to a limited extent, attendants find themselves in an environment which frees energy from frustration and anxiety for constructive purposes,

and gives them opportunity to hear and participate in considerations of patient care, thus fostering their development as
increasingly useful and effective members of the therapeutic
team. These same conditions, moreover, lessen the status conflict between nurses and attendants, and provide inexperienced
nurses with the chance to learn needed psychiatric skills more
successfully and quickly.

Nurses and attendants have been discussed at this length
because they are the personnel most closely associated with
patients. Space unfortunately does not allow detailed reference
here to the importance of those other categories of staff that
have become part of psychiatric hospitals, such as social
workers, clinical psychologists, and occupational and recreational therapists. Their contribution has proved indispensable,
but as yet they have only rarely made the impact on the patient
in the ward setting that is so sorely needed.

We come now to the second working hypothesis: *The utilization of* EVERY *form of therapy available requires planned and
systematic use of the whole environment, consisting both of
physical resources and social interaction between all categories
of staff and patients.*

CONTRIBUTIONS OF SOCIAL SCIENCE TO THERAPEUTIC ACTION

To the growing conviction among the staffs of psychiatric
hospitals that the therapeutic potential of such institutions can
be appreciably broadened, sociologists, social psychologists,
and social anthropologists have recently lent their support. A
few of the hypotheses created by behavior scientists have been
tested by them for validity in the hospital setting, or have been
used as the basis for action-oriented research in the improvement of patient care. Other hypotheses have attracted the attention of therapists who are beginning to determine the extent
of their usefulness. It has already been noted that the social
science concept of social adjustment is now being reworked
into the more dynamic generalization of social efficiency, while
Harry Stack Sullivan's concept of interpersonal relations that
has done so much to extend horizons is being enlarged to in-

clude interpersonal competence and techniques for its development.[1]

Illustrations of Helpful Concepts

As studies of different facets of the hospital social environment increase in number, the variety of concepts employed for
analytical purposes naturally becomes progressively larger.
Reference, at least implicitly, to some of these concepts appears
throughout the following pages. Two that have furnished useful frames of reference for many of the studies and that need
to be emphasized because of their direct bearing upon ways
to broaden the therapeutic potential are social structure and
role. So indispensable did they seem to the staff of the Russell
Sage Foundation Project, concerning which much of this book
deals, that they form recurring themes until they are included
in the final chapter among the emerging guideposts to social
treatment.

When social scientists began to examine the average large
mental hospital, they almost immediately questioned why the
chronic psychotic patient who is supposedly free from gross
brain damage remains ill. Is it because of incurable inner conflict, or because of the restrictive procedures, inadequacy of
communication, and general emotional impoverishment of the
institution? As persons trained to look at environmental factors,
their attention was focused upon the second possible alternative. Close observation revealed that these hospitals were often
so traditional in outlook that they gave almost no attention to
reexamination of their organizational pattern and many of their
procedures. The several services and departments were largely

[1] In spite of the great attention that has been devoted by social scientists and
psychiatrists to the process of socialization, particularly in children, and to the
development of relationships between persons or groups, no comparable attention has been devoted, except possibly by industrial psychologists, to study of
relationships between persons and things or objects. Professor David Riesman
once observed, after visiting industrial plants, that probably for many Americans
their most comfortable and rewarding relation was with machines. For some
individuals it is with seed catalogues, books, mountain climbing, fishing, or
even collecting sunsets. Through encouraging the creation of objects, occupational therapists foster the development of this kind of relatedness. Systematic
examination of its nature, depth, and value might lead to conclusions that could
be fruitfully applied in helping patients toward better behavioral adjustment.

independent of each other, and hence failed to concentrate joint attention on the fundamental problem of what was good for the patients. Opportunities for consideration of this problem were not only little developed, but channels for exchange of essential daily information and consultation were so poor that rumor and gossip frequently replaced needed communication.

The number of physicians and nurses in administrative and supervisory positions was meager indeed when compared with that deemed essential by the general hospital. As almost inevitably happens in institutions where the organizational structure is inadequate to support the functions that must be performed, authority was often assumed by unauthorized persons or groups who either wanted to "get things done" or wanted the gratification of increased power. Perhaps one of the most surprising and disconcerting discoveries was the degree of power that could be exercised by persons in charge of the purchase or requisitioning and distribution of supplies for the institution, and by those whose function it was to make repairs and maintain plant and equipment. By their withholding supplies and services, which were always too few, from some parts of the hospital and providing them to others—or merely by their being suspected of showing favoritism in an institution where rumor was rife—they could seriously damage staff morale. Even in hospitals that were on a much higher level of administrative competence, many road blocks to fostering therapeutic goals appeared to exist which might have been removed if they had been perceived not as merely individual barriers but as signs indicating basic organizational weaknesses.

Because therapists have had their attention so largely focused upon the individual patient and upon psychiatric research and resulting advances in practice, they have shown relatively small awareness of the extent to which the social structure of the hospital creates an environment that may be therapeutic or nontherapeutic. Although sociologists particularly have been interested in the general problem of social structure for many years, their writings have not been readily available to members of the medical and nursing professions responsible for operating psychiatric hospitals.[1] Only now are studies of hospitals based upon theories of social structure beginning to reach the press.

The most comprehensive one yet published is *The Mental Hospital:* A Study of Institutional Participation in Psychiatric Illness and Treatment by Dr. Alfred H. Stanton and Dr. Morris S. Schwartz, issued in 1954 by Basic Books. In it a psychiatrist and a sociologist have set down a detailed analysis of the formal and informal organization of a particular hospital and also of one of its disturbed wards. In addition, analyses are included of the closely related subjects of the system of communication and the structure of power. A second undertaking to which reference must be made is the recent sociological examination of a large public hospital in Canada and the resulting reorganization of aspects of the entire social structure but particularly the policy, structure, and function of the nursing hierarchy. A paper on this undertaking is scheduled for publication in a psychiatric journal under the authorship of Dr. Elaine Cumming, formerly the consulting sociologist, Dr. I. L. W. Clancey, the clinical director of the hospital, and Dr. John Cumming, formerly senior psychiatrist. When this article and a second one by Elaine and John Cumming on the locus of power in a large mental hospital become available, they should provide hospital administrators with further basis for judgment both about the importance of social structure, and the usefulness of sociological analysis as a tool for indicating changes to be made.

The second concept on which social scientists have placed much reliance is role. Already several references have been made to it in the preceding section, with the expressed assumption that by altering the roles assigned to members of the staff, particularly attendants, patient care could be appreciably improved. In order to consider the value of this assumption within its social context, it is necessary to note how the staffing of an

[1] In 1954 Penguin Books published *The Social Psychology of Industry,* written with a minimum of technical language by the British psychiatrist, J. A. C. Brown. This book, which attempts to supply the reader with an understanding of the social background of industry, is almost as applicable to the hospital.

institution, for other than a relatively few individualized positions, is determined and what the results are.

Like other large corporate endeavors, administrative planning by psychiatric hospitals has been primarily mechanistic, in terms of functions to be performed and the way those functions should be grouped for efficiency of operation. Once functions had been listed, they were then moved like checkers into place with relation to each other. The next step was to employ personnel, much as machinery is bought, according to the specifications of functions to be performed. Unfortunately, machines capable of carrying out tasks where interpersonal relations are involved could not be used. Human beings had to be utilized—but human beings with attitudes, needs, and aspirations that were the result of their total life experience. Hence, they were often not amenable to functional imperatives. Here was the great dilemma that most hospitals have not yet resolved, particularly for those large categories of personnel at the bottom of the hierarchical structure.

It is this dilemma that role theory can help to reduce by shifting emphasis from the mechanistic concept of function that loses sight of the person expected to perform the function, to the dynamic concept that behavior can be so modified on the basis of psychological knowledge that worker and function are brought more nearly into harmony. Many studies, particularly of industry, have shown that all workers want employment that provides them with a sense of self-respect and importance, and opportunity for increasing recognition. These considerations are often more important to them than wage increases. The worker who finds himself in such a position tends not only to perform the functions expected of him with enthusiasm and effectiveness but as if he preferred it to almost any other. From such studies industry has been learning that the concept of role provides a flexible instrument for improving employee morale and hence increasing motivation. Therefore, the social scientist concludes that those mental hospitals which are attempting differentiation in the role of attendants or creation of a totally new role may look forward, if other conditions are favorable, to conspicuous improvement in patient care. Similarly, reexamination and possible modification of current roles of every other category of personnel might yield fruitful results.

Useful By-Products of Experimental Research

Research in the mental hospital based on social science theories has not only supported the belief of many members of the staff that the therapeutic potential could be broadened, but has emphasized various devices for achieving that end, particularly alterations in the ordering of organizational relationships and recognition of the needs of personnel. In addition, social science experiments in changing environmental situations have produced several by-products that have themselves been important in fostering the same end.

Experimentation in which considerable numbers of hospital staff participated in planning for and making changes and in evaluating the results achieved, has proved at its best an effective instrument for sharpening perception, furnishing additional channels of communication, and heightening motivation. Action-oriented research of this kind requires bringing together many persons, often from different categories of personnel, who have previously had little contact with each other. Thus, serious failures in communication, characteristic of almost all large institutions, may become alleviated and status barriers reduced. And with these changes—particularly if there is opportunity for the therapeutic expression of old resentments and hostilities—attitudes may be so altered as greatly to increase interest in one's work and in cooperating with others.

Second, research requires stating the problem to be studied. The very process of definition is capable of sharpening the perception of many administrative and staff members who have been so involved in the day-by-day process of meeting necessary routines and emergencies that they have not reviewed the purpose, to say nothing of the success, of their procedures. Often clearer definition alone furnishes new perspective that becomes in turn the basis for altered policy determination. Once the problem has been defined, techniques for carrying out the experimentation and evaluating the results must be found. Here again the necessary discussion may both produce creative ideas as yet untried, and encourage the participants to discover what techniques in use elsewhere could be adapted to the requirements. Then comes the process of getting the experiment into operation and maintaining its level and tempo. This process is potentially dynamic enough to challenge the staff to sustained effort, particularly nurses and attendants who have generally been permitted little opportunity to share in experimental work. Sometimes wholesome competition is created between wards or other areas selected for the experiment, or even between those not thus designated and those selected. When this occurs, motivation is so increased as to be felt throughout considerable portions of the hospital.

Research directed toward action goals may, however, encounter many pitfalls. Staff who find themselves in areas not chosen for experimentation or which are labeled "control" areas can suffer frustration and decreased motivation unless preventive measures are taken. To be able to maintain control areas at all is almost an impossibility if interest in the project is intense and widespread, for under such circumstances staff may unconsciously alter the social situation. Personnel participating in the experiment, particularly if long continued, need to be rewarded by encouragement and praise. Nothing is more serious than failure to make frequent reports on evaluation of progress or the results of tests administered. The time lag between the administration of tests and the analysis and interpretation of data not infrequently permits anxiety and suspiciousness to develop and motivation to decrease.

Also high on the list of liabilities is the lack of experience as yet among social scientists in acting as team captains in the planning and operating of such undertakings. Dr. Richard H. York, who assumed this role with exceptional skill in the Project reported in this book, has several times commented, "If only I could do it over again after what I have learned!" In spite of such difficulties and current inadequacies in research techniques, attention needs to remain focused on social experimentation as a positive means for helping staff to move toward higher levels of patient care and more satisfaction in their work.

We conclude, therefore, with a third working hypothesis: *For purposes of making effective therapeutic use of the social environment of the hospital, including improvement in the motivation of personnel, concepts and methods of research developed by the behavior sciences should be tested and utilized wherever feasible.*

"THE RUSSELL SAGE PROJECT"

We come finally to a description of the origin, nature, and results of the specific undertaking that was labeled by the cooperating hospitals, the Russell Sage Project. Before the closing of the experimental school for psychiatric aides in Topeka, Dr. Bernard H. Hall, its director, discussed with Russell Sage Foundation the possibility of a study of the activities involved in providing ward care to hospitalized mental patients. This was viewed primarily as a functional analysis on the basis of which determination might perhaps be made about the training of ward personnel. Light should also be sought, Dr. Hall suggested, on questions of how more nurses and better attendants might be recruited, how the morale of the latter might be improved, tenure lengthened, and level of performance raised.

From these discussions a memorandum was prepared that received budgetary approval from the Foundation's Trustees in November, 1951. According to the plan outlined, the Project was to consist of two distinctly different but supplementary parts. There was to be a nationwide survey of patient care as currently provided in supposedly representative hospitals, particularly of the state variety. At the same time there was to be a scientifically oriented experiment in one community of the extent to which principles and practices of patient care evolved by small and relatively favored psychiatric hospitals could be applied in much larger and less well-financed institutions. Because of the Foundation's interest in fostering interrelationships between behavior scientists and the professions that work directly with people, it was predetermined that the survey would be conducted by a social scientist, and that persons representing the behavior disciplines would collaborate in the experiment with psychiatrists, nurses, attendants, and other categories of personnel.

Through a fortuitous circumstance the experimental part of the Project was begun some eighteen months before the survey. Although this book deals exclusively with the former, a further brief note about the survey is in order here. During the interval before appointing as its director Dr. Otto O. Von Mering, Jr., a social anthropologist who was then completing a two-year research study in a psychiatric institute, the Foundation revised its original decision concerning the nature of the survey. It had already become obvious that the account of the experiment would of necessity include data about ward conditions in the teaching and research institute, the state hospital, and the Veterans Administration hospital selected, and it was believed that the picture presented would be broadly representative of conditions elsewhere in these three types of institution. Differences would be primarily in degree rather than in kind. Because patient care in large psychiatric hospitals is generally on so low a level of development, any report on staff functions, morale, and tenure in a score of typical institutions throughout the United States would be largely repetitious and generally discouraging.

What seemed to be needed was a report of *achievements*, primarily in state hospitals since their difficulties are the greatest, which could serve as patterns for improvement elsewhere. Hence, emphasis was shifted from a survey of representative conditions and functions to one of *encouraging trends* in patient care. From a variety of sources information was obtained about institutions in all regions of the United States that were sponsoring promising new developments. After a year of travel, visits to more than 20 such hospitals have been completed. The report that Dr. Von Mering is preparing for publication will attempt to analyze and evaluate the importance and the usefulness to other institutions of the many truly hopeful undertakings, often almost unknown elsewhere, that he has found.

For the experimental part of the Project the Foundation requested Boston Psychopathic Hospital to establish cooperative relations with a state and a neuropsychiatric Veterans Administration hospital in the vicinity, in order to test the applicability of principles and practices such as those used by it. This Hospital is a small institution of 120 beds and an outpatient service for the acutely ill. It is maintained for purposes of diagnosis, treatment, teaching, and research by the Commonwealth of Massachusetts and the department of psychiatry of the Harvard Medical School. Several reasons contributed to its selection. The Foundation considered it to be among the best of those teaching and research institutions that are concerned with the advancement of psychiatric treatment. Dr. Harry C. Solomon, its superintendent and medical director, had already expressed his belief that the behavior sciences hold the key to an understanding of social management, comparable in importance perhaps to clinical management of patients, and had invited the Foundation to sponsor social science research in the Hospital. Finally, it was situated in a geographical area where psychiatric and educational facilities could be called on in great abundance.

Initial discussions between the Foundation and Boston Psychopathic Hospital resulted in the creation of a committee of three persons to direct the Project. They were Dr. Robert W. Hyde, assistant superintendent of the Hospital, who customarily gives much attention to the development of hypotheses and experiments dealing with the improvement of patient care; Dr. Milton Greenblatt, the psychiatrist in charge of the research laboratories; and Dr. Frederic L. Wells, previously a member of the staff, who has contributed greatly to the establishment of clinical and social psychology in the United States.

The Foundation had already elicited interest and ready assent from the central office of the Veterans Administration in Washington to have its federal hospitals included in both parts of the Project, and the writer had visited the Bedford V.A. Hospital, an exclusively neuropsychiatric facility of 1,800 beds in the Boston area. Bedford had profited greatly from the reorganization of all Veterans Administration hospitals after the war and from its own efforts toward upgrading. In the estimation of its staff, however, it was still below the level of motivation, coordination of effort, and maximum utilization of resources that might be expected of such a well-provided-for institution. Because of the steps already taken, the question of what federal institution Boston Psychopathic Hospital should invite to partnership in the Project did not arise.

The choice of a state hospital, however, was more difficult since a half-dozen were less than an hour's drive away. One that might logically have been chosen was passed over as being too highly developed to be representative. In a decade it had raised itself, through the ability and dynamic personality of the superintendent and the staff he had assembled, from a typical to a vastly improved, experimentally minded institution that was pioneering in nurse-led group therapy and in rehabilitation of chronic patients. The Metropolitan State Hospital in Waltham, an 1,800-bed institution including a children's unit, was finally selected. Its buildings were relatively new and pleasantly located; its peripheral recreation or work rooms were bright and cheerful. But it was short of staff of all categories, of fresh paint and basic supplies, and of provision, particularly on the wards, for the simplest amenities of living. With economic impoverishment, that stagnation had crept in which is so often characteristic of neglected public institutions. Improvement of patient care there would provide the Project with a real challenge.

During the early winter of 1952 several meetings were held at Boston Psychopathic Hospital attended by nurses, aides, physicians, and others chiefly in supervisory positions from Bedford V.A., Metropolitan, and also McLean Hospital, a well-known private sanatorium affiliated with the Massachusetts General Hospital. The purpose of these meetings was exploration of the facets and goals of the proposed experiment in improvement of patient care. Initially each hospital displayed great interest in describing its particular problems, but many of them—such as problems of morale, communication, social climate—proved to be common to all. A little later, persons attending the meetings began to make large numbers of suggestions for improving their services. They wanted to try new procedures with special groups of patients: senile, women, chronic, acute; they wanted to utilize special groups of staff in the "action" research: nurses, attendants, physicians, occupational therapy workers, and so on. Those who were experimentally inclined insisted that before instituting any changes there be clear definition of criteria and indices of improvement that would apply to ward programs of all kinds and to varied types of patients. Those clinically inclined were impatient to start ward changes at once.

From this ferment came acceptance in March of responsibility for participation in the Project by Metropolitan and Bedford hospitals; spontaneous formation of committees in the two institutions to forward the undertaking; and decision to hold monthly meetings, which would rotate among the hospitals, to facilitate overall planning and reporting on progress made.

In April Dr. Richard H. York, a clinical psychologist, was appointed to act as the liaison representative between the institutions and to assist with the experiment within the state and the federal hospital. His role, as he conceived it, was that of "participant observer." Shortly afterward he was joined by Miss Penelope Lambros, who served as executive secretary and research assistant in all phases of the field work. For the very reason that Dr. York was neither a psychiatrist nor a staff member of the Boston Psychopathic Hospital, but was experienced in various aspects of social research in hospitals as well as in group relations generally, he was accepted with ease in the two institutions. His appointment was particularly fortunate, for already some representatives had felt that Boston Psychopathic Hospital was trying to show them "how to run their wards." Although that institution believed it was acting with genuine humility, the very attempt to establish close collaborative efforts among several hospitals was so new an experience that anxiety had been created which it did not know how to allay.

The decision was made at this time to attempt no specific demonstration on the wards of the participating hospitals of practices that had been effective at the teaching and research institute. Instead, the needs of each institution, and what it thought it could and wished to do to improve patient care, were to be the determinants of experiments undertaken. Principles, however, were to be obtained from every possible source as guides in setting up and evaluating the experiments. How specific plans were formulated for action programs at Bedford V.A. and Metropolitan State, how the programs evolved, what were the interrelated institutional factors that made for greater or less success in each hospital, and what measurements were used to evaluate the results—these are among the topics analyzed by Dr. York in Parts II and III of this book.

Before ending this Introduction we must comment on a few further aspects of the Project and indicate some of its by-products that are perhaps in process of becoming, as by-products often do, more important than the original undertaking.

Attention should be directed to the fact that the number of persons who had an opportunity to engage directly or indirectly in the experiments ran perhaps into hundreds. At the Bedford V.A. Hospital alone, 72 aides participated directly, to say nothing of ward nurses and physicians, and members of the administrative staff and of the physical medical rehabilitation service. What they gained in individual development and improved interest and skill in patient care, regardless of the many frustrations encountered, was only partially evaluated but is known to have been great. The original intention was to list at the beginning of the book the names of those who had served on the committees of the individual institutions, on the inter-hospital committee, or who had otherwise rendered conspicuous service. But how could we omit the names of all those who had translated into day-by-day action the planning done in committee meetings! They were the persons who had truly accomplished the task. Therefore, it was decided reluctantly to mention no names except the few that appear in the text.

Just as it has been impossible to mention individually the participants in the experiments, so has it been impossible to include large bodies of data collected. One reason is lack of space; the other is the technical nature of many of the scales and other procedures used to gauge attitudes and evaluate results. Extensive testing was done of the opinions and feelings of attendants, nurses, physicians, and even patients about a variety of hospital situations and techniques of patient care and also about mental illness itself. The instrument of cardboard "dolls" representing staff and patients and the reproductions of typical hospital situations, devised by Richard Hobson with the help of an artist for encouraging persons interviewed to talk more freely while assembling a picture, is worthy of a monograph for clinical psychologists. Its inclusion would be inappropriate in this book, the primary aim of which is to stimulate more immediate and direct interest in improvement of patient care. The same is true of the results of an opinionnaire administered by Dr. Doris Gilbert, on "ways of thinking about mental illness and some related social problems," that have already been utilized in a doctoral dissertation submitted to Harvard University.

One subject, however, could not be left out, so central was it to the purpose of the book, namely, the description of developments that had occurred over more than a decade at Boston Psychopathic Hospital in social aspects of patient care. For the very reason that the Hospital had not been requested to engage in experimentation within its own institution in connection with the Project, omission would have been logical. But readers would have been denied the report of a twelve-year, sequential evolution that is particularly rich in indications of what may and may not be accomplished in a growth process that even in this teaching and research institute still depends more largely upon practical experience than scientific planning for guidance.

Prior to Dr. Solomon's superintendency the Hospital had been distinguished for its neurological research, but patients had received little individual attention except diagnostically. For such an institution, ward conditions were shocking. Small change has been built continuously on small change until the results are impressive. But the end is not yet in sight. Particularly valuable during recent years has been the increasing use of social science research. Even while the Hospital was giving much time and attention to the Russell Sage Project in the collaborating institutions, it was carrying on several studies, one of which was on the role of psychiatric nursing made possible by a subsidy from the American Nurses' Association.

In Dr. Greenblatt's suggestion that he write the report of developments at Boston Psychopathic lies the first of several encouraging by-products of the Project. Because he began his residency training at the Hospital in 1942, he has had an opportunity to see and participate in many of the changes that have occurred. On the other hand, he has been so closely associated with the direction of the research laboratories which were long primarily physiological and particularly with the two large studies of lobotomy, that the therapeutic potential of the social environment of the Hospital had partially escaped his attention. From his reexamination of events has come the conviction that this potential merits the utmost in careful evaluation and expanded use. So strong a testimonial from him will create interest among many psychiatrists elsewhere.

Another by-product is the initiation of interest at Saint Elizabeths Hospital, Washington, D.C., in having social scientists collaborate with its staff in experimental studies. This results in large part from the fact that Dr. Jay L. Hoffman, who has recently taken an administrative post there, was chief of professional services at Bedford during the early stages of the Project and gave it both devoted assistance and close scrutiny. The experiment proved, to his satisfaction, that patients, relatives, and personnel were more satisfied with their hospital and their work. He concluded that no administration could further delay the introduction of programs of patient remotivation when evidence was available of what could be done to help even long-hospitalized chronic patients.

Provision has been made for continuation of the interhospital meetings, although less frequently, with perhaps additional neighboring institutions invited to join. In this connection the remarks of a psychiatrist, who had watched the Project from outside with considerable interest, are pertinent. He reminded the writer that two years earlier he had doubted whether several psychiatric hospitals with representatives of all types of personnel could be brought together in a close working relationship. That very accomplishment had, in his estimation, set in motion various forces that although small and not easily definable were sufficient to increase flexibility in many psychiatric circles in Boston.

A further result of the Foundation's undertaking was the initiation of interest by Dr. P. Stefan Kraus, a member of the Bedford psychiatric staff, in finding social science theories that could be used for the purpose of moving long-chronic patients ahead therapeutically, and new scales to measure their social improvement. He had recently been assigned to a building of nearly 200 seriously regressed patients, many of whom had been hospitalized for years, when its wards became an experimental area. A later chapter recounts the pronounced degree of patient improvement and the lightening of the atmosphere of those "back wards" that were accomplished by him, a small corps of aides, and a charge nurse. It had been hoped by the writer that Dr. Kraus could maintain this position for several years, and be given every opportunity for systematic study of how far such a group of patients might be helped toward recovery and toward a life outside the hospital. However, he was "advanced," as so often happens, to a larger administrative position where his time is now occupied with the reorganization of the acute service.

Probably the single most important outgrowth of the Project was the decision made by Boston Psychopathic Hospital to seek a teaching and research facility in the area of chronic disease. Obviously, such a facility would be in one of the state hospitals. After conferences with Dr. Jack R. Ewalt, commissioner of the Massachusetts Department of Mental Health, Dr. Solomon asked Metropolitan State Hospital for the privilege of establishing an affiliation with it. There was tacit understanding that in return for the affiliation Boston Psychopathic Hospital would attempt, through the resources of its own staff and such other resources as it could solicit, to help make provision for some of the existing deficits in personnel, supplies, and motivation. Thus, dynamic forces would be set in motion whereby Metropolitan could raise itself to a level appropriate for teaching and research purposes and for greatly improved patient care.

Since the winter of 1953 the two hospitals have been grappling with the exceedingly difficult and complex problems of how to make the rapid changes needed on the one hand, and how to establish comfortable interrelationships on the other. There have been times when both hospitals have felt so threatened psychologically that retreat must have seemed momentarily like the easiest solution. Understandably, the reorganization has been particularly hard for Metropolitan, for it is rarely easy when accepting assistance from a more favored relative to realize that what the giver receives in return may prove of inestimable value to him. Neither is it easy to be objective about conditions of impoverishment even though one is aware that they are largely the result of society's neglect.

But the prognosis appears good. Boston Psychopathic has moved outside itself, and in so doing has prevented any possible growth of complacency that often comes with success. The Metropolitan has at last the opportunity to develop into an outstanding and widely known hospital, whereas the odds against it were formerly too great. And in this alliance (as well as in other similar developments elsewhere) is being forged perhaps a pattern for the future, when teaching and research institutes may exercise more responsibility for experimentation in social as well as clinical treatment and in the care of chronic patients, and when state hospitals may feel free to call for such help as a right and without embarrassment.

ESTHER LUCILE BROWN, PH.D.
Russell Sage Foundation

PART ONE

TOWARD A THERAPEUTIC COMMUNITY

MILTON GREENBLATT, M.D.

1. Beginnings of Growth

CENTURIES OF BEATING, STRAITJACKETS, ostracism, dispossession, and neglect of emotionally disturbed persons have not solved the riddle of mental illness, diminished man's fear of insanity, or allayed his troubled conscience. In our own time we vacillate between thrusting mental illness completely out of sight and out of mind, and yielding to humanistic inner promptings to cure these "sick souls." Today our state hospitals represent a crude and unfortunate compromise between such conflicting trends. As late as 1909 in the Commonwealth of Massachusetts, a state supposedly advanced in the care of the mentally ill, laws for the sensible care of patients suffering from acute psychotic turmoil did not exist. Fortunately, after 1909, with materialization of a psychopathic hospital, the possibility of decent management of mentally ill people at the onset of their illnesses began to emerge, and with it the hope of coming to grips with the whole problem of mental disease.

This section of the book traces the rapid evolution of concepts and practices in the care of the mentally ill in recent years at Boston Psychopathic Hospital, which for the most part treats acute cases of psychosis. It is the chronicle of the experience of an institution that for more than a decade has explored ways and means of improving the care of the mentally ill through more effective use of the physical and social environment of the hospital. There is no claim to priority in any of the procedures employed. Some institutions are known to have long antedated Boston Psychopathic Hospital in the elimination of various "evils," while others have perhaps carried many of the positive undertakings described here to a higher level of success. What cannot be gainsaid is the writer's profound satisfaction

37

in having participated in these experiments; his deepened respect for the possibilities inherent in the social sciences for making hospitals into more truly therapeutic communities; and the gratifying realization that what has thus far been learned is perhaps only the beginning of a long chain of developments in the improvement of patient care.

Parts II and III comprise Dr. Richard H. York's report on improvement of patient care at Bedford Veterans Administration Hospital and Metropolitan State Hospital, where primarily chronic patients are cared for in large numbers. What has been learned in all three institutions through study of the hospital social system and analysis of ward care, and through direct experiments has wide application, it is believed, to the institutional treatment of mental disorders, as well as the broader problems of mental health and disease.

EARLY HISTORY OF BOSTON PSYCHOPATHIC HOSPITAL

Before Boston Psychopathic Hospital was opened as the primary receiving hospital for acute mentally ill patients in Massachusetts, an intolerable condition of neglect existed in the Commonwealth. Citizens suffering from mental disturbances were sent to jails, police stations, or the House of Correction, like offenders. They often remained there for days before being removed to mental hospitals for medical and psychiatric treatment. Many of these cases are cited by L. Vernon Briggs in his *History of the Psychopathic Hospital*.[1]

John F. Naven, 35 years old . . . was taken to the Relief Station of the Boston City Hospital . . . suffering from pneumonia. They said insanity had developed, which was probably delirium; so . . . he was taken to the City Prison where it was claimed no attention was given him, and when Dr. Dunn finally arrived, on December 9, 1907 [how long after admission is not stated], he was found lying dead in his cell. There was an autopsy and the official cause of death, as rendered by the medical examiner, was acute lobar pneumonia.

A newspaper account on May 31, 1908, tells of the case of a

[1] Briggs, L. Vernon, and collaborators, *History of the Psychopathic Hospital, Boston, Massachusetts*. Wright and Potter Printing Co., Boston, 1922, pp. 25–26, 55.

man who was "nabbed" by policemen in front of the City Prison and put in a padded cell for safekeeping. One of his stunts was to walk on his hands and knees and try to bark like a dog.

Patrick Welch, aged 35, in September, 1909, was found on the sidewalk on Lincoln Street, acting as though intoxicated. He was booked for insanity. Later he was sent to the City Prison and confined in a padded cell, where he was found by one of the guards, a short time afterwards, groaning upon the floor. Dr. Dunn, the prison physician, was summoned and advised the man's removal to City Hospital, at which time the doctors found him suffering from a fractured skull. He lived but a few hours.

On November 28, 1909, William J. Mulkern, aged 28 years, was taken to the City Prison from the Relief Station, and the next day was found dead in his cell. An autopsy was performed, and the cause of death given as "oedema of the brain; dilatation of the heart; chronic tuberculosis of the lungs."

Aroused citizens led by Dr. Briggs attracted public attention to the issue, with the result that between 1909 and 1911 the Massachusetts legislature, by a series of humane acts, first brought the care of acutely psychotic citizens under the responsibility of the state, then provided for the building of an observation psychopathic hospital where mental cases could receive quick and efficient diagnosis and treatment, and finally charged the State Board of Insanity with the emergency care of patients in the Boston State Hospital until the Psychopathic Hospital should be ready for occupancy. At this time only the Commonwealth of Massachusetts and the State of New York possessed laws by which acutely ill mental cases could receive immediate hospital care.

On June 24, 1912, Boston Psychopathic Hospital was formally opened as a receiving department of Boston State Hospital. Its first director was Dr. Elmer E. Southard, a man of remarkable gifts and broad vision. He was renowned as a neuropathologist, and held the chair of professor of neuropathology at Harvard Medical School. Dr. Southard had great interest in a wide range of activities, and in addition to neuropathology, he was versed in etymology, philosophy (he took over Josiah Royce's seminars at Harvard when the latter was ill), sociology, neurosyphilis, and chess. He had the intangible quality of being able to surround himself with men of drive and spark.[1] Immediately, the Hospital became a place of intellectual stimulation. Under Southard the state and the Harvard Medical School joined hands in the care of the mentally ill and the functions of the Psychopathic Hospital were broadly interpreted to include not only treatment, but also research into the causes of mental illness and the teaching of many student and professional groups.

Although the capacity of the Hospital was only 110 beds, the turnover was rapid. In the first fiscal year more than 1,500 patients were treated, and in the second year more than 2,000. This number far exceeded the original estimate, even though a very broad range of services had been expected from the Hospital. The result was that both the director and his staff were overburdened with administrative details. To prevent the diverting of their energies from clinical, scientific, and research work, the position of administrator (chief executive officer) was introduced into the organization in 1915. This action eventually led to the problem of divided control and conflicts over policies concerning patient care.

As the activities of the Hospital became differentiated, the help of many persons of diverse skills was required. Thus, there were early created departments of psychology, occupational therapy, hydrotherapy, social work, pathology, therapeutic research, as well as a large and thriving outpatient facility. Southard emphasized also laboratory tests and procedures and gave attention to the proper medical "work-up" of each case. A training program for physicians from state hospitals was added to the work of teaching medical students and others. As the reputation of the Hospital grew, there commenced an influx of personnel and visitors from all over the nation, while the rapid turnover of staff members reflected growing recognition of the importance of the training as a springboard for im-

[1] Some of the original members of Dr. Southard's team were: Administration, E. H. Cohoon and A. P. Noyes; Chief Medical Officers, H. M. Adler and A. Myerson; Outpatient Department, H. M. Adler, A. W. Stearns, D. A. Thom; Psychology, R. M. Yerkes; Social Work, M. C. Jarrett; Pathology, M. M. Canavan and O. J. Raeder; Therapeutic Research, H. C. Solomon.

portant positions elsewhere. However, while the intellectual stimulation was considerable, the orientation was in many respects away from the patient, especially his immediate living problems. Enthusiasm was primarily for hydrotherapy, chemicals to control distraught behavior, and studies of metabolism, neuropathology, and syphilis of the nervous system with its dramatic neurological signs.

In 1920 the second director of the Psychopathic Hospital, Dr. C. Macfie Campbell, took office.[1] During his long tenure from 1920 to 1943 the basic lines of work laid down by his predecessor were carried forward. Dr. Campbell became famous for his intensive teaching of resident physicians. He was one of the early exponents of dynamic psychiatry, and helped many young men begin their careers in psychoanalysis, although he criticized the doctrinaire thinking of some of the psychoanalysts. His basic point of view was Meyerian, that is, emphasis on the individual's total adaptation to his environment. He was an energetic student and thinker, a master of the literature in many fields, and one of the most gifted men of his time in precise formulation and description of psychiatric processes. But ward care of patients still lagged and the deeply personal significance of hospitalization to the mentally ill was largely glossed over. There were relatively few attempts to use the physical and social environment of the Hospital for the patient's benefit, and its therapeutic possibilities were not fully appreciated.

In 1943 Dr. Campbell was succeeded by Dr. Harry C. Solomon, who had been closely associated with the Hospital since its opening in 1912, and had collaborated with both Southard and Campbell. Our discussion of the ward-care program of Boston Psychopathic Hospital as outlined in the fol-

---

[1] Although originally a branch of Boston State Hospital and under the superintendent of that institution, the functions of the Psychopathic Hospital were so obviously different, in view of its research work, instruction of medical students and training of specialized workers, the large turnover of diagnostic problems, and involvement in the larger problems of general psychiatry, that a separate organizational plan of administration was soon deemed desirable. In 1920, a few days before the death of Dr. Southard, Boston Psychopathic Hospital became an independent unit of the Department of Mental Diseases.

lowing pages is essentially based on developments after 1943. These developments stemmed from a number of reforms in patient care, some of which had taken shape in the thinking of Dr. Solomon during his years of private practice, teaching, and research, and some of which arose from active trial and error by the psychiatric staff which he assembled. Immediately upon his accession to the position of medical director, however, he was confronted with the problem of control of hospital policy.

PROBLEMS AND PHILOSOPHY OF THE NEW MEDICAL DIRECTOR

For years authority had been divided between the medical director, whose lines of communication were mostly with Harvard University, and the chief executive officer, who was the administrative arm of the State Department of Mental Health.[1] Theoretically, the chief executive officer was subordinate to the medical director, but practically he controlled the purse strings and generally called the tune. This could, and often did, hamstring the medical director in developing his program of ward care. His suggestions for improving the physical appearance of the wards, providing a better social and recreational program, and even altering procedures for medical care could be tabled or vetoed in the name of "economy." During the twenty-three years of Dr. Campbell's regime as head psychiatrist, a succession of executive officers were in power, some of whom collaborated amiably with the distinguished psychiatrist, some were indifferent, and some openly antagonistic to his plans for the treatment of patients. The executive officer rationalized his position when necessary by contending that a relatively neutral person, that is, one more distant from patients, would not be carried away by impulsive enthusiasm in regard to care of the sick; and could therefore run the Hospital more efficiently and economically. To some extent this was based upon the distrust that many administrators charged with effi-

[1] This division of responsibility and authority at the top grew in part from the excessive demands upon the medical director for teaching, research, and writing, resulting from his position as professor of psychiatry at the Medical School.

cient management of hospital affairs have toward "the intellectual."

At Boston Psychopathic Hospital the turn of events was as follows. With the change of Commissioner of Mental Health of Massachusetts in 1941 and appointment of a new medical director in 1943, a plan for bringing all administration under the direction of the latter was adopted. As soon as authority was centered in one person there was the advantage of control of hospital policy and flexibility. The medical director no longer had to ask for administrative approval for every move.

A broader and more flexible role having been worked out, the Department of Mental Health lent the Hospital a half-time administrative assistant in 1944 to get the business office in order. We mention this only because it was the first important test of the authority of the medical director and presaged a new era of administrative freedom. In both personality and theory of hospital management the administrative assistant differed from the medical director. At times critical differences of opinion arose, but when the medical director made his wishes clear they were promptly carried out. For example, the administrative assistant felt that he should countersign all letters written by hospital personnel. The medical director believed that this was an abuse of professional freedom and department responsibility, and that it was an unnecessary centralization of authority, which in the long run could only reduce department identity and breed resentment. His judgment ruled and the practice was discontinued.

There soon emerged a pattern of changes in hospital administration that showed even more clearly the thinking of the new director. His intention was to delegate as much authority as possible and thus spread the responsibility among the entire staff—nonmedical as well as medical—deepen their sense of importance, increase their contribution to the functioning of the Hospital, and through them reach the patients. He felt that patients had great potentialities for improvement if they were put in a favorable environment. By and large this consisted of a personnel-patient relationship founded on understanding, sympathy, kindliness, and recognition of the rights of the individual. Opportunities for development of self-respect by personnel and patients alike would have to be provided, with a chance for release of initiative, and reward in terms of acceptance of their ideas and behavior.

THE "SECURITY MOTIF"

In accordance with this general philosophy attention was turned to the details of the patients' lives. The first attack was against the concept of "security"—"security" against suicide, "security" against damage to others, and so on. Not only were the aids to good living meager, but a great variety of restrictive practices prevailed. The windows were barred, the heavy ward doors locked. On the admission wards there were seven seclusion rooms for 28 patients, a ratio of one to four. In addition, six tubs for prolonged baths were almost constantly in use. If seclusion and tubs were not adequate for these 28 patients, packs and physical restraints were called into service. Also, attempts were frequently made to treat or prevent adverse behavior by the use of sedation.[1]

In the name of "security" a number of further indignities were visited on the patients. They could not have their own clothes but were required to wear hospital pajamas, drawers, or torn, bedraggled dressing gowns, the purpose of which was to prevent escape or, in the event of escape, to simplify their identification and apprehension. Patients wore soft slippers because shoes were considered dangerous weapons, especially women's high-heeled shoes. Soft slippers, moreover, would make it more difficult for escapees to get far, especially in the rain or snow.

Furniture consisted of large heavy chairs and tables, uncomfortable and uninviting but heavy enough so that they could not be swung. The use of matches was largely prohibited for fear of damage by fire. Smoking was allowed only in small toilet rooms, under supervision, with matches and cigarettes supplied by nurses and attendants on request from the patient.

[1] See Chapter 2.

There was no place to sit while smoking other than on the toilet. Usually the patient took a few puffs while standing.

All of these measures, it must be noted, failed to accomplish the objective for which they were devised; they were essentially self-defeating, since they tended to promote a feeling of restriction and repression, of fear and punitiveness. Seclusion, packs, tubs, chemical and physical restraints failed to reduce disturbed behavior. Exchanging ragged, unsightly apparel for the patient's own clothes did not prevent escape. Substituting torn slippers for shoes did not stop running away or dangerous assault. The patient proved equal to the challenge of turning heavy furniture to diabolical ends. Finally, since smoking was largely prohibited, or permitted under the most unsatisfying conditions, the patients stole or smuggled matches and cigarettes, and fires frequently broke out in remote corners of the corridors, and even in seclusion rooms in which patients had been locked.

ADMISSION OF PATIENTS

Before the change in administrative policy the admission of patients was a classic example of man's insensitivity to man, under the guise of psychiatric treatment. The old admission office was in the rear of the Hospital; the entrance was through a large swinging iron gate. The room was bare, undecorated; the admission officers abrupt, impersonal. Patients, sometimes manacled, who were disturbed or fearful, were hurried through a series of questions and then given over to an attendant for introduction to the seclusion section of the ward, by way of a forbidding back staircase. This series of potentially traumatic events was known as the "admission procedure." A large percentage of patients offered physical resistance, but admitting personnel knew how to deal with *that*.

As soon as the patient appeared on the ward, he was forced to take a bath. Attendants and nurses had been inculcated with fear of contamination; each new patient was considered a potential source of filth, disease, and infestation. Not only were his clothes removed (and he never saw them again unless, at a later date, he was transferred to the convalescent ward), but he was deprived of spectacles, dentures, money, rings, everything personal or sentimental. Although it was recognized that patients with gross defects in visual acuity would be handicapped without their glasses in attempting to cope with the new environment, the practice of immediately putting all spectacles under lock and key continued for years. Removal of dentures sometimes made communication difficult and the none-too-palatable hospital food indigestible. Forcibly stripping and bathing patients and removing possessions of sentimental value often gave rise to, or exaggerated, delusional fears, such as that the patient was to be castrated or raped, that the Hospital was a house of prostitution, or that the individual was the victim of white slave traffic. Imagine the fears of a young woman supporting the strain of separation from her husband in military service when wedding ring, trinkets, and photographs were taken away from her.

Not a little of the turmoil of admission, it must be said, was due to misguided relatives and friends, who in desperation were forced to bring disturbed or unmanageable patients to the Hospital, despite their own fear of psychiatric institutions. The patients, too, harbored many of the fears of mental illness and of the mental hospital that prevailed in their community. Although satisfactory classification of the gamut of anxieties they suffered cannot readily be made, the following rather primary terrors were recognized as needing elimination: fear of being locked up and of never being released, fear of danger from other patients and of brutality from personnel, and fear of not receiving treatment.

A study of patients newly admitted to Massachusetts mental hospitals revealed that some of them were so preoccupied with fear of brutality from personnel, or of danger from other patients, that they had no time to worry about not receiving treatment.[1] A concern with treatment often represented the

[1] Elwell, Richard N., "Brief Study of Admissions to a Psychiatric Hospital." Paper presented in a graduate course in psychiatric nursing at Boston Psychopathic Hospital, May, 1951.

beginning of a more positive response to their environment, and in many instances was welcomed as a favorable sign.

Patients' anxieties are best conveyed in their own words. A paranoid bank-teller tried to rush out of the ward whenever the door was opened. Later, after he had improved he explained, "Because the doors are locked it seems more like a jail. I have no fears about the ward, I am just worried about my wife and children." At a meeting of Patient Government one of the members exclaimed dramatically to the staff, "We are here waiting on time. I want some of your freedom to go home and pay my gas bill. You are killing my nature locking me up and putting the keys in your pocket." Another patient, aged forty, was depressed and suicidal following the loss of his job three weeks prior to admission. He felt unable to face his responsibilities, and suffered progressively disturbing phobias that had begun in mid-adolescence and had become aggravated since his marriage.

> When I came to Ward 2, I was afraid. When they gave me a bath, I saw them move the controls and felt that they were going to spray me with cold water. You know all the stories you hear about hospitals and how the patients are treated. Day by day I saw that those things didn't happen here. The other thing I feared most was being sent away to one of the larger state hospitals. I got over that when I saw patients going home from here.

Still another patient remarked that when he was asked to remove his clothes he expected to be put into a straitjacket. One young veteran who had been a patient at various times in four different psychiatric hospitals expressed fear of not receiving treatment as follows: "I hope that they can do something for me here. I've been in hospitals before but all they do is let you lie around. I want to get treatment but I'm afraid I'll be sidetracked again."

While the majority of newly admitted patients fear the mental hospital, fear incarceration, fear chronic disease, fear death ("the only way I'll get out of here is in a box"), a few psychotic persons suffer from such intense feelings of persecution in their family and community setting that the hospital may be em-

braced as a haven of refuge. Their fears of the institutional
environment are dwarfed by comparison with their fears of
the outer world. For example, one patient suffering from delusions of impending disaster and suspecting that the F.B.I. was
following him, felt relatively greater security and safety on
the ward. The knowledge that seclusion rooms were available
as a place of refuge gave him comfort.

SOFTENING THE BLOW OF ADMISSION

The first attempts at Boston Psychopathic Hospital to improve the admission procedure were to make the admission
office more attractive by adding furniture, pictures, bright
draperies, and a carpet. Admitting personnel—consisting of the
physician who obtained identifying data about the patient and
tentatively appraised the nature and severity of his disorder,
a male attendant, and a female attendant or nurse—were requested not to hurry the procedure, to give the patient adequate
time. The male attendant was instructed to stay in the background, and the female attendant or nurse was assigned to
take the patient to the ward. There the latter was *asked* if he
wanted a bath. His own clothing and personal possessions were
not taken away from him. Instead, he was introduced to his new
surroundings and instructed in the use of facilities in much the
same manner as in a college dormitory.

Once their interest was aroused in reducing the traumatic
aspects of admission, attendants and nurses cooperated in a
gratifying manner. Doubtless, they remembered their own
experiences in attempting to gain acceptance in a new environment, whether neighborhood, school, club, or social gathering.
Discussions concerning the problem of introducing new persons
to the ward showed the personnel highly sensitive to patients'
needs and often imaginative in devising ways of reassuring
them. For example:

ATTENDANT E: When I admitted Patient A, I apologized for the
fact that no patients were on the ward and told her they were
in occupational therapy or hydrotherapy. I was alone with her. I
went through the routine of admission, and then took her to the

kitchen and gave her a glass of milk. She told me that she was a nurse and had been taking insulin. I asked her if she had come to continue her treatment and she said that she didn't think so. She was very quiet. I took her to the sun porch and gave her some magazines.

PHYSICIAN: When the other patients came down from occupational therapy did they talk to her?

ATTENDANT E: I introduced her to them.

PHYSICIAN: How do you decide whom to introduce the new patient to?

ATTENDANT J M: Usually we decide which patients on the ward are most cooperative and introduce the new patient to them, and ask them to show him or her around. If the most friendly patients are grouped together playing cards, I take the new patient up to the whole group.

ATTENDANT J B: I have found that if a patient is confused and fearful it is best not to introduce him to more than one or two persons. It may confuse and frighten him to have to meet too many at once.

PHYSICIAN: How much does the head nurse have to do with it?

HEAD NURSE W: When I was on the admission ward, I used to introduce new patients to the friendliest persons and tell them the rules and routine of the ward and the entertainment schedule. I told them that in warm weather they would be able to go out in the yard. I told them that this would be their home for a while and we would try to make them happy.

ATTENDANT E: If the new patient arrives just before mealtime, I look for a vacant seat and introduce the patient to a talkative group, explaining that this is his or her seat. It gives him an opening to talk to the others.

ATTENDANT J D: Once when I was admitting a patient, the ward was a mess. The head nurse was straightening things out. I explained to him that the ward was not always like that. Then I told him of the routine regulations of the ward, that we had a list of regulations posted on the bulletin board, and I suggested that he make himself familiar with it. Most of the patients were off the ward at occupational therapy. When they came down I introduced him to members of the patient governing committee and suggested that they take him around to meet the other patients, make him feel at home, and explain at length the other things that I had not had time to mention. He seemed quite happy about it. In a very few hours he felt quite at home.

Each experience that the patient has with personnel and

with other patients may serve either to dispel or aggravate his fears. There is no physical escape from the ward in which he is locked. He must adjust to the new situation as it exists despite his state of disturbed perception and inner turmoil. Hence, he has powerful motivation to test it out and see if his fears are justified. Alleviation of fears depends not only on his finding that they are unfounded, but upon meeting someone who is friendly and understanding. It is usually through a particular individual that introduction to the group takes place. One patient told of the careful attention given to her sore arm by the admitting physician as the key to relief of her fears. Another found a generous patient, who offered him an extra shirt just at the moment when the attendant was apologizing for a shortage, the key to his first positive feelings. "The nurses made me feel safe," said one man who consequently believed he could always turn to them for help. The paranoid bank-teller said, "My opinion of the attendants is that they are all right, conscientious, on the job, pleasant, which sometimes means a great deal more than being capable." A hospitalized graduate student commented, "Mr. C [attendant] introduced me to the ward; he very much wanted to be a good guy. He seemed to understand and take an interest in me. I also liked the fact that no one held it against a patient when he was violent. When he came out [of seclusion] everybody was friendly."

How great an influence may be exerted by the young nursing student on a male disturbed ward is apparent from the remark of a fearful patient. "I was a bit leery about coming here. To tell the truth I was scared of what the patients might be like until I saw those young kid nurses. I said, 'What the hell! If they can be here, it can't be so bad,' and I wasn't scared after that." A large proportion of women admitted to the disturbed ward gave credit to the admitting social worker for softening the blow of admission. She had explained in detail the stresses to be expected. On several occasions the technique has been used by social workers and staff psychiatrists of bringing the patient to visit the ward some time before his actual admission, introducing him to the staff, explaining the functions of the hospital and showing him around, so that he could become familiar with the environment in which he was to live. Some caution must obviously be exercised in utilizing this technique, for the patient's tour through the ward is counted on to allay, rather than exaggerate, fears and anxieties.

A link with the world outside the hospital, a reminder that one is in touch with the community, can be an important security-giving experience. One patient was pleasantly surprised when he found that there was an old friend among the patients to whom he was introduced. "One of the nicest things was turning on the radio and feeling that the outside and inside were one," was another revealing insight. "It was a pleasant experience to find such activities as ping-pong . . . and I'll never forget when they wheeled the television set in."

Thus, the orientation that the patient receives may spell the difference between fear and security. During the strategic hour of arrival not only attendants and nurses, but other patients are a vital part of the therapeutic environment. As we learn more about this critical period, we may be able to make assignments of particular patients or personnel to help new arrivals. Since patients themselves have all experienced the stresses of admission, they should be freely consulted as one of the most insightful resources for improving admission. This is a function in which Patient Government manifests deep and continued interest.

REORGANIZING THE FRONT OFFICE

Attention to details that might disturb the impressionable patient was found to lead to improvement in the physical surroundings; it also heightened the staff's awareness of the traumatic aspects of hospitalization, and brought into the foreground the need for still greater sensitivity and understanding in personal relationships with patients. This new awareness soon brought further changes. For example, the admission office was moved from the rear to the front of the Hospital. Patients came in through the main door as in most general hospitals, and the whole admission procedure was brought into public view. Some employees warned the Hospital that the strange behavior of psychotic patients and their struggles against admission would greatly upset persons in the front lobby. Such fears were unfounded. As with all other changes which removed causes of unpleasantness and added a feeling of acceptance and security, the patients responded in a most perceptive manner. The admission procedure became less stressful and tumultuous.

Before 1943 two executive physicians occupying the "front" or "executive" office handled incoming calls, dealt with relatives, and admitted patients. Here were highly trained physicians performing tasks that were considered "routine administration" or essentially nonmedical; tasks that could have been performed with perhaps more enthusiasm by a skilled secretary or receptionist. In this setting, contact with relatives was often impersonal and perfunctory; hence, permission for diagnostic studies, such as lumbar punctures or special x-rays, was difficult to obtain and treatment recommendations were often rejected by the relatives or accepted reluctantly. Not infrequently the contact left family members with a feeling of coldness, or lack of flexibility of personnel in response to special requests that they believed to be for the comfort or convenience of patients.

The retirement of one of the executive physicians made possible a change. No new person was appointed to replace the senior officer; instead, his junior was elevated in rank. A clerk, who had shown especial proficiency during several years of service in the record room, was selected as secretary, and Miss Anne P. Ogilby, a psychiatric social worker, with family agency experience and skill in working with individuals and groups, completed the trio. This reshuffling made the admission procedure unhurried, improved the handling of relatives, and extended personal service to more individuals. The executive psychiatrist began to function more at the supervisory and policy-making level, while the executive social worker undertook the task of providing continuity of service to patients from admission, through hospitalization, to discharge.

The patient "waiting list," which had always been something of a bone of contention because of the clamor for beds, came in for considerable revision. For years this list had been made up of names of prospective patients whose physicians or relatives were pressing for their admission. The honor of a bed at the Hospital often went to a patient whose physician could talk most plausibly about an emergency, or who had the greatest influence with the admitting officer on duty or with some member of the senior staff. This procedure tended to create a feeling of injustice and resentment on the part of physicians in the community who felt they were not on the "inside." A new policy of admission based on strict adherence to consecutive order on the waiting list plus, so far as possible, an impartial review of the treatment potentialities of each case, did much to improve relations with physicians in the community and strengthen their confidence in the Hospital.

The executive social worker immediately began to cultivate the strategic possibilities of her position. She became acquainted with a patient and his relatives before admission; at the time of admission she carefully explored with them plans for his rehabilitation in the community, and during the hospitalization period she became an information and social service center. Upon the patient's discharge she brought to realization the plans that had begun to develop at the moment he crossed the threshold of the institution. With the integration and unification of the social service functions of the Hospital through this social worker, a great improvement in morale was noted. Relatives began to see hospitalization much more as a temporary procedure, and patients as possessing potentialities for recovery. Questions about where the patient would live, who would look after him, how his social life could be enriched, and whether his job would be kept open for him began to replace the former expectation of chronicity of disease, prolonged hospitalization, and closing of community ranks against the unfortunate deranged. With hope aroused, relatives began to show eagerness to contribute to the therapeutic process. Their resistance to giving permission for diagnostic or treatment procedures, which had so often been the focal point of combat between them and hospital authorities, thus delaying therapy for extended periods, evaporated like mist before a bright sun. The combined efforts of social worker and relatives toward making or keeping a place in the community for the hospitalized patient facilitated the process of discharge, saved the Commonwealth of Massachusetts the cost of countless patient days, and in effect, ended the transfer of certain patients from "The Psychopathic" to a chronic hospital because "they had no home to go to."

2. Eliminating Major Evils

THIS WRITER WELL REMEMBERS how, on his first psychiatric rounds at Boston Psychopathic Hospital in December, 1941, the noise, tumult, and disorganization of the admission ward struck him with depressing force. Bare and repelling, it was home to 28 patients—who ate and slept there. Some were without clothes except for fragments of bathrobes and "johnnies"; many were without shoes or slippers and were walking around barefoot. The patients were disheveled, agitated, grotesque, posturing. Some retreated into corners or approached us with profanity; others demanded favors, hungry for attention. To a young intern the total scene was frightening, but it was as nothing compared to the shock of seeing patients in seclusion.

SECLUSION

At the back of the ward were seven seclusion rooms from which emanated most of the noise, confusion, and odor. One peered into these cells through narrow windows at revolting pictures of deteriorated life. There one often saw naked persons living in their own excreta, terribly hostile, repressed, or crushed. Few physicians were brave enough to make rounds on secluded patients without being accompanied by attendants, whose obvious role was that of bodyguard. To enter these cells was to risk vituperation or physical attack. Upon leaving a seclusion room the physician stepped lively, fearing either his own capture or sudden escape of the patient.

On many occasions one witnessed the degree to which tensions were produced in patients and personnel alike when fellow human beings were physically overpowered, dragged screaming and kicking through the wards, protesting in panic that they were to be burned, flogged, or killed—which in their deluded state they believed to be true.

Once in a seclusion room, how did patients behave? They raged for hours, pounded on the door until knuckles were raw, tore holes in the wall plaster, destroyed the "indestructible" mattress, broke windows and screens, ripped soundproofing from the ceilings, or removed ventilators. Often they turned against themselves, ripped their clothes, or pounded their bodies. Behind locked doors and without easy access to toilet facilities, they emptied bladder and bowel. Any physician with experience in hospital psychiatry has seen all this and more— fire-setting in the seclusion room, hangings, ingenious escapes, barricadings. Not infrequently physical complications set in: dehydration, infections of bruises and lacerations, exhaustion and delirium, fevers and sepsis.

Reaction of Patients and Personnel

Patients themselves leave little doubt as to their feeling about seclusion. In gathering data in several institutions about the attitudes of patients and staff toward many aspects of hospital life, Richard Hobson, who has already been mentioned in the Introduction, used the device of presenting to both staff and patients a series of pictures depicting ward life.[1] One of the pictures shows a man, lying naked on a mattress in a seclusion room, an attendant standing by. This is a familiar scene to workers in psychiatric hospitals and to many patients who have suffered or witnessed this form of "treatment." One patient, who had been in seclusion, said: "It reminds me of being treated just like an animal, but even an animal has more shelter than that. He can do nothing but curse, get rid of his emotional irritation. I can't see any benefit from that kind of treatment."

Said a second patient: They [secluded patients] have an awful horror of being locked up. They can stay in a room, but let them bar a door and then those guys will say, "I'm gonna get out of here, or else." It's like a padded cell, stripped of everything. Strip him of his clothes so he won't hang himself. The only thing is that if he gnawed away the mattress he could have all the bloody

[1] The writer is indebted to Mr. Hobson for permission to use these data.

rope in the world. The string that ties the mattress would give you enough twine to hang 40 men. You should see what Henry R can do to an indestructible mattress. He gets a thumbnail into a corner of it, extracts a piece, and the first thing you know he's made it look like shoelaces.

Another patient remarked: No human being should be thrown into a room with the door locked, because it's the most atrocious thing—I would say that it's almost like Christ crucified on the cross. I was in seclusion with no clothes at all, with a dirty, lousy mattress. When they threw the food in, they just threw it on the floor. You eat like a dog and when the attendants take you out they give you a punch in the stomach. I'll think of that the rest of my life. You're very uncomfortable, your body is dirty, you're itching with bed bugs and crabs. The rooms are not clean at all, they are smelly, and the floors are messed up.

And still another declared: The worst they could ever do to a patient. I'll tell you the actual experience of being in one. I was all that night on the floor. I was all drugged up. You say, "What the hell good is living?" You say, "The first so-and-so that gets to you, you are going to let him have it." Like a dog when you chain him and then let him loose, he is going to go wild.

Reactions of patients who have *not* been in seclusion are worth noting. The tensions of living in close quarters with disturbed or excited individuals led a few to admit to Mr. Hobson that they were relieved when excited members of the ward were "out of the way." One modified the statement "Sometimes we just wish they would get locked up" by adding the significant clause "but not for as long as they are," while another said, "It makes a difference if the person is really bad—I don't feel so unhappy about his being in seclusion if he is really bad." In contrast to such views several patients declared that they were "scared to death" of being put in seclusion; that excited patients should be given something to do; that seclusion probably did not make individuals calm down. One person expressed this last idea as follows: "It is depressing to see someone else in a bare, locked room. Like taking an animal out of a forest. It makes him more wild." Another person said of seclusion, "That's the way I was punished as a child—locked up."

Ward staff have confused feelings about seclusion and difficulty in accepting it as treatment. Three nursing students, for example, faced with the problems of adaptation to a new environment, offered different interpretations. One said that it was done for punishment: "Then patients get rebellious because they think you have put them there." A second viewed it as a protective measure rather than a punishment, while a third added that it was for the patient's protection as well as for that of other patients. A characteristic comment of many nurses was this: "Sometimes we feel guilty; we should have seen the situation coming up so that we could have done something about it."

The underlying punitive meanings that most patients and personnel attach to seclusion became obvious one day in a lively discussion during a psychodrama session at Boston Psychopathic Hospital on the theme of "justice," in which both patients and staff participated. One head nurse suggested that when there is a ward disturbance, it is hard to question everyone and make the right decision about who is responsible. Thereupon Patient A inquired what one had to do to be eligible to be locked up! Patient B replied, "Almost anything. It just isn't fair. The nurse doesn't get the details. She whams the first person in without being sure it is the person who started it."[1] Patient C agreed that "that is just what happens an awful lot." He wanted to know why the staff did not keep records of behavior and watch patients all the time.

Thus, the ward atmosphere is clouded by fear of punishment and a sense of injustice, to say nothing of the sense of guilt of personnel who have participated in an act of degrading other human beings against their will. Unrelieved guilt leads to self-justifying attitudes, which make the situation even more difficult.

Seclusion Can Be Reduced

At Boston Psychopathic Hospital seclusion was for many years one of the recognized and accepted practices most heavily relied on for the management of disturbed patients, and the thought of doing without even one seclusion room was, as late

[1] While a physician's signature is required for all patients in seclusion, the head nurse is often given considerable latitude of judgment as to which disturbed person or persons should be secluded, especially in "emergencies."

as 1943, almost inconceivable. The staff attitude was that seclusion was necessary to protect both patients and personnel
from belligerent, unpredictable persons. Without seclusion,
attendants would have no choice but to resort to roughness and
physical violence in order to subdue dangerous patients.

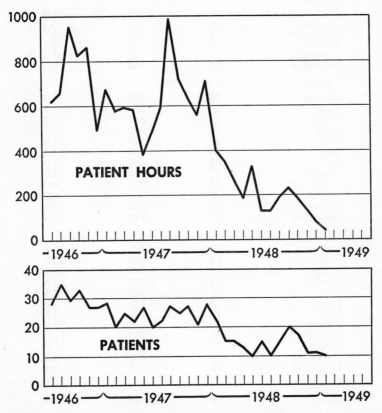

CHART 1. PATIENT HOURS AND PATIENTS IN SECLUSION, BOSTON
PSYCHOPATHIC HOSPITAL, JULY, 1946 TO JANUARY, 1949

Although pressure toward reduction of seclusion was steadily
maintained by the Hospital's administrative psychiatrists after
1943, it was not until July, 1946, that a sustained attack was
made on this problem. Even then there was marked fluctuation
for a year and a half in the use of seclusion rooms, as indicated
by the accompanying chart and table which detail the number

TABLE 1. DECREASING USE OF SECLUSION, ALL WARDS
OF BOSTON PSYCHOPATHIC HOSPITAL, JULY,
1946, TO JANUARY, 1949, BY MONTH

Month	Patients in seclusion	Patient-hours in seclusion	Hours in seclusion per patient
1946			
July	28	614	21.9
August	35	657	18.8
September	29	952	32.8
October	33	829	25.1
November	27	862	31.9
December	27	494	18.3
1947			
January	28	673	24.0
February	20	580	29.0
March	25	597	23.9
April	22	582	26.5
May	27	386	14.3
June	20	480	24.0
July	22	595	27.0
August	27	996	36.9
September	25	725	29.0
October	27	636	23.6
November	21	558	26.6
December	28	714	25.5
1948			
January	22	405	18.4
February	15	352	23.5
March	15	256	17.1
April	13	189	14.5
May	10	335	33.5
June	15	131	8.7
July	10	131	13.1
August	15	192	12.8
September	20	233	11.7
October	17	188	11.1
November	11	135	12.3
December	11	81	7.4
1949			
January	10	46	4.6

of seclusion hours for all wards, month by month, between July,
1946, and January, 1949. September and November, 1946,
figures stand out as conspicuously high with another peak in
August, 1947. During September, 1946, a total of 952 hours of
seclusion was reported. The patients in seclusion numbered
29 (17 men and 12 women). In November, 1946, the total

seclusion hours were 862 distributed among 17 men and 10 women. In August, 1947, 11 men and 16 women were in seclusion for a total of 996 hours. *There were many months during which one-quarter to one-third of the patients in the Hospital were either locked in seclusion at one time or another or subjected to physical restraints for disturbed behavior.* Throughout this period the whole hospital atmosphere reflected the strain of forcibly separating so many patients from the ward society and keeping them separated against their will.

The period from January, 1948, to January, 1949, was one of rapid abandonment of seclusion as a major method of control of disturbed patients. In January, 1949, four men and six women saw seclusion at some time during the month (for a total of 46 hours). The figures show that in a relatively short period a virtual mastery of the problem was achieved. To talk about seclusion hours, however, intellectualizes the problem and takes away the impact of suffering that each hour represents to the patient, and to all those persons on the ward who may believe he is being unnecessarily isolated. One must constantly be reminded that every seclusion hour means *punishment* to all but the exceptional patient who needs the feeling of added protection, whereas sick, hospitalized persons have a right to expect understanding and constructive treatment.

Since the question is still raised whether the drastic reduction in seclusion accomplished at a small institution with a large staff such as Boston Psychopathic Hospital can be repeated in a large hospital with appreciably smaller staff, we wish to point to the favorable results achieved in the two other institutions of 1,800 or more beds, which will be described in later sections of this book. By a direct frontal attack upon this problem, Dr. Jay L. Hoffman, chief of professional services,[1] and his staff, succeeded in reducing seclusion in the Bedford V.A. Hospital from 2,900 hours in February, 1952, when the pro-

[1] The position of chief of professional services as defined by the Veterans Administration is broader than that of clinical director in most hospitals, inasmuch as it connotes administrative responsibility for all categories of professional personnel. However, the more familiar term "clinical director" will be used interchangeably with chief of professional services in this book.

gram started, to 26 hours in November, 1952. The number of secluded patients during this period fell from 18 to one. At the Metropolitan State Hospital, with extremely limited personnel and with a very large complement of chronic patients, seclusion has also been greatly reduced. The remarkable work of Granville Hopkins and others at Metropolitan in making this possible will be discussed subsequently by Dr. York.[1] Indeed, it appears that whenever a determined and steadfast effort has been initiated to cut down on the use of seclusion, success has followed. There is every reason to believe that excessive *dependence* on this method of "treating" psychotic individuals can be as much outgrown as the chains which were struck off the mentally ill in 1792 by Philippe Pinel.

Administrative Role in Reduction of Seclusion

Analysis shows that three factors contributed to the reduction of seclusion. The first was the conviction of administrative personnel that seclusion could be reduced, with their support and the encouragement of ward staffs who were directly concerned in bringing it about. Experience suggests that active psychological support by the administration is essential, for in any change of hospital functioning as radical as elimination of seclusion, a stressful period of readjustment is encountered and unless new methods of doing things are repeatedly and actively rewarded, the old equilibrium tends to reassert itself.

We were interested to learn from the medical director of Boston Psychopathic Hospital how and when he became convinced that seclusion and other forms of restraint could be eliminated. Dr. Solomon's experience in private practice first led him to believe that disturbances in the behavior of patients could often be traced to procedures in managing them and not to the disease. Time and again he was called to attend patients with depressive, agitated, or schizophrenic trends, who in their home settings were behaving quite satisfactorily. When sent to the hospital they flared up violently as the probable result of the cold environment, impersonal handling, and the coercive,

[1] See Chapter 17.

punitive attitude of the staff, implemented by restraint, tubs, packs, chemical sedation, and seclusion. In 1917 he visited a large psychopathic hospital in Toronto, in which there was virtual absence of personnel because of the severe wartime drain upon Canada's manpower. Patients were admitted to the wards directly, without elaborate procedures, clothes were not removed, admission baths were not forced upon them. Despite the paucity of personnel, patients were amazingly well behaved.

Another observation that contributed to Dr. Solomon's attitude was the successful administration of a small private hospital near Boston. Largely as the result of a progressive program instituted by the resident director, Dr. George Schlomer, a man of vast clinical experience, acute psychotic patients were managed essentially without packs, seclusion, or prolonged baths. Dr. Schlomer took what others would have regarded as "risks," risks which at that time required courage, but which led to a more relaxed environment with wide limits to permissiveness, greater trust, and less disturbed behavior of patients.

The conviction of the clinical director of Bedford that seclusion could be eliminated came after learning that in some other Veterans Administration institutions, not so generously staffed as his own, restraints and seclusion were things of the past. Said Dr. Hoffman:

In 1948 I attended a meeting of 30 clinical directors from various hospitals throughout the country. Because the meeting was held in a small town and there were no hotel facilities available to accommodate us, we found ourselves placed in a ward in the hospital with 30 beds. We got around to exchanging experiences, and I learned much from my colleagues. I remember one doctor from a hospital somewhere in the South, who told me that there were no restraints in his hospital; and at Bedford at the time we had three types of restraint—sheets, packs, and tubs. Another doctor spoke of having two swimming pools, thereby cutting down on hydrotherapy. At Bedford we had the hydrotherapy room open twenty-four hours a day, seven days a week; we have since cut this down to seven hours. From another doctor

I got the idea of taking the doors off the seclusion rooms. I said to him, "What happens when you do this?" He very calmly replied, "Nothing, it works out very well." I came away from the meeting feeling very humble; if they could do it with so few facilities, why couldn't we do it at Bedford where we have so much?

Inclusion of Attendants in the Treatment Program

The second factor contributing to successful elimination of seclusion was the conscious inclusion of attendants (and other ward personnel) in the treatment program.[1] This step is a *sine qua non* in any project for improved ward care of patients not only because quantitatively the essential manpower in mental hospitals resides in their ranks, but also because the attendant is the proximal individual with whom the patient interacts.[2] In his actions he embodies the tone of the institution: either watchdog, cold, distant, and threatening; or relaxed, friendly, and interested. It is largely the attendant-patient relationship that determines the amount and type of disturbed behavior of patients, the level of fear, the degree of arbitrary authoritarianism, and the point at which seclusion becomes the answer. The attendant can make or break the patient. He can arrange the situation so that a patient whom he fears, or against whom he harbors deep antagonism will eventually land in seclusion— and by the physician's order. It is therefore imperative for psychiatrist and head nurse especially to understand the attendant's mind, and to educate him into junior partnership in the treatment team.

Bringing attendants into membership in this team implies, first, that they be accepted as individuals; that the fears, tensions, and frustrations facing them in the performance of their jobs be recognized and handled; that steps be taken to improve their skill in dealing with sick persons who present inexplicable behavior; and that they be given access to sources of informa-

[1] The term "attendant" is used in this discussion to include psychiatric aides and technicians.

[2] The degree to which attendants are successfully incorporated into the treatment program depends in large measure on how the nurse has been educated, since in most ward programs the attendant follows her leadership.

tion that help to guide the physician in his elaborate considerations of the welfare of the patient. A goal imposed upon the attendant that carries the expectation of additional work and responsibility without increased recognition is not likely to be reached. Only by participating with the attendant in a common effort, including planning, policy-making, and carrying out projects, with full acknowledgment of the partnership and reciprocation involved, can the social aims for ward patients be achieved. If the physician is not *for* the attendants, they are almost surely against *him*.

Group sessions led by a physician, head nurse, social worker, psychologist, or other person interested in the large potential contribution of attendants to ward care, provide an excellent medium for the latter to unburden their fears, and for the formulation of better principles of patient management. If the leader assumes a nonauthoritarian and sympathetic role, the attendants gradually begin to express themselves, and to give opinions and suggestions, which when incorporated into the ward program, add immeasurably to their sense of personal worth and contribution to the goals of the institution. One attendant at Bedford said that prior to the initiation of such meetings he "felt more like a watchdog or a member of a labor battalion than a contributor to a therapeutic team." When the attendants were permitted to contribute, their own thinking was productively stimulated. They "dropped their watchdog attitude and instead of passing the tour of duty with the aid of a comic book, engaged patients in such activities as ping-pong, cards, checkers, table games, volleyball, badminton, ring-toss, and the like." A sense of common purpose, security, and belonging replaced that of isolation and self-depreciation. After the attendant had this vital experience, he was impatient for the mentally ill person to achieve the same sense of relief.

Centering these group meetings around patient problems gives the sessions vital significance not only because they teach the attendant more effective methods of handling patients and illuminate his own reaction patterns, but also because they involve him immediately in the clinical atmosphere that pervades the hospital. For example, Patient B, who presented the familiar problem of "negative" behavior, was discussed at one such meeting.[1]

ATTENDANT W: When I was bringing a patient back to the ward from evening activities, Mr. B stood at the ward door demanding to take part. I told him activities were over so he couldn't leave the ward. He tried to crowd past me, and Attendant C and I had quite a time getting him back into the ward. He fought and kept fighting and we had to place him in seclusion. I had the feeling that he knew that his demand to leave the ward was unreasonable, that he actually did it to provoke a struggle, and that he really enjoyed the struggle.

ATTENDANT S: I felt the same. He is medium size and wiry, and he almost acts as if he enjoyed making us struggle with him. He will pound on a window, harder and harder, until we come and stop him before he breaks it and cuts himself. When we ask him to stop he hits it harder, and when we take hold of his arm to prevent his hitting the window, he fights.

ATTENDANT W: He can talk quite rationally, and I feel he understands what he is doing.

DOCTOR H: So you both think he is provoking you to use force with him?

ATTENDANT W: Yes, we feel that he is not assaultive in the usual sense of the word. He has never attacked anyone, but he does things that we must interfere with.

DOCTOR H: And this isn't helping him?

ATTENDANT W: No, we realize that, but don't know what to do.

DOCTOR H: Perhaps you can let him break a window or go out of the door. You might ask his doctor if he objects to noninterference.

ATTENDANT W: This is a rather radical point of view. We spend so much time preventing these things.

DOCTOR H: You understand what he means by his aggressive gestures, but have you told him so? Have you said to him, "You seem to be trying to aggravate me by doing things I'll have to stop. Are you trying to provoke a fight?"

ATTENDANT W: No, I never told him that. Maybe I should.

DOCTOR H: You would merely be putting his action into words. You understand him very well, but you aren't letting him know that you do.

[1] Hyde, Robert W., in collaboration with the Attendants of Boston Psychopathic Hospital, *Experiencing the Patient's Day:* A Manual for Psychiatric Hospital Personnel. G. P. Putnam's Sons, New York, 1955, pp. 172–174.

[The very next day, Dr. H learned that the discussion had borne fruit.]

ATTENDANT W: You remember Mr. B. We tried what you suggested. After the meeting yesterday we returned to the ward. Mr. B had been placed in seclusion; we took him out. He demanded that we let him into the bathing room to help attendant S K paint. Then he didn't want to paint and started picking things up and spilling them. I followed your suggestion and asked him if he was just trying to provoke a fight. It worked, and he came out of the room without trouble.

DOCTOR H: Just how did he respond?

ATTENDANT W: It was effective in giving him considerable emotional release. It was much as we had figured. He said, "Yes, I'm trying to get you to scuffle with me. I'm guilty, I've sinned, and the only satisfaction I can get is having you punish me." He said this with a lot of emotion. It was really just what he felt.

[Later when Mr. B wanted to open the locked door and go out, Attendant W went with him, and when he wanted to go to occupational therapy, he was taken there. He was then willing to return to the ward.]

In this case, talking with the psychiatrist, who was the leader of the meeting, led to clarification of attitudes and specific positive suggestions as to how to handle the patient. When the punitive meaning of seclusion to patient and attendant was verbalized by both partners in the struggle, the patient's behavior improved and the issue was resolved.

Patients' problems are legion and their infinite variety presents material for continuing attendant classes. The attendant soon learns to accept some basic facts of human relationships: that his capacity for empathy varies with the type of patient; that his likes and dislikes, which appear at first to be reflex and uncontrollable, may be traced to his own special experience and upbringing; that knowing the patient better implies better understanding of himself; and that increased self-understanding gradually brings his own response under more conscious control. As the seasoned psychiatrist might suspect, in overcoming his deeper prejudices the attendant is often faced with a long slow process of maturation. This factor makes it necessary, therefore, to train the attendant by some such device as clinical teaching sessions throughout the period of his service, just as psychiatrists in training are expected to attend clinical staff conferences and teaching rounds throughout their years of postgraduate education. Although the attendant has a great deal to learn, attendant meetings, in the hands of a skillful leader, have proved to be a potent and constructive method of handling a large variety of stressful social relationships on the ward.

The following example of attendant discussions illustrates how a strong racial bias among ward personnel determined the untoward behavior of one patient, and how behavior improved as insight was rapidly gained. A Negro patient cried and wanted to fight whenever another patient insulted him because of his color. He was put into seclusion for four days because of his belligerency; he tore off the ventilator, ripped up two mattresses, and threw a tray at an attendant.[1]

ATTENDANT G: I dislike him. I can't seem to feel anything in common with him. We haven't experienced the same cultural level. I think he really doesn't want to fight. Whenever he is going to fight with another patient and we tell him to stop, he does right away and seems relieved.

DOCTOR H: It looks like panic. His hostility may be defensive.

ATTENDANT G: When he was being forced into the seclusion room, one attendant put an arm around his neck causing oxygen hunger. That's reason enough for fear.

ATTENDANT McG: How does Attendant A [Negro attendant] get along with him?

ATTENDANT G: No better. The patient says Attendant A doesn't like him.

All agreed that no one had been interested in sitting down and talking with the patient. They recognized that they could not forget the association of Negro patients of this type with knife and razor fights, an association which was repeatedly strengthened by his threat, when angry, "I'll cut you."

This session helped several members of the group identify themselves with the feelings of isolation and fear suffered by him. The next day at staff conference the ward nurse felt free to reveal her feelings about this patient, admitting concern be-

[1] Hyde, Robert W., *Ibid.*, pp. 191–192.

cause he ate so much and stole other patients' food. Affiliate nursing students were disturbed because he exposed himself. However, positive feelings also came forth. Three attendants said that after the previous day's discussion they understood the patient better, and that talking about their attitude toward him increased their liking for him. The patient soon responded to this sudden liquidation of barriers against him and stopped causing disturbance on the ward. In addition, he was taken down to physical therapy, where he seemed to be able to vent his spleen on the punching bag. He became much more relaxed.

One further lesson becomes clear in consideration of this case, that basic to any improvement in ward care is a deep understanding of the genesis of fears by personnel. The same patient may threaten different staff members in different ways, each according to the personal defenses that are most vulnerable in the situation. Here attendants feared physical assault, students feared sexual assault, while the head nurse feared disruption of her responsibility for the feeding of patients.

These are but two of many examples in which informal discussions with attendants in groups at Boston Psychopathic Hospital spelled the difference between seclusion and no seclusion. At Bedford V.A. Hospital the elimination of seclusion was made possible by the introduction of meetings with psychiatric aides, first weekly, then twice weekly. Dr. Ian Funk who pioneered in this experiment at Bedford, wrote:

> As the patients were taken out of seclusion it was quickly evident that a more tolerant attitude on the part of everyone, and especially the aides, would be necessary. For instance, B H, a patient who had been in seclusion for several years, would impulsively break anything made of glass, especially a window. I felt the only logical attitude was to ignore these actions. Just about every window in the ward that the patient could reach was broken. They were not then replaced as warm weather had set in, and after about four weeks, the patient no longer showed this behavior except on very rare occasions.

Without meetings that sought to achieve change in attitudes, this patient could never have been removed from seclusion, because the attendants were under the pressure of their own fears and those of the other patients who regarded him as a hopeless case. His orgy of window-breaking would not have been tolerated if the attendants had not felt closely identified with Dr. Funk's all-out attempt at rehabilitation. It is well to remember that to permit window-breaking is heresy against the conventional attitude that seems to place more emphasis on the preservation of hospital property than upon the treatment of patients through permitting expression. It further challenges the old fear that if pieces of glass are lying around, they will be used for suicidal or homicidal purposes.

ATTENDANT: Dr. Funk gave the order to let him break windows. He said it was because the patient wanted to get back into the seclusion room. I think it's so myself.

QUESTION: Did you notice any reactions of other patients to his breaking windows?

ATTENDANT: They resented it and they told him he was doing it out of meanness. That may have had some effect. When he tapered off from breaking windows, he would hit patients.

QUESTION: How did you handle that?

ATTENDANT: Say, he hit somebody in the morning, we would leave him in the seclusion room for only a couple of hours, and after that we would tell him to go into the day room, and he would be O.K. Now in the morning we will open the door and he'll get up, put his clothes on, and help us with the dishes.

Another patient had been secluded continuously over a six-year period because of extremely abusive behavior toward both patients and personnel. He would spit at anyone who passed. During this long period he had regressed so far as to smear feces on the walls and on his person. With the aid of chemical sedation, this patient was allowed gradually increased periods in the day room, and finally became a member of the ward society. He received much attention from all personnel, and a generally permissive attitude was adopted toward the crude and primitive displays of affection which he manifested. When he was ultimately given a chance to eat with patients whose behavior was most acceptable, his table manners even surpassed theirs. Group meetings, however, had been necessary before positive attitudes could supplant aversion sufficiently for the patient to be permitted to eat at the dinner table with his fellow patients.

Whatever helps to bring attendants into the treatment orbit, increases their identification with the goals of the hospital and makes them responsible parties in the patients' total welfare. In addition to attendant meetings, a further technique that has helped personnel see how their actions may affect patients is psychodrama. As used at Boston Psychopathic Hospital, psychodrama has many forms. One of the principal methods is to have attendants and other personnel act out their approaches to a sick patient with the goal, for example, of helping him accept some treatment that he fears, or of drawing him into some kind of social or recreational activity. Other patients who sit as a kind of jury then describe their reactions to the various approaches, and analyze the good and bad points of each. The patient upon whom the various approaches are tried comments also on how it feels to be dealt with by individuals with different personalities and techniques. One interesting modification of this procedure is to ask an attendant to play the role of the sick patient; and a complete reversal can be had when patients play the part of personnel.[1]

Through psychodrama an attempt is made to learn directly from patients, rather than from authority figures or from intellectual rationalization. This is another example of application to the ward-care process of the principle of improved communication. Communication from patient to personnel teaches the latter how patients feel about what they do, and in the reverse direction it teaches patients why personnel do the things they do. Bilateral communication leads to deeper appreciation by each of the role of the other.

Access to Records. Much can be accomplished in raising attendant morale by group meetings or psychodrama emphasizing the clinical approach, but these aids are not enough. Without access to recorded information about patients, the attendant can hardly feel that he is being admitted to the therapeutic family. Unfortunately, it is common policy to deny him

[1] Psychodrama is discussed in greater detail in Chapter 8.

the privilege of consulting patients' records, and even to exclude him from conferences in which case presentations are
being discussed. Some of the reasons given are: the attendant
does not have enough education to appreciate the significance
of the material in the record; his attitude is nonprofessional;
his interest is morbid; his knowledge may reach the wrong ears
within the hospital, and he will pass on confidential information
about patients when gossiping with friends outside the institution. It is feared that by knowing more about the patient he
may somehow interfere with the doctor's therapeutic program,
perhaps make a wrong statement, gesture, or interpretation to
the patient.

Experience, however, strongly contradicts this view. By
opening up to the attendant accurate sources of information,
he becomes more responsible rather than less so, both within
and outside the hospital. In knowing about his charges he
moves closer to them, and when he shares knowledge he becomes a better ally of the physician. Instead of basing his
understanding of the patient on gossip, conjecture, or stolen
fragments of information, he may with dignity consult the
reliable official sources. This helps to organize and professional-
ize his knowledge. Not only is it highly desirable that records
be made available to the attendant, he should be encouraged
to read them, ask questions of the nurse and psychiatrist, both
informally and in conferences, and contribute to their understanding of patients from his fund of knowledge gained through
long hours of observing the latter on the wards. It is also highly
beneficial to morale when nurses and doctors freely share their
thinking about the patient with him.

Eliminating Social Discrimination. All these measures for
raising the status of the attendant can be nullified, however,
if there is social discrimination against him or against other
ward personnel who are members of the treatment team. Generally speaking, communication between physicians and attendants is rare, the former scarcely know the attendants' faces,
let alone their names. Few words of greeting or recognition
pass between the two groups. Physicians also communicate

rarely with nursing students, although both they and attendants have the closest contact with patients.[1]

During the war years often the only people available as attendants, other than conscientious objectors in some areas, were those rejected by the armed services because of instability, inadequacy, or alcoholism. They had little interest in their job, and under the difficult working conditions then prevailing in mental hospitals, they often quit after brief service. The poor quality and rapid turnover of attendant personnel, together with the long-standing prejudice against this group of hospital workers, only perpetuated the social discriminations shown them. In many hospitals, Boston Psychopathic Hospital included, nursing students were forbidden to fraternize with them when off duty. An attendant could not "date" an affiliate. The control of both student and attendant by the despotic nursing office extended to their private lives. If the two were drawn to each other, they could meet only clandestinely, far from hospital grounds. Always present was the fear that an affiliate might marry an attendant, which would mean for her a serious loss of social status, and stories of unhappy marriages of nurses with attendants who were alcoholics or "bums" were often told. Reinforcing this ideology was the affiliates' concept of an attendant as an "orderly," a notion based on their experience in the general hospital, where the orderly was someone who performed many of the undesirable tasks. Students had to learn that attendants were not orderlies but attendant-nurses on whom the hospital was dependent for developing a therapeutic climate.

Before 1943 little recognition existed of social needs of attendants and affiliates at Boston Psychopathic Hospital. There was no place to entertain, no parlor nor lobby that either group could call its own. Space is at a great premium in a small hospital having many activities, and it would have been easy to deny personnel a place for social activities on this basis alone. Perhaps no act in the Hospital's history more clearly records the philosophy of the medical director than his assigning his

[1] See Chapter 7.

own pleasant office, waiting-room, and adjoining lobby as a place where nursing students and attendants could see their friends and visitors in the evening hours. One can imagine its significance in elevating the status of attendants and students, inasmuch as by this act the director implied that he was assuming responsibility for their social welfare, accepting their friends, and trusting them to behave in a mature manner.

In the days when hierarchical barriers were very apparent, affiliates and head nurses rarely ate with attendants. It was frowned upon by the superintendent of nurses. Although attendants might confer with nurses (to a limited extent) concerning the care of a patient on the ward, such discussion did not flow over to the meal hour, which would be a natural time for relaxed conversation between team members regarding ward problems. Communication, though inadequate, was limited to formal working hours, and informal interaction was specifically interdicted.

How did this affect the ward care of the patient? The patient was chiefly in the hands of the attendant, who was demeaned as a person by the rest of his co-workers and largely ostracized from their society. Patients sensed the antagonism between personnel, and heard hostile and belittling statements made by one against the other. Differences among staff members were "taken out" on patients, who, being extraordinarily sensitive to these antagonisms, often suffered an increase in anxiety and disorganization of behavior. Those with more paranoid proclivities played one member of personnel against the other. An unfortunate and trying situation not infrequently arose when the nursing student who had thus been put in the position of snubbing the attendant had to call upon him to protect her if the patient became violent or abusive.

Social discrimination against the attendant began to disappear with the recognition of the importance of the social environment of the Hospital, the place of the attendant in that environment, and the absolute necessity for including him in the treatment team. The ban against attendants and nursing personnel going out or eating together was lifted. Promoting the attendant's social life was recognized as important to morale, and definite forward steps were taken, such as that by the medical director mentioned above. Improvement in the quality of men engaged after the war helped also to raise their status. Toward the end of the 1940's students in the social sciences began coming to the Hospital for specialized study of the mentally ill; their instruction included practical experience as attendants or auxiliary occupational therapy workers. There was also an influx of medical students, who found they could learn much about patients and the Hospital through informal chats with attendants and nurses. Both groups helped to forge links between their teachers, the psychiatrists, and ward personnel. Further recognition of the importance of the attendant's work occurred when graduate students were engaged in connection with research projects, to function in the role of attendant in several Massachusetts hospitals and to attempt to describe the stresses of the job.

Opportunities for growth and development were greatly enhanced by the inauguration of continuous on-the-job training, which will be discussed in a later chapter. As soon as it was recognized that nursing students and attendants would get along better if each understood the other's task, the latter began to take part in the orientation of new affiliates. Participation in all major clinical events was encouraged; attendants contributed to ward meetings, ward rounds, staff conferences, total treatment conferences. A final boost in morale occurred through the promotion of some attendants to positions with higher status—one became recreational director, another the chief x-ray technician, and others found jobs in research teams.

Assimilating the Patient into the Ward Milieu

A third and most important factor in any program for reduction of seclusion is that patients removed from seclusion must not flounder in a group situation with which they are totally unfamiliar, or which might become threatening. Those who have for a long time been in enforced privacy can be successfully assimilated into the ward milieu only by a major rehabilitation effort on the part of ward personnel. All possibilities for engaging them in salutary activity or diversion must be explored. Some have been admitted to hydrotherapy or physical therapy, others to group activity, games, sports, occupational therapy, or work programs. On occasion they may prefer to remain for a time in a quiet, cheerful day room. Aggressive or belligerent individuals have been successfully controlled by oral medication that was tapered off as they became accustomed to the new environment. Perhaps most important of all in helping the formerly secluded patient adjust to the ward is a relaxed, nonfearful, accepting attitude by both patients and personnel. When a person comes from the seclusion room into the ward, it is like being admitted to the hospital all over again, except that he has acquired a reputation as a trouble-maker and the attitudes of the ward group have hardened against him. Once more it is the trusting kindly individual who is essential to the necessary bond, and then the accepting group that entwines him in the social network.

"They look forward to activities during the day," said one attendant concerning patients recently removed from seclusion. "In the evening they have something to talk over among them-selves—they can carry on a conversation. They are interested in the games. I have heard them tell other patients about going swimming, or bowling so many strings. At night they are tired, more like normal folk, and are able to sleep better without medication." Although at first apprehensive and skeptical about the possibility of taking patients out of seclusion, especially those with bad reputations, attendants are pleased and gratified when the program succeeds. "Five years ago you would have 8 to 15 patients in seclusion on one corridor, with aides on guard all the time," said one attendant of long experience at Bedford V.A. Hospital. "That was hard for both the aide and the patient. With the new setup it is good for personnel and patient." When asked about his feelings in anticipation of the program he said, "At first I thought it wouldn't work, that it would be murder."

After the first few successes there is a profound shift in atti-tude of personnel. Putting patients in seclusion as a "preventive measure" is no longer sanctioned as desirable practice; on the contrary, the "good" attendant uses interest and imagination in contriving ways and means of integrating the patient into ward life. Any breakdown in the patient's behavior is first examined as a possible consequence of a poor relationship developed between the attendant and the patient in question.

Recently, for example, a student attendant had a front tooth knocked out by a psychotic patient. When the incident was reported, the psychiatrist attempted to discover what the student had done to cause the patient to strike him, rather than assuming that the assault had been without provocation and that the patient should be secluded for the protection of the ward. Discussion revealed that the attendant had indeed provoked the patient by a number of indignities and contemptuous remarks.

A final stage in the evolution of a philosophy concerning seclusion is possible when fear of patients, hostility, and desire to punish them are not adequate reasons to resort to seclusion, but when seclusion is justified only on rational therapeutic grounds, with careful weighing of indications and contraindications in relation to the patient's total problem and possible consequences to himself and the ward. Experience suggests that occasionally disturbed, unpredictable psychotic patients may profit from seclusion; that some manics may benefit from a cooling-off period; that some paranoid patients with overwhelming fear of the social situation may gain a measure of comfort from being temporarily separated from their fellows. Patients irritated by the pressures and annoyances of ward life, may obtain rest and quiet in a seclusion room, if no better retreat is available. Defining specific therapeutic indications and learning how to use seclusion judiciously require a good deal of observation and experimentation. An *absolute policy* against seclusion can deprive ward personnel from developing and demonstrating individual judgment and skill. However, in the hospital of the future, if seclusion is used at all, we believe it will be used sparingly, for selected patients and only for brief periods.

CONTINUOUS BATHS

Prolonged baths in the treatment of psychoses began in Germany in the early 1900's. The method was heralded as of great value and it was claimed that patients could stay almost indefinitely in the tubs without ill effect. Some patients had remained for thirty days. The purpose was to calm excited, violent patients or those with agitated depressions.

The usual procedure was to introduce a constant flow of water into a tub at body temperature; the patient was then placed on a canvas hammock in the water and another canvas sheet was pulled up over him leaving only the head exposed. Treatment usually consisted of immersion for three to eight hours each day until symptoms subsided or it was obvious that this method of treatment was of no avail. When the physician came on rounds, the expectation was that all tubs would be in use and a list of those patients who might "profit" by this treatment would be made available to him. In this way treatment personnel often postponed the day of working in close therapeutic relationship with the patient. Habit and convenience, coupled with either ignorance or unwillingness to try to modify the routine, resulted in perpetuation of this system. Perhaps over the years the attitudes of personnel in many hospitals underwent a slow and insidious change: from use of baths to calm dangerous and assaultive patients, to employing baths for those who became a nuisance, to using them as a punitive device under the guise of "prevention." However, the battle royal that frequently ensued before patients would submit to being put in a tub left little doubt that the psychotic individual often saw this procedure as arbitrary or punitive.

For punishment, or to say the least restraint, to masquerade as medical treatment is a basic deceit recognized by patients. Many mental disorders revolve around the patient's feeling of the injustice, but not being heard, he becomes increasingly vehement and obdurate. When the hospital officially sanctions forced "hydrotherapy" as "treatment," the basic delusional tendencies of the paranoid patient are intensely activated, thus prolonging and worsening, rather than alleviating his illness.

TABLE 2. DECREASING USE OF CONTINUOUS BATH
TREATMENTS, BOSTON PSYCHOPATHIC
HOSPITAL, 1925 TO 1946

Year	Patients receiving bath treatment	Number of bath treatments	Aggregate bath hours	Hours per treatment
1925	730	3,569	24,920	7.0
1930	462	2,422	15,374	6.3
1935	548	2,141	13,841	6.5
1940	318	1,466	7,704	5.3
1941	341	1,419	8,101	5.7
1942	335	1,482	8,412	5.7
1943	—[a]	721	4,317	6.0
1944	178	1,105	5,594	5.1
1945	103	605	3,257	5.4
1946	2	4	8	2.0

[a] Not available.

Statistics at Boston Psychopathic Hospital dating from 1925 show the decrease in use of continuous baths. In that year 730 patients were thus treated; this number represents roughly one-third of all those admitted. These patients were soaked under the trained eye of hydrotherapists or assistants for a total of 24,920 hours. Approximately 500 days of staff time were spent restraining patients in the tubs and standing guard. Probably very little time was devoted to talking to the patient or getting to know him better, for therapeutic reliance was placed in the magic of the bath, rather in the healing power of human contact.

Gradually over nearly a quarter-century, continuous baths at this Hospital were reduced, and in the latter part of 1946 the tubs were finally removed altogether. Not only did this release personnel for other necessary tasks, but it increased the available physical space, which was then used for a locker room and a recreation room. The locker room made it possible for the first time for patients to assume responsibility for their own clothes and possessions; the recreation room permitted an increase of ward activities. More will be said about both these subjects in Chapters 3 and 5.

WET SHEET PACKS

To be wrapped in a wet sheet pack, tightly bound around the arms and legs with no free motion allowed, was understandably something that disturbed patients hated and feared. The pack was so great a physical restraint that only writhing or tensing of the muscles was possible, which often further increased apprehension and frustration. Since the moist sheets covered by rubber or a blanket tended to retain the heat eliminated by the body, sometimes fever and hyperthemia developed. It was generally recognized that a low but definite mortality accompanied this procedure, and that some patients with recognized limited cardiac reserve had died as a result of the writhing. Often patients emerged from packs more disturbed and angered than before, so that after a minimum period of rest they were once again forced into them. To many this procedure was degrading. Those who were quieted were perhaps the ones who could endure bodily limitation without great discomfort, were able to submit to the reality of force, or what is more probable, gained something from the personal interest, attention, or kindness of exceptional hydrotherapists or attendants, who imparted a feeling of trust and security that surpassed the discomfort and restraint of the pack.

Wet sheet packs disappeared from the scene at the Hospital in 1943, and the department of hydrotherapy, which had been responsible for continuous baths and packs, as well as for the use of the needle spray, salt rubs, saline baths, and the electric cabinet, underwent considerable change. It was equipped to give diathermy, infrared and ultraviolet ray treatments, and vapor baths. Quite as importantly emphasis was placed upon having it encourage sports, games, and exercises. Provision was made for badminton, volleyball, basketball, tennis, golf practice, and the use of a rowing machine, bicycle, and pulleys. Thus, free activity could be substituted for the restrictions of continuous baths and wet sheet packs. Finally, the hydrotherapy suite was physically improved to create a spa-like atmosphere, insofar as was possible with limited funds and an old and functionally inadequate building. Here, under the friendly interest and leadership of Harold S. Byrne, the physio-therapist, patients could enjoy either rest or activity in an environment that gave them a feeling of personal warmth and well-being.

CHEMICAL RESTRAINTS

More insidious than seclusion, and often more damaging to the patient's welfare and to ward morale, was the repeated and excessive use of sedative drugs, like barbiturates, bromides, and paraldehyde. Before 1943 the practice at the Hospital was to leave orders on evening rounds for heavy doses of barbiturates to be administered during the night in the event of restlessness, disturbed behavior, or sleeplessness. The purpose was to ensure a good night's rest for both patients and physician. Throughout the day, when situations arose demanding the immediate handling of a difficult patient, and all seclusion rooms, packs, or tubs were in use, the physician resorted to medication. It seemed a natural solution, particularly when the patient pre-sented somatic complaints, such as pain, gastrointestinal dis-comfort, palpitation, tremors—symptoms for which the familiar procedure in the general hospital, where the doctor had served his internship, is the prescription of one or another form of sedative medication. Needless to say, the bill for drugs in those days was a large item of budgetary expenditure.

The new administrative policy favored the reduction and finally the almost complete elimination of sedative medication in the management of psychotic patients. The staff learned that most mentally ill patients tolerate barbiturates poorly, that the repeated use of such sedation even in small doses tends to intoxicate them, blunt their finer sensibilities, reduce their inte-gration and control, and lead to a more rather than a less-disturbed ward. Considerable determination and fortitude were required initially for the ward physician to deny medication upon the urgent demands of the patient, or the entreaties of ward personnel. Often a patient who had been heavily medi-cated for some time would go through a highly agitated period during the withdrawal phase. Yet when the withdrawal was complete and both personnel and patient were convinced that drugs could no longer be resorted to, it was remarkable how calm the patients became, how quiet the ward. Many who for weeks declared that they were unable to sleep without medication, often slept soundly once they became fully convinced that sedative drugs were not the answer to their problem.

Not to be confused with barbiturates are certain new drugs in which such intense interest is currently being taken that a word of explanation is in order here. Chief among them are chlorpromazine hydrochloride (thorazine) and serpasil, which possess little hypnotic action but apparently exert a favorable influence on some states of anxiety, tension, and excitement. Studies are now in progress to delineate more specifically the indications and areas of usefulness, as well as to determine their toxic effects. Although no final evaluation can be given as yet, and some early enthusiastic reports may be discounted, it would appear that these drugs are in a different class from the barbiturates. Unless new information contradicts present impressions, they are a promising addition to the therapeutic armamentarium in psychiatry. Sometimes patients who have not been benefited by other psychiatric procedures will be helped by one of them. Since they may calm distressed or excited persons and allay anxiety, they reduce fear and apprehension in both patients and personnel, and thus may make the resocialization program for the patient easier and more effective.

FORCED FEEDING

A difficult complication in the care of the psychotic patient frequently arose when he refused to eat because of great fear, depression, or suspiciousness. Some patients refused food and drink altogether, others would eat or drink very sparingly. When the condition lasted for more than thirty-six hours, there was considerable alarm for the patient's physical well-being. Physicians resorted to the unhappy practice of forced feeding, often supplemented by additional saline injections to maintain the water and salt balance of the body. Twice a day the recalcitrant patient was forcibly restrained, a tube was passed through the mouth or nostrils to the stomach and a rich solution of liquid food and vitamins administered. Much time was required for resident physicians and nursing staff to attend to the physical condition of these patients. The procedures were never without risks, for tube feeding carried the danger of pulmonary inspiration of nutrient solution, which was very irritating to the bronchi and lungs, and subcutaneous fluid infusions carried the danger of sepsis and tissue breakdown.

All personnel were grateful when the improvement of ward atmosphere led gradually to the disappearance of forced feedings. Many factors contributed and it is difficult to weigh the relative importance of each. Concentration on interpersonal relationships, and lavishing time and attention upon patients who were recalcitrant did much to allay fear and suspiciousness. Somatic treatments contributed by rapidly resolving severe depressions and breaking up catatonic reactions. The use of sodium amytal intravenously was highly effective in some cases, causing valuable catharsis which brought with it both an understanding of the patient's reasons for refusing food and drink, and often a rapid resolution of the resistance. Gradual reduction of seclusion and other restrictive practices, together with greater involvement of patients in ward social activities, were certainly helpful. A better attitude toward meals, more palatable food, a chance to sit down and relax during mealtime with less pressure from personnel to hurry were probably also helpful.

THE NATURE OF THESE "EVILS"

All the procedures mentioned in this chapter as "evils" arose originally through the sincere efforts of hospital therapists to help patients. When first introduced, continuous baths and wet sheet packs were hailed as excellent therapeutic devices; a great deal of time and attention went into training personnel properly in these techniques, and many cases were proudly pointed to as having been "cured." Chemical restraints were considered a humane method of overcoming aggression, agitation, and hyperactivity. (It was years before observant psychiatrists noted that mental patients were sensitive to sedative drugs that could be used for the most part with impunity on nonnervous subjects.) Seclusion was an unfortunate reality that developed from the grim necessity of removing someone from the ward society to protect himself or others on the ward. Forced feedings were obviously indicated to save the patient from death by starvation and dehydration. There appeared to be no choice.

All this, we must remember, was consistent with the best psychiatric practice of the day. Indeed, baths, packs, chemical sedation, and seclusion still have strong adherents in many quarters. We must admit that in some hands they are remarkably efficacious and that we do not yet completely understand the indications and contraindications of each. In what, then, does the "evil" consist?

When new procedures are introduced in psychiatry by earnest, enthusiastic persons, success frequently follows. This success is perhaps attributable to the therapeutic value of the accompanying interest and human devotion, which are quickly sensed and utilized by patients. When these qualities are lacking, when interest flags, when procedures become routine and monotonous, then the restrictive and punitive aspects of such "therapies" begin, and the gulf widens between patients and personnel. It is likely that these procedures had little value in themselves in curing patients, and that as soon as personnel were no longer vitally interested in them, they had outlived their usefulness. *The "evils" we have discussed consist, therefore, essentially in overroutinization, emphasis upon procedure rather than the person, lack of knowledge concerning patients' feelings or poor communication about these feelings among the staff, and lack of adequate motivation for serving the basic psychological, as contrasted with physiological, needs of patients.*

3. Improving the Physical Environment

ONCE THE "SECURITY MOTIF" had been challenged and found wanting, interest shifted rapidly toward making the patients' physical environment more attractive. The theory of the use of the physical environment as a positive force in patient therapy had not yet been formulated; it was to evolve only slowly. But there was general recognition of the immediate desirability of having patients dressed in a more dignified and esthetic manner than bathrobes, slippers, and the heterogeneous apparel permitted, and of providing them with brighter, pleasanter, and more comfortable wards and day rooms.

However, the obtaining of suitable clothes and even the decision to allow disturbed patients to wear them presented many problems. The fear persisted that if patients who came to the Hospital appropriately dressed were permitted to wear their own clothes, they might tear them to shreds during destructive outbreaks; and their families would be antagonized unless the loss were made good. Patients referred from the courts frequently appeared in so disreputable a condition that they needed to be completely outfitted. Almost no money was available at this time for purchasing clothes and early attempts to obtain funds through official channels met with failure. The situation was somewhat relieved by gifts from the staff and their friends who contributed second-hand clothes in reasonably good condition, or readily repairable by the hospital seamstress. Families of patients, too, were asked to cooperate and contributed willingly and generously. Once the patients' needs were known, help also came from many unsolicited sources. Gradually the cooperation of state budgetary authorities was obtained on a yearly basis and a small fund was created that could be used for clothing. By shrewd buying from big stores with automatic markdowns, by purchasing slightly damaged merchandise at low cost, and by encouraging relatives, personnel, and friends to participate further, eventually all patients were wearing either their own clothes or presentable garments supplied by the Hospital.

The patients showed considerable pride in their appearance, sometimes to a surprising degree, especially on social occasions such as dances or parties when men and women were allowed to mix freely.[1] Furthermore, they manifested a gratifying degree of responsibility in looking after themselves, so that there was progressively less soiling and destruction of apparel. The problem of repair, therefore, diminished to all but negligible proportions. Permitting patients to have their own clothes inevitably gave rise to the question of where the clothes could be kept. A later fiscal allotment made possible the purchase of lockers. Pride and responsibility were enhanced by this change, and patients demonstrated that they were capable of managing their personal belongings. It was obvious that attractive clothes and accessories had conspicuous therapeutic value.

By this time personnel were beginning to suspect that patients could rise to surprising heights of self-respect and acceptable behavior if encouraged by opportunities made available at strategic points in their recovery curve, and by a ward atmosphere where expectation of progressive assumption of responsibilities was the rule. When it appeared that, by changes in the environment and in social expectation, patients might be led step by step to high levels of achievement, creativity and motivation were greatly stimulated. How many patients could be brought to recovery or discharge through social therapy alone without the aid of somatic treatments or intensive, costly, prolonged individual psychotherapy? As the challenge began to unfold, the staff became more sensitive to the many ways in which rigid hospital routines, thoughtlessly accepted as good practice, might prohibit or retard the growth of patients. The more alert offered suggestions for improvement

[1] See Chapter 5.

which were often eagerly accepted for trial. Thus, began the release of imaginative suggestions from the ranks of personnel.

DECORATING THE HOSPITAL

A new conception soon gained acceptance, namely, that patients rarely destroy things which they feel keenly are for their own benefit, or which they thoroughly enjoy. Thus, it was possible to plan for major physical or esthetic improvements with less fear that they would hang themselves on draperies or destroy beautiful pictures. The process of interior decorating was a slow one, and was delayed by a tight budget that had been drawn up in previous years with an eye to economy and not necessarily with the patients in mind. Again contributions came from relatives and interested friends of the Hospital. Gifts of furniture and pictures were often received from people who heard, quite indirectly, of the Hospital's drive to brighten up the dull ward environment.

A significant contribution toward improving the physical appearance of the institution was made by the medical director, who felt the importance of setting an example to others. He ordered the complete redecoration of his office and that of his secretary, at his own expense. Since a great deal of the activity of the Hospital centered around his office, which had been shabby indeed, the change served as a dramatic example to the rest of personnel that he was seriously interested in developing the physical as well as the interpersonal aspects of a warm homelike environment, and that decorating could be done without depending on slow, routine channels.

Paint in attractive colors was put on every part of the hospital building and patients who showed an interest in helping were encouraged and utilized to the utmost. Once the spirit of decorating took hold, practically no effort was necessary to recruit patient workers. Not infrequently a nurse would report, "I have a master painter on my ward. What can be done to keep him occupied?" Patients cooperated with nurses in obtaining materials for all sorts of refurbishing, and the assistant superintendent particularly was on his mettle to facilitate the carrying out of these projects. The life of the institution had changed to a point where initiative was encouraged and rewarded, and where patients and personnel challenged administrative officers to keep up with their demands to improve the environment which was their home.

Some of the more talented patients undertook to decorate the walls with murals. The first of these was painted on a wall of the hydrotherapy suite by a modern artist who was being treated for schizophrenia. He portrayed his impression of what physiotherapy was accomplishing for patients. Much interest was displayed in this painting which was of obvious merit and symbolic richness. Later the Hospital was treated to its first large mural done by a team of workers, all patients, who showed great originality in organizing the work and differentiating their roles to their own satisfaction. One patient, obviously the most talented, was the master worker. Another patient was the guide who brought visitors and relatives to show off progress without disrupting the artists' creativity. As many as six patients worked together, giving mutual support and encouragement. None had ever before painted a mural although several had had previous artistic training. There was a freedom and scope to this painting which grew out of the novelty of the idea, the camaraderie of a group project, the pride of decorating one's abode, and the appreciative attention of many patients, relatives, and personnel. After discharge from the Hospital one artist voluntarily returned to help finish the project.

More and more wall space thus became covered with framed pictures or murals. Patients began to look upon the walls as belonging to them to use as they pleased. Paintings remained until patients tired of them, or wanted some other kind of decoration. When this occurred, they painted over old decorations to make way for new ones.

ASSISTANCE OF BOSTON PSYCHOPATHIC HOSPITAL AUXILIARY

After initial steps had been taken and momentum developed toward making wards and day rooms decent places in which to live, the Boston Psychopathic Hospital Auxiliary, which

was formed in 1945, stepped naturally into the role of further-
ing the work of decorating. It consisted of an organized body
of friends of the Hospital with a base in the community, and
therefore with access to resources not otherwise available to
the institution. At first, it was composed largely of wives of
trustees, staff psychiatrists, and hospital consultants and their
close friends, but gradually the organization grew to include
many women in the community who, for one reason or another,
felt a need to improve the condition of the mentally ill. As their
numbers increased to a present total of some 400, functions became differentiated: fund-raising to provide an income more
flexible than that allotted by the state; recreation and entertainment to expand the Hospital's facilities for enriching the social
life of the patients; community education to spread word of
the goals and functions of the mental hospital, the recent advances in psychiatric treatment, favorable results in treatment
of the major psychoses, and the great need for hospital-com-
munity cooperation; and volunteer procurement and assignment to swell the ranks of those who wished to help patients
develop skills and interests. Hand in hand with personnel,
members of the Auxiliary applied their considerable talents
as homemakers to the benefit and comfort of patients.

It is now difficult to imagine how the Hospital could thrive
without their assistance, or the assistance of some equivalent
task force of flexible, adaptable, idealistic persons willing to
fill in the many gaps in patient care as they arise. Without
such warm ties with the community any psychiatric hospital
is almost certain to be bereft of dignity and respectability.
Perhaps their greatest contribution, aside from the innumerable individual services rendered, is the feeling they have
imparted to patients and personnel that the community in
general cares about the mentally ill.

With comfortable and attractive furniture, and pictures on
the walls; with patients dressed more like civilians; and with
seclusion, tubs, packs, and chemical restraints largely eliminated, the wards began to take on an almost inviting appearance. Those who visited them after a long absence were struck

by the dramatic changes, which to the personnel sometimes seemed to be almost imperceptible progress against hard resistance. Patients who were later readmitted were especially gratified by the changes. Their happier frame of mind, and less-disturbed and withdrawn behavior reaffirmed the validity of the physical and social therapeutic approach.

4. Effect of Somatic Treatments

Somatic therapy at the hospital still consisted in 1943, as has been seen, primarily of drugs, packs, and prolonged baths used chiefly for the purpose of sedating disturbed patients. In addition, the arsenicals and fever, produced by malaria, typhoid injection, or fever box, were employed specifically in cases involving syphilis of the central nervous system. In those days a large group of patients with neurosyphilis were being cared for as outpatients; from this group those with the most serious disturbances, essentially organic psychoses, were admitted to the Hospital. Electric shock treatment was used rarely, although several practitioners in the community and some private hospitals were employing it extensively. Metrazol had been tried in a few cases, primarily as a research endeavor; and although some patients appeared to benefit, the procedure was abandoned after a brief research report. The effects of both electric shock and metrazol had been studied to some extent with the aid of the electroencephalograph, but since the rather extensive changes that occurred in the brain waves in the course of these therapies were interpreted as bad, their use was not encouraged. There was no insulin treatment, and psychosurgery or brain surgery for mental illness, was only a name.

TRIUMPH OVER NEUROSYPHILIS

The intensive investigation and treatment of syphilis of the central nervous system had been one of the Hospital's major functions for more than two decades. Not only was an active outpatient service supported, but two separate wards totaling 20 beds were provided for the care and treatment of hospitalized cases of neurosyphilis. In addition, many of the more ad-

91

vanced cases, those with profound behavioral disturbances, confusion, belligerency, unpredictable outbursts, were cared for on the admission wards. Approximately 10 per cent of the cases admitted to the Hospital over a long period of years suffered from this disease. Some of the most deteriorated patients, very difficult for personnel to manage, fell into this category. Medical science at this time had a few major weapons to work with: the disease could be diagnosed by serological and spinal fluid tests, and it could be treated with arsenicals and fever. With these powerful instruments, a remarkable job was being done in returning a large majority of cases affected with neurosyphilis to the community and to socioeconomic independence. However, experts were impatient for the widest possible spread of diagnostic and treatment facilities, since they knew that the medical tools at hand were sufficient to turn the tide if full community cooperation could be obtained.

A number of trends converged during the 1940's that virtually eliminated neurosyphilis as a numerically important problem in the community. Among the most important of these trends were the propaganda efforts of the Surgeon General of the United States Public Health Service and of state and local agencies in behalf of early diagnosis and treatment; enactment of state laws requiring blood tests before marriage; and the intensive diagnostic and therapeutic services offered by the armed forces during World War II. In addition, the use of penicillin, in both the early stages of the disease and in late complications of the central nervous system, greatly increased the efficiency of medical treatment.

At the Hospital these events were significant from two standpoints. First, as patients with neurosyphilis became rare, a reduction in the number of disturbed, difficult persons on the wards occurred; once more the amount of aggression, belligerency, and deteriorated behavior fell. Second, personnel who for years had been occupied with the medical treatment of neurosyphilis were released to assist in other forms of therapy, while two more wards became available to patients with functional psychoses. One ward was converted into an insulin suite for the intensive treatment of schizophrenics. The other was converted into an open convalescent ward for female patients almost ready for discharge. It later became a center for electric shock therapy for both outpatients and inpatients.

In treating patients with known lesions of the central nervous system, which were partly or largely reversible by strictly medical measures like drugs and fever, almost the exclusive emphasis was understandably upon somatic remedies. Indeed, early and effective use of these measures might spell the difference between invalidism and cure based on restoration of normal brain function. Psychosociological management of such patients therefore received little consideration. However, as neurosyphilis began to dwindle and then disappear, the idea of brain lesion as a leading cause of mental illness began to fade. Although pathologists had been searching for generations, no clear evidence of lesions had been produced in schizophrenic, manic depressive, involutional, neurotic, or psychopathic cases, which constitute the essential types now represented in mental hospitals. This is not to say that medicine had given up the hope, or even the expectation, that neurophysiological exploration would eventually provide a more satisfactory basis for both understanding and treatment of psychiatric disorders. For the present, however, these cases, practically, could be formulated only as problems in disturbed life experience and emotional development. Hence, as anatomical brain lesion was deemphasized, psychological and sociological aspects of patient care assumed greater importance, but not at the expense of the somatic therapies described below.

INTENSIFICATION OF ELECTRIC SHOCK TREATMENT

Great intensification and extension of the shock treatment program was undertaken subsequent to 1943 for depression, manic and involutional psychosis, and paranoid or catatonic cases of schizophrenia. Fully one-fourth to one-half of the patients in the Hospital began to receive such therapy. This therapeutic enthusiasm was in direct contrast to the conservatism of the old regime. The medical staff was being taught the value of intensive treatment for every patient, as well as the importance of medical responsibility for his entire twenty-four-hour day. The need for an empirical approach to all forms of treatment was recognized, and it was felt that every procedure for which there was a reasonable claim should be given a fair trial. This empiricism was coupled with a strong interest in establishing the therapeutic efficacy of every procedure in simple but concrete terms: What were the comparative effects of each treatment on symptoms, on the patient's ability to live in the community, to hold a job, and to make a contribution to his own support and that of his dependents? To what extent were the patient, his family, and the community satisfied with the results achieved? This pattern of thinking dominated the approach to new or modified therapies and guided much of the clinical research.

Just as the writer was privileged to witness the last days of neurosyphilis, so he was gratified to see, as a result of the extension of electric shock treatment, the rapid resolution of many cases of profound depression that would otherwise have gone on for months or, in the instance of the agitated midlife psychoses, for years. The resident staff was counseled to speed the cumbersome workings of diagnostic procedures, to decide on a desirable course of action as soon after the patient's admission as possible, by a quick marshaling of data and consideration of alternatives. They were asked to keep constantly in mind that every day saved helped to keep symptoms from becoming rutted or ingrained; that it meant a quicker return of the patient to his former place in the community, less disruption of his way of life, less financial and social loss, less stigma, and less strain on the family circle.

The earlier and bolder use of convulsive shock treatment further reduced the amount of disturbed, and threatening behavior of patients on the ward. A depressed patient preoccupied with self-destruction, who might be considered a severe suicidal risk would be evaluated and treated without delay. Often within twenty-four hours the threat of suicide would be lifted, and both personnel and patients could breathe with relief. An excited manic, or a catatonic schizophrenic patient out of contact with reality, frequently improved in a short time, so that effective communication was possible and psychotherapy and sociotherapy could be undertaken.

The success of inpatient shock treatment in quickly lifting depressions later led to its consideration as an outpatient procedure, to avoid hospitalization altogether whenever it was possible. The results were equally dramatic, with the happy addition that separation from family and home and the stigma of hospitalization were avoided.[1] In many instances patients were able to complete a course of treatments without losing any substantial portion of time away from their work. The sting of mental illness was thus greatly reduced.

Complications of Electric Shock Treatment

The more extensive use of electric shock, however, brought into view a number of undesirable complications. Fortunately, mortality was negligible, but on occasion there occurred torn ligaments, fractures of transverse processes of vertebrae and long bones, or dislocation of arm or mandible, although their incidence was never great enough to override the advantages of treatment. In addition, patients complained of confusion and memory disturbance after treatment. Although the undesirable mental symptoms cleared rapidly with time and skeletal complications were handled with increasing skill, it appeared advisable to take specific steps toward further improvement of this form of treatment which had already proved its great worth. There seemed to be two major directions in which progress could be made: by altering the properties of the electric current so that the clinical effects could be obtained with least possible disturbance to the brain, and consequently the least possible memory impairment and confusion; and by reducing the strain on muscles, ligaments, and bones through decreasing the force of the convulsion.

Research went forward in both directions.[2] It is beyond the

[1] Mezer, R. R., and H. C. Solomon, "Value of Electric-Shock Treatment on Outpatients," *New England Journal of Medicine*, vol. 250, April 29, 1954, pp. 721–722.

[2] Investigations in this area were carried out by Dr. William L. Holt, then chief medical officer, assisted by several residents, in collaboration with Reuben Reiter, electrical engineer.

scope of this report to discuss in detail these investigative developments. To a large extent the not inconsiderable progress made was due to the collaboration of psychiatrists with the electrical engineer, a professional man who had previously found no place in the psychiatric team. His inventive skill came to bear marvelously upon the problem of altering current properties in order to obtain the most good with the least stress to patients. He reduced the amperage to one-tenth the amount formerly used, and so altered current characteristics that confusion and memory disturbances were greatly reduced or eliminated, while the strain on muscles and bones was minimized. Later modifications brought respiration under better control, which added a greater safety factor to the treatment procedure. These changes also decreased postshock excitement and overactivity, which had been minor but definite hazards in some cases.

Research directed toward reducing the strain of the convulsive seizure on muscles, tendons, and bones took the form of investigating a number of drugs with known quieting effects upon nerves and muscles. By administering such drugs to patients shortly before the production of the seizure, the convulsion could be greatly softened without reducing its beneficial effect on the psychosis. A series of experiments soon disclosed pharmacologic agents with the requisite characteristics. Perhaps the most promising development has been the recent use of a combination of two drugs given just prior to application of the electric current. One drug (sodium pentothal) is given intravenously and quickly puts the patient to sleep. The other drug (succinyl choline hydrochloride) follows immediately by the same route and induces a very brief paralysis of musculature so that the electric impulse when applied produces little or no convulsive movements of the body. Thus, it is at last possible to assure the patient that there is no "shock" and essentially no "convulsion." In fact, so far as he is concerned, it is merely "sleep" treatment; he will awaken within the hour, fully in possession of his senses, in all probability feeling much better and able to carry on the day's activities.

Social Measures to Reduce Fear

While these advances were being made, it became obvious that more could be done to minimize the fears of patients about to undergo electric shock treatment. This was not a matter of either bioelectrical or pharmacologic research, but a problem of understanding the total situation or environment in which shock therapy takes place.

It is difficult even now to communicate with patients or relatives about this form of treatment without using terms or evoking memories of former procedures that are anxiety inducing. The words "electric shock" arouse the layman's fear of electricity, short circuits, painful jolts from house currents. Interruption of consciousness may be alarming to persons who suffer from one of the many varieties of usually benign but frightening dizziness, "blackouts," or fainting spells. The former thrashing about that followed the passage of current was like an "epileptic seizure" or "convulsion." Acceptance of electrically induced convulsion by patients as a therapeutic force was therefore often achieved only after an uphill fight against prejudices and misapprehensions. One of the obvious early mistakes was to allow patients to see others during the convulsive seizure or in long and deep unconsciousness during the recovery phase. Few sights are more awesome than the picture of a full-blown convulsion. Patients obtained the impression—completely erroneous though it was—that those under shock were suffering excruciating pain, or that personnel had done something aggressive against them. Thus, they came to treatment apprehensive, fearful, and uninstructed.

In 1949 a study designed to cast light upon the attitudes and feelings of electric shock patients while waiting their turn for treatment was made by Miss Harriet M. Kandler, who subsequently became director of nursing. Verbatim recordings of spontaneous conversation by these patients, made by Miss Kandler, verified the hypothesis that waiting for shock heightened anxiety. On the morning of November 23, 1949, for example, while eleven women and two men (seven depressed, one manic, and three with involutional melancholia) were on the sun porch next to the treatment center, the following conversation and actions were recorded:

MRS. F: One of the worst angles is sitting around waiting for treatment.

MRS. G: The last time I had treatment I felt pain up and down my legs. I'm not going to have any more.

MRS. H: Why do I have to have any more treatments? I am not going to have any more.

MRS. I: They'll deposit you right on the table and it will be over before you know it.

MRS. F: They have a depressing effect upon my whole system; I feel like a chronic invalid.

MRS. J: I get nervous just sitting around waiting for the treatment.

MRS. K: [Comes into sun porch; had been wandering in and out.] I would feel much better if they would leave me alone.

MRS. N: [Turns the pages of a newspaper.]

MR. O: [Walks into sun porch, looks around at patients, then goes back to corridor. Shortly returns and sits down.]

NURSE 1: [Walks into sun porch, looks at patients, then leaves.]

MRS. I: I am getting so grouchy from these treatments.

MRS. G: The last treatment I had was the first time I didn't feel fine afterward. I've seen Mrs. H get better. You're acting fine now, Mrs. H. But for me, enough is enough.

NURSE 2: [Comes to get Mr. O for treatment. They leave the sun porch talking together.]

MRS. G: [Comes over to sit where Mr. O had been sitting.] I'd feel much better if I got dressed and went down to the gym or something . . . you go without breakfast sometimes . . . once you start these treatments you can't do without them and they're expensive.

MRS. K: You have to pay for them, too. [Mrs. K and Mrs. G talk together.] [There is noise from the treatment room, Mr. O is having his treatment. General tension, unrest, and apprehension seem to pervade the group, all of whom turn their attention fearfully to the noise next door.][1]

Although electric shock had been in active use for six years, this problem was not systematically investigated or attempts made to solve it prior to Miss Kandler's study. Fundamental steps decided upon were to explain to patients and relatives in

[1] Kandler, Harriet M., "Studying a Problem in Psychiatric Nursing," *American Journal of Nursing*, vol. 51, February, 1951, pp. 108–111.

greater detail the facts about electric shock treatment; to separate those awaiting shock from those who were recovering from it; to escort anxious, complaining patients directly from the ward to treatment, so that they would not raise the level of anxiety of less tense persons; to engage patients in the waiting room in distracting conversation; and to initiate card games. All of these measures had something to recommend them; the most rewarding results, however, came when one of the patients began to play the piano during a waiting period and was joined by several others in singing, like the proverbial whistling to keep up one's courage in the dark. The record notes: "Mr. N finds music and plays a popular song. The effect is remarkable. All the fussing stops. Mr. K settles down to play solitaire and listen to the music. The five remaining patients group themselves around the piano and sing. A nurse enters to get Mr. M for treatment. He goes without complaining."

On several other occasions piano playing and group singing proved their worth. Sometimes music was provided by the patients, sometimes by other persons recruited for the task. Additional possibilities suggested themselves, such as moving pictures, occupational therapy, and group therapy sessions, but none of these was adequately explored.

INSULIN TREATMENT

In view of the empirical attitude of the Hospital, it was inevitable that insulin therapy, like electroconvulsive treatment, was at last to be given its chance. Since no funds were available in the budget for a nurse specialized in insulin therapy, who is indispensable in this type of treatment, money was found by the Harvard Medical School. A capable nurse-physician team then had to be developed to organize this endeavor and to supervise it, because as is well known, definite risks to life are attendant upon repeated lowering of the blood sugar to unphysiologic depths. The patient therefore must be watched constantly to guard against deepening coma, and careful consideration given daily to adjusting doses of insulin to obviate untoward effects of sudden changes in insulin sensitivity or resistance. Plans for a six-bed unit went into effect in 1944. From the moment of inception the unit was used to capacity, and practical experience confirmed reports from medical literature that many schizophrenic patients who responded slowly or not at all to other forms of therapy showed improvement when given a course of insulin coma. Eventually the capacity of the unit was raised to 17 beds, without completely meeting the Hospital's needs. In addition to the use of large doses of insulin to produce coma, insulin was also tried in small subcoma doses to allay anxiety, excitement, and agitation, and proved a helpful adjunct to the other hospital therapies.

It is difficult to overestimate the effect on both patients and personnel of increased care and attention given persons receiving somatic treatment. Many hospitalized patients suffer specifically from lack of interest in and concern about their welfare; and staff members who are not doing something for patients, with a reasonable chance of helping them, tend to stagnate. If insulin treatment contributed nothing in itself but only served as a medium through which personnel could relate closely to patients, its use might still be justified—though we should question the necessity for such curiously indirect methods of encouraging interaction. When we consider the social impoverishment of the average schizophrenic patient, aggravated by the barren hospital environment, compared with the amount of wholesome human interaction necessary to bring him out of his retreat, almost any activity is justifiable on the basis that it is better than none at all.

Whether it was the zeal of personnel, the increased attention given patients, or specific physiologic effect of repeated hypoglycemias upon the brain, the fact is that insulin helped a definite proportion of patients not benefited by electric shock, hospital social therapy, or other measures. It was a common experience and a gratifying one, to see the day-to-day resolution of schizophrenic symptoms, especially in paranoid patients. First, a gradual reduction in the intensity of hallucinations and delusions occurred, the patient appeared less preoccupied, less driven to bizarre behavior. Then, his attention began to turn outward from the self toward the environment; meanwhile, the disintegration of the schizophrenic state began to be replaced by more coordinated psychological functioning. Finally, the patient's disruptive tensions receded into the background or disappeared altogether; he commenced to relate himself in a more meaningful way to his fellow human beings. Anyone who has watched this process again and again cannot fail to appreciate the importance of insulin shock as a therapeutic instrument, particularly since its chief area of effectiveness is in the paranoid conditions, which are affected little or not at all by electric shock techniques.

An interesting kind of solidarity springs up among insulin patients which may also contribute to their sense of well-being. There are indications that a strong kinship is felt, which plays a role in their attitude toward treatment, and thus probably in its efficacy. One of those receiving insulin wrote a poem for the hospital "Patients' Press" which paraphrased a well-known Boston rhyme:

> Here's to the home of the buzz and the prod,
> Where the shocks speak only to insulins
> And the insulins speak only to God.

This conception of a hierarchy of importance based on the therapy received came from the patients at a time when enthusiasm for somatic treatment was at its height. Later when psychotherapeutic interest came into the foreground and the successes of somatic treatment were accepted as routine, patients' feelings of importance were correlated with the number of psychotherapeutic hours they received from their psychiatrists.

There have been numerous instances in which patients were known to have helped other patients understand somatic therapy and be less fearful. Few arguments are so convincing to the apprehensive individual awaiting his first electric shock or insulin treatment as the statement of a fellow-patient who says: "I have been through it all. It is not so bad as you think. Look what it has done for me!" A vast patient-to-patient network, of which we are largely unaware, may be of crucial importance to recovery. Such examples make one acutely conscious of a reservoir of therapeutic strength that may lie in the patients themselves.

LOBOTOMY

Perhaps the most controversial form of somatic therapy, but one which is gradually winning a place for itself, is lobotomy or psychosurgery. Objections to this type of treatment arise primarily from the fact that it involves cutting fibers in the anterior part of the brain which subsequently do not regenerate. Physicians are understandingly slow to adopt methods that are irreversibly destructive, unless their efficacy is established beyond doubt and no treatment of lesser proportions will suffice. Although destructive operations, such as removal of a kidney, or portion of stomach or bowel, are commonplace in surgery today, they are rarely performed except in cases where anatomic pathology has been demonstrated, and where the diseased specimen can be examined on the pathologist's table. In the psychoses for which lobotomy may be used, there is no evident pathology, gross or microscopic, although neuropathologists have searched for decades. That is not to say that the brain is functioning normally, but only that lesions cannot be demonstrated by the methods of the neuropathologist. Actually, there is a considerable amount of behavioral and psychological evidence of nervous system dysfunction; and in recent years physiologists have noted disordered brain functioning beyond the reach of the pathologist's techniques.

Justification for the operation derives from the fact that in general lobotomy has been demonstrated to benefit one-half or more of the patients on whom it has been performed.[1] Follow-up studies of five to ten years' duration of patients operated on at Boston Psychopathic Hospital have revealed that *if improvement once begins* it may continue in a remarkable way over a long period of time; some patients have shown

[1] Greenblatt, Milton, R. Arnot, and Harry C. Solomon, editors, *Studies in Lobotomy*, Grune and Stratton, New York, 1950; Greenblatt, Milton, and Harry C. Solomon, editors, *Frontal Lobes and Schizophrenia*, Springer Publishing Co., New York, 1953.

slow but steady progress for at least seven years.[1] Relapses, moreover, are relatively infrequent. It is as though the operation releases a hidden potential, which once asserted, becomes established.

Further justification for surgery derives from the fact that lobotomy is used only in those cases which are regarded as having a "hopeless" prognosis under prevailing conditions and facilities for treatment. Of the patients who populate the "back wards" of our many custodial institutions, not more than 1 or 2 per cent show sufficient improvement each year under present conditions to permit their discharge into the community, and among those discharged the tendency to relapse is very great. In contrast, out of more than 500 patients lobotomized at Boston Psychopathic Hospital during the period when it served the entire Commonwealth, 35 to 40 per cent were released to the community, where they have been able to remain for years. Beyond this, there is a distinct improvement in behavior for many who have not yet reached a level sufficient for discharge. They are more contented with themselves and their environment, less wracked by disturbing emotion, more outgoing; and are often able to make some contribution to hospital life.

A survey was published in 1950 of opinions of superintendents of Massachusetts state hospitals concerning the value of lobotomy to patients who continued their residence after operation in these hospitals.[2] It recorded uniform agreement as to the beneficial effects on ward life that resulted from the great reduction in overactivity, aggressiveness, and belligerency. This result was particularly welcome during World War II, when wards were poorly staffed and the few available personnel were forced to give an undue share of their attention to disturbed patients, frequently neglecting all others. One superintendent commented that he could tell a hospital in

---

[1] Greenblatt, Milton, E. Robertson, and Harry C. Solomon, "Five Year Follow-up of One Hundred Cases of Bilateral Prefrontal Lobotomy," *Journal of American Medical Association*, vol. 151, January, 1953, pp. 200–202; Greenblatt, Milton, M. Wingate, and Harry C. Solomon, *Work Capacity of 86 Cases Five to Ten Years After Bilateral Prefrontal Lobotomy*, unpublished manuscript.

[2] Greenblatt, Milton, R. Arnot, and Harry C. Solomon, editors, *Op. cit.*

which lobotomy had been used, because the atmosphere of the disturbed wards was below the critical level of agitation.

Since the introduction of lobotomy into America in 1935, much investigation has been directed toward reducing the amount of brain damage incident to surgery while maintaining the beneficial results. Lack of emotional depth, reduction of initiative, or "blunting" of emotions followed lobotomy in a significant number of the patients operated on by the earlier techniques. Great strides now appear to have been made toward the desired goal. Patients subjected to limited operations are reported on the whole to have shown more initiative and spontaneity, warmer and more appropriate emotional response, greater interest and participation in social activities than was generally observed following the more extensive surgical procedures.

The impact of lobotomy surgery upon the attitudes of ward personnel at the Hospital was considerable. At first, there was resistance to the performing of a brain operation upon psychotic patients. Then, when the staff saw patient after patient whose condition had been considered hopeless improve and return to the community, a new surge of interest not only in acute but also in chronic mental illness swept through the wards. Until then it had been the general feeling of personnel that through good hospital care, psychotherapy, electric shock, and deep insulin coma many patients with mental illness could be successfully treated, but a large proportion who were resistant to these therapies would still remain. The lobotomy operation brought successful results to so many of this "hopeless" group that the staff began to feel that perhaps all functional psychoses were curable. They were inspired to work harder with the more difficult cases.

There was another significant, although incidental, effect of having the Hospital used as a statewide center for lobotomy surgery. As the "worst" patients from the other institutions arrived to await determination concerning surgery, it was discovered that their destructive and assaultive behavior, which had kept many of them in seclusion for long periods, changed dramatically. For the first time personnel had partial evidence that such outrageous behavior could be the result of resistance to and retaliation against a fearful, rigid, and nontherapeutic ward atmosphere. Prior to this, the staff had always questioned whether Boston Psychopathic Hospital was not skimming off the cream of the "better" patients, and that only those better patients would respond to the freedoms of the "Psycho" community. Now they learned that their attitudes toward patient care had perhaps universal applicability. This realization brought increased pride and confidence, and the assurance that they were, in fact, effective agents in the therapeutic community.

5. Resocialization

MOST CASES OF SERIOUS MENTAL ILLNESS are characterized by progressive desocialization. One by one, under the influence of the psychotic process, the patient gives up his ties with society. When asked about the nature of schizophrenia the famous psychiatrist, Dr. C. Macfie Campbell who had studied this condition all of his professional life, replied that it consists of progressive stages of maladjustment. As he saw it, many patients traverse these stages in regular sequence; in others the condition becomes arrested at one or another stage of evolution, while some patients appear to skip stages. First, there is a reduction in interest, initiative, and spontaneity. The patient responds to frustrations of instinctive strivings by a damming up of affect and a turning inward of attention. He takes less pleasure in family, friends, and social contacts, and withdraws from painful interaction. Then there is a growing preoccupation with his own mental content, accompanied by disturbing internal trends. He broods about a variety of topics, about sex, ambitious wishes, religion, primitive aggressive impulses. His judgment is impaired and he tends to see the world about him as in odd imbalance.

A third stage may be discerned in which the individual deals with deepening tensions by attempts at restitution, by striking out blindly and aggressively against those who are near to him, by confused attempts to reestablish himself in the social milieu, often by projecting his troubles upon the outer world via delusions, hallucinations, or other distortions. Not a few persons go through a fourth stage which may be characterized as one of further disorganization and of deterioration, a dead end of surrender or regression. Here a crude and unfortunate compromise is made between the demands of the inner self and the frustration of the outer world, a compromise that enables the individual to survive with minimal pain. The awful price which the patient pays, however, is his unwillingness to have his equilibrium disturbed. Clinically, this means chronicity.

If it is true that the individual's social deficit is symptomatic of the disease, then logically the hospital environment should promote resocialization by presenting to the individual a rich assortment of socializing possibilities, especially suited to his needs, together with subtle coercions indirectly invoking his own social motivation.[1] In addition, a system of rewards should be provided which strengthen the patient's satisfactions in engaging in easy interchange with his fellow human beings. But so often the reverse is true! The hospital environment is a complete break from the outside community, less attractive, less wholesome, and far from encouraging interaction it makes some forms of it wholly impossible. Often the environment is socially stagnant, the individuals not members of a living group, but units occupying space.

FORMER LOW LEVEL OF WARD SOCIALIZATION

Observation in 1943 of the wards of the Hospital revealed almost incredible social inactivity. Books, magazines, puzzles, checkers, cards were insufficient in quantity or wholly absent. The first logical step was to make available various types of equipment for recreation and diversion that could be readily obtained, easily replaced, and were customarily utilized in homes and social gatherings. Gradually these materials were

---

[1] All efforts of psychiatric hospitals to get the patient well, even by the use of strictly somatic treatments, might be viewed by social scientists as attempts at resocialization or improved socialization. At the extreme of the most seriously regressed patient, resocialization involves retraining in habits acquired during early childhood: use of toilet, table manners, dressing, and keeping oneself clothed. At the other extreme of the patient who although acutely psychotic is less dissociated from reality, resocialization focuses upon helping him to behave comfortably and appropriately with individuals and groups, and to carry on those social activities, including work, that are characteristic of the milieu from which he comes. It should be noted that the terms "socialization" and "resocialization" are used in this chapter in the latter limited sense to refer to those efforts directed toward increasing social interaction in socially accepted ways. E.L.B.

supplied, and soon it was observed that without coaxing or cajoling but simply by putting them in plain sight, many patients would use the games and reading matter on their own initiative. With coaxing, a large majority, even on an acutely ill ward, would become interested in some activity.[1] Only the most distant or regressed patients failed to respond. It was obvious that an enormous latent interest existed which could be evoked. What was learned about this interest and how it might best be directed is described later in this chapter under the more positive topic heading Effectiveness of Games.

One fact had to be accepted, that an adequate supply system was an absolute necessity in order to maintain the facilities offered to patients. Materials were lost or destroyed. One misplaced card meant that a deck was useless. A few lost checkers discouraged patients from playing the game. Two or three additional packs of cards per day for each ward were sometimes required. These were supplied largely by friends of the Hospital, sometimes by appealing to clubs for their slightly worn or marked decks. When supplies ran low personnel were occasionally inclined to brand patients as wasteful and destructive, but the hospital administration resisted all attempts to be restrictive. Instead, it carried on subtle propaganda to the effect that as ward life improved, the patients would appreciate their advantages more, and the loss due to destructiveness, misplacement, and misuse would diminish. This prediction in general proved to be true.

VALUE OF MUSIC

As late as 1946 there was no radio on any ward.[2] Even "canned" music piped in from a central broadcasting system such as was being used in many hospitals was not available.

[1] Hyde, Robert W., Richard H. York, and Anne C. Wood, "Effectiveness of Games in a Mental Hospital," *Occupational Therapy and Rehabilitation*, vol. 27, August, 1948, pp. 304–308.

[2] Had there been more interhospital communication and less working in isolation, this Hospital might have undertaken experiments in music therapy at a much earlier date. This is clearly an area where it has lagged behind many other institutions, especially in its failure to encourage active participation of patients in choral and instrumental groups.

Questioning of patients revealed that they preferred their own radio sets to being a captive audience to "canned" music. Quickly radios were bought or contributed until each ward of 28 patients had at least one. Others were kept in the nurses' closets and the electrician's shop in case of failure of those in use. The patients appreciated the opportunity of selecting their own programs and adjusting the volume to suit themselves. They even began to form discussion groups around programs of special interest.

Occasionally arguments developed. Perhaps the radio was too loud for the comfort of some ward members. Sometimes a dispute arose over the selection of a program, or the radio might be turned on by one patient and off by another. At first, personnel were likely to intercede in a quarrel, introducing control and arbitrary authority, but they soon learned that disagreements rarely came to fisticuffs. Tolerance emerged when the staff learned that an argument was, after all, a type of social intercourse, to be preferred to apathy and lack of interest; that it might indicate psychological "movement" for patients to show aggression over something external, concrete, and meaningful instead of solely in relation to their psychotic content. Fears over the consequences of manifestation of strong feeling were allayed when it was observed that a dispute mobilized feelings of other members of the ward group, who consequently took sides and by a show of strength usually decided the issue. It was surprising how often the majority ruled. Democracy and a sense of fair play ran deeper than we thought.

Radio programs play so important a part in the life of the average American, both for recreation and information, that to deprive a sick person of the opportunity to enjoy them is all but inhuman. In the hospital, moreover, radio seems to be appreciated not only for its entertainment and educational value, but because it provides a stimulus to interaction and a realistic link with the outside world.[1] The question often arises as to whether psychotic patients respond to music in any deep sense;

[1] Derr, R. C., *Radio Therapy: A Study of the Use of Radio on the Male Acute Ward.* Unpublished observations at Boston Psychopathic Hospital, 1947.

whether it has therapeutic value. A study made in 1952 by Carola Korda of 27 patients, who were given the opportunity of listening to selections from classical, semiclassical, and popular music, suggests that mentally ill patients have a high sensitivity to sounds, rhythms, and musical moods.[1] Depressed patients found sad music difficult to tolerate; they said it made them sadder or more miserable; but they could enjoy songs with a light motif. Other patients who were primarily schizophrenic commented that in general they found "release and satisfaction," were "uplifted," and able to give vent to "pent-up emotions." The music helped them "solve problems"; many said that it was "soothing and relaxing" or "good for the nerves."[2] One described its effect as "like a heady drink" that "overwhelms and exhilarates me." Only one patient seemed to have "no music in him." "I haven't thought about music for fifty years," said a man almost sixty with involutional melancholia. "Other things are more important." The remarks of the other 26 persons clearly indicated that listening to music gave them great satisfaction and enjoyment. Many improved patients felt that it had played an important part in their recovery.

After radios came phonographs; first on the two convalescent wards, later on all wards. Partly through gifts and partly through hospital funds a supply of records was built up. Increased emphasis on music led to the inauguration of music appreciation classes by interested persons who volunteered their services. Some gave lectures, others elicited discussions from the patients. Generally it was felt that a strong need was being satisfied.

Pianos, always easy to obtain for the price of transportation from homes where they have outlived their usefulness, followed

[1] Korda, Carola, *The Meaning of Music to Psychiatric Patients.* Unpublished observations at Boston Psychopathic Hospital.

[2] One dramatic experiment was conducted by a graduate theology student, the Reverend Lee A. Thigpen, during the summer season when the sicker patients were taken out to play volleyball in an enclosed courtyard. Most of them were very immature, withdrawn, and lacking in interest in the game. With the best skill of the physical therapist only a tenuous degree of participation could be achieved. Mr. Thigpen set about playing music of different types on a phonograph in the courtyard. He selected either stimulating or quieting pieces; depending on his selection, he could consistently start or halt the participation of the patients in the volleyball game.

radios and phonographs to the wards. On the convalescent wards they were accepted as a natural part of the setting, but because of the rough handling they received on the acute wards, some members of the staff objected to having them where there were disturbed patients. Resistance died away, however, in a short time and pianos are now accepted everywhere without complaints from either patients or personnel. This illustrates what we believe to be a general principle: *With each change in the social pattern, there is temporary resistance from some individuals, abuse of the new privilege, and predictions of disaster. After this period a plateau of acceptance and adoption is generally reached. It is only then that the true value and significance of the change can be properly assessed.*

EFFECTIVENESS OF GAMES

Since the schizophrenic patient is often paralyzed by fear and hostile or negative affect when in contact with other persons, it is frequently easier to establish communication with him through forms of intercourse that are relatively impersonal, such as simple games. One can sit down and play checkers or cards with him without arousing tension that might interfere with the development of a relationship. He can withdraw to the shelter of the game whenever the personal impact is threatening. By a gradual process of testing and feeling out his partner, he is likely to develop sufficient security to tolerate a closer relationship. Such reactions are not appreciably different from those of normal persons. All of us utilize a variety of tension-allaying devices when we meet others, especially strangers. We carry on superficial and stereotyped patter, "throw parties," serve cocktails, or go to entertainments. These devices to reduce interpersonal tension have an even wider range of usefulness in the mental hospital where patients are defective in socializing skills, than outside where there is presumption of efficiency. They are also helpful to hospital staff, volunteers, and students who are not without their own anxieties in dealing with badly disturbed persons.

Interpersonal tensions such as those suffered by schizophrenic patients breed inactivity. But inactivity accentuates and prolongs their lethargy, sluggishness, and self-involvement. Hence, it is doubly essential that they be encouraged to undertake even those limited forms of activity like games in which they are able to participate. If they are too disturbed to go to the recreation or occupational therapy department, activity must be brought to them in the ward day room.

With these considerations in mind the Hospital decided to take a more careful look at what was going on in activities on the ward as well as in the recreation areas. Inspection of the wards early in 1947 showed, in addition to the radios, phonographs, and pianos to which reference has already been made, ping-pong, and a considerable variety of card and other table games. During a period of five months, 43 unannounced fifteen-minute visits at different hours were paid to the smoking-room of the acute male ward for the purpose of noting whether games were being played, and if so, what kinds, number of players and of watchers, and so on. During 28 of these observations a total of 40 games were in progress. On 19 occasions only one game was going on, on six occasions two games, and on three occasions three games. Eighty-three patients out of a possible 447 who were present in the smoking-room during the observation periods participated, and some 46 additional patients actively watched. Hence, slightly under 30 per cent were involved to some extent.

Of the 40 games played, 27 were initiated and conducted by the patients themselves, nine with the help of nurses or attendants, and four by occupational therapists who came to the smoking-room for the purpose of stimulating social interaction. In comparing games played by the patients themselves with those in which personnel actively took part, it was noted that an average of 2.8 patients participated in the first instance as compared with four in the second. The greater the number of patients engaged in the game, the greater the number of watchers, so that personnel-stimulated games attracted not only more participants, but more observers as well. Only occasionally did a patient playing solitaire or working on a puzzle attract watchers, but three-quarters of the games involving three or more participants attracted them.

An effective technique for introducing games to a group of patients was found to be that of using a "stooge" who played as if he were one of the patients and thereby aroused interest in addition to that directly created by the therapist. Much depended on his personality. If he were spontaneous, joyful, he was able to interest many more than a person who was quiet and unenthusiastic. Competition, furthermore, intensified participation and concentration. Bingo, table baseball, table horse racing, and betting—all of which can be played in the ward day room—proved capable of mobilizing many patients at one time as participants and observers. The following notes made by a staff member indicate how cooperation and concentration can be sustained for relatively long periods:

No formal introduction to the game was made. I brought the large box into the occupational therapy playroom, took out the wheel, the chips, and the "wager" cloth. I busied myself laying out the cloth, sorting the chips, adjusting the wheel, conscious that several of the patients were watching me. One asked me what this was, but before I could answer a second patient had volunteered the proper information. By the time the apparatus was set up, there were four patients around the table.

None of the patients knew the rules, so I set about teaching them as simply as possible, without actually asking them to play. I distributed the chips and was about to proceed when one patient asked me if this was "for money." He appeared very much relieved when I said that we didn't play for money here.

We started simply. I showed them the various betting possibilities and before long the patients were trying all sorts of combinations. After some fifteen minutes, there were easily over fifteen players and others were watching, ready to take over when an opportunity presented itself.

Not only were the patients playing, and apparently enjoying themselves, but were speaking to each other, advising, coaching, cautioning. In one instance a patient who had "lost" his chips was given more by another patient. The emotions of the players varied with the ups and downs of fortune. We began the game at three o'clock; at four when the signal was given for the patients to leave, they were reluctant to go. One of the patients asked for "just one more spin of the wheel." Several asked if they could play again the next day.

In March and April, 1948, a series of horse-racing games was tried on one ward to note the effect of rewards on patient interest and participation. The game consisted of a race track upon which six horses could run, the advancement of each horse depending on the roll of the dice. Hurdles were placed across the racing board at intervals, and in order to move past the obstacles the number of the horse had to be rolled as a double. There was room for six participants, each of whom "rode" a horse, and a seventh who could be brought in as dice-roller for the group. Several "afternoons at the races" demonstrated that this type of game generally attracts many patients, especially if rewards are offered. When prizes such as candy and cigarettes were given, the number of watchers averaged seven per game, whereas when none was given, the figure dropped to 2.4. Many of the patients commented on how rapidly the time passed and asked if they might play the game again.

These several observations led the Hospital to conclude that recreational supplies should not only be made readily available to patients on the ward, but that attendants and nurses should be encouraged to engage patients in group activities as part of their regular functions. Before this concept gained acceptance, the ward staff had rarely played games with patients. They had not conceived of recreation as part of their role and the institution had not sufficiently emphasized the importance of patient interaction. The affiliate students in particular felt distinctly uncomfortable when they discovered, upon arrival from general hospitals, that they were expected to spend time sitting down playing cards or other games. Certainly they would be considered "loafing on the job!" When they saw an occupational therapist on the ward using her skill to mobilize patient attention, however, they gradually began to understand that this, too, was a part of therapy. Attendants and nurses also played more often if an occupational therapist came to the ward occasionally to reinforce interest, indicate ways to achieve participation at a higher level, or help to introduce competition and reward as motivating forces.

BRINGING MEN AND WOMEN PATIENTS TOGETHER

Since the Hospital had embarked on an attempt to make the institutional environment as nearly like the community as possible, it was inevitable that the lack of communication between men and women patients during their whole period of hospitalization should be questioned. The hypothesis that bringing men and women patients together might have a salutary effect upon both had to stand trial. The medical director, who believed that the change should be tried, discussed with the occupational therapists and nursing supervisors the possible advantages of such a move. Later he argued, cajoled, and even pleaded for a trial, but to no avail. There was deeply intrenched resistance both on the part of the occupational therapy service and the heads of the nursing service. The latter, having served the Hospital since its inception, had a deep personal loyalty to the old way of doing things. Since no free communication had been allowed between the sexes for thirty years, they freely predicted disaster if men and women psychotic patients were allowed to intermingle.

Finally, a direct order from the medical director that men and women be sent to occupational therapy together, an order that could not be evaded, resulted in an almost complete emptying of the male and female wards into that department. Seriously disturbed patients were sent there, including some of the partially clothed men. The crowding, concentration of agitated people, and expectation of disaster soon led to an impossible situation of wild excitement which had to be broken up by the return of patients to their respective wards. This proved to the nursing service, beyond all doubt, that men and women psychotic patients could not be mixed.

Later, when one of the occupational therapists was on leave, a volunteer took her place. Again the experiment was tried, men and women patients met in the occupational therapy department, this time on a selective basis. But now, the experiment was a success, and by the time the occupational therapist returned from her leave of absence, the presence of men and women together was an accomplished fact, smooth and ongoing, which most people accepted with good grace.

It may be instructive to consider for a moment the problem of resistance to change on the part of senior supervisory personnel with absolute devotion to the welfare of the mentally ill. Despite years of service none of them had had previous experience with such radical changes in patient care. Their education was not based upon the principle of progress by experimentation, with recognition of the immense unknown territory in psychiatry which had yet to be conquered. Over the years they had had relatively little direction or interference from the administration of the Hospital and from physicians. To a considerable extent resistance to *this* specific change was based upon fear that aggressive sexual feelings might be released. They were familiar with the crude expressions of patients on the ward relative to repressed sexual drives, and had often seen masturbation practiced openly. Besides personal squeamishness there was anxiety about what relatives and public authorities might say if any indiscretions occurred. Thus, it is understandable that they considered mixing psychotic persons of opposite sexes to be foolhardy and dangerous. The actual events, however, showed how unwise it is to prejudge pessimistically the ability of the mentally ill, under appropriate conditions, to behave as rational human beings.

All the uncouth practices of men without women vanished. The men tucked in their shirt tails, buttoned their trousers, combed their hair, and their language became acceptable. The women took more pride in their personal appearance; they, too, combed their hair, and used lipstick. Interest in personal appearance was later furthered by special beauty culture and postural exercises through courses given by the physiotherapist to the women, and the opening of a beauty parlor on the women's convalescent ward. Friendships between men and women developed which added meaning to life. Aggressive or crude sexual behavior diminished sharply as sexual interest was directed into more wholesome channels of socialization.

The battle over permitting men and women to be together underlined how little the ancillary services, such as occupational therapy and nursing, had been drawn into the thinking and planning of the administrative leaders. If progress toward a therapeutic community were to be accelerated, it appeared necessary to increase communication between departments, so that each could feel a greater sense of participation and a stake in all new projects.[1] The occupational therapy department in particular became better integrated with the rest of the institution as a clearer functional conception evolved, peculiarly suited to the developing needs of the Hospital.

OCCUPATIONAL THERAPY AND ITS PLACE ON THE WARD

Two distinctive types of functions appeared appropriate for the department of occupational therapy to cultivate. First, it was to be considered an intrinsic part of the facilities of the hospital community for self-expression, and providing means for the ever-increasing wishes of patients for activity, recreation, social communion. Hence, the department was not expected to wait for a physician's prescription before helping patients; the privilege of using the occupational therapy and recreation rooms was viewed as a part of the patient's right to live the better life as he wished to explore it. Second, after the physician had become better acquainted with a new patient and an appraisal of his needs had been made, the psychiatrist was to confer with a representative from occupational therapy about a specific type of recreation or task most suitable to produce emotional release, improve communication, or achieve some other end. This oral conference was substituted for the former written communication in recognition of the need for more effective interaction between occupational therapy and medical staff, whereby the latter might become better acquainted with occupational therapy philosophy and techniques, and the former more enlightened about the patient's problems and the dynamics of therapy.

Thus, it became standard practice for patients from both the male and female convalescent wards, roughly 60 to 65 per cent of the hospital population, to be admitted to occupational

[1] For a detailed description of techniques for improving intrahospital relations, see Chapter 8.

therapy on a blanket prescription, morning or afternoon, unless directly counterordered by the psychiatrist. This was for purposes of general socialization and rehabilitation. During the course of their hospitalization, a specific program was formulated for individual patients as the occasion demanded.

The expanded conception of occupational therapy to include all those patients able to enjoy the activities offered, without medical prescription, but merely on the approval of the ward nurse, led directly to the question of taking occupational therapy to the wards for the benefit of patients unable to go to the workshops and recreational rooms. It led also to the larger consideration of responsibility for further utilization of patients' leisure time and of how that responsibility could be divided between the department and the nursing service. Although such an extension of occupational therapy seemed staggering, ways were found to make a modest beginning.

First, students of occupational therapy were sent to the wards for experience; later, one salary block belonging to the nursing roster was transferred to the department of occupational therapy for the purpose of engaging a person to work exclusively on the two disturbed wards. The therapist was under the administrative jurisdiction of the head nurses on these wards, but under the professional guidance of the occupational therapy department. Because she functioned as a liaison between the department and the nursing service, it was possible for the ward nurses and attendants to think of themselves as more closely related to occupational therapy. They began to view occupational therapy as a skill they needed and could learn. Consequently, members of the department instituted classes for them. One occupational therapist, Mrs. Marion Plotnick, became so much interested in whether attendants generally might be helped to serve patients more effectively, that she made arrangements with a local state hospital to serve as an attendant for several weeks. In this way she hoped to gain experience and intimate knowledge of the role they play in patients' lives, and how the skills possessed by occupational therapists might be utilized by them. The following are excerpts from the diary she kept as she rotated through various services of the large hospital.

All during my three days on the senile ward I wished we had just a few of the materials from the occupational therapy department at "Psycho." The radio didn't work and there were no books or magazines available. One patient went to the occupational therapy department and made a very beautiful needlepoint article. However, although all the other patients were interested in it, she wasn't able to explain to them how she had done it. I felt that not so many baths [for incontinence] would have to be given and not so many disciplinary measures taken, if there was something interesting for the patients to do. Many of the hours we spent in the kitchen could have been made useful if we spent them with the patients, either reading, teaching them embroidery, making pot holders, or just tuning in radio stations. I thought the patients' lives were very dull. With a little activity on the ward the attendants' job might not have been so hard. They would not have had so many physical duties if they had been able to sit down and help patients with activities.

[During her tour of the medical ward, Mrs. Plotnick wrote]: After I had finished the ward routine I noticed that one of the patients was tatting. Since I had always been interested in learning to tat, I asked her if she would show me how and she agreed. . . . Many of the patients became interested in the lesson, and before we left a few of them had learned to tat along with myself and another attendant. I couldn't help feeling how interesting this work would have been for all of these patients. They were so eager to learn. The personnel's attitude was excellent. Two attendants were willing to learn, and if they had been given supplies they would have carried on almost any activity that the patients needed. The free time available added up to about one hour per day for each attendant.

[Of the admitting ward she noted]: I spent two days not working hard physically, but being worn out from exasperation at the lack of activity. I got the day-long job of guarding the sunporch doorway so patients couldn't return to the ward dormitory. The nurses were tired from inactivity and would have gladly welcomed a change from this routine. They had a pleasant room in which puzzles, card games, and craft activities might have been carried on very effectively with student nurses helping out. The only thing lacking was initiative.

[Finally Mrs. Plotnick wrote of her experiences on the children's ward, considered one of the most difficult assignments in the hospital.] When I arrived on the ward through a large porch with drab gray plaster, the girls [adolescents with severe behavior problems] were all grouped around the beds talking while the attendants were frantically trying to break up their conversation. I asked them whether they would like to fix their hair. They appeared dubious, but that afternoon we got combs, bobby pins, and water . . . and they had a wonderful time doing each other's hair. They copied the styles from pictures of movie stars. This took most of the afternoon. The charge attendant said it was the first time in a long time that they had worked together.

The younger children, who were psychotic, were huddled together in a back room with two attendants to look after them. These attendants were college students and they understood that the children were ill but they had no materials for them to play with, so they tried to fill in the time with story telling. This was rather hard since the children varied so much in behavior, age, and attitude. One of the attendants said she was so tired at the end of a day she wondered if she would be able to return the next day.

In good weather there was a playground available for these children but all the attendants did was to see that they didn't harm themselves or each other. The attendants had plenty of time to direct activity programs but didn't know how to start.

This trained occupational therapist in the attendant's role could see limitless opportunities lost for patient betterment, simply because no program had been worked out for a systematic exchange of professional information and skills between occupational therapists and attendants. She found that approximately one-half of the attendants were interested and able, but were handicapped by never getting the proper orientation concerning, and instruction or supervision in, means of activating patients. They were receptive to leadership, to learning more about occupational therapy, and to trying out the materials. Furthermore, she found that even though the Hospital was understaffed, attendants had a significant amount of time they could spend in promoting socialization, provided that instruction was given them.

This experience increased Mrs. Plotnick's understanding of the role of attendants and deepened her respect for their service to patients. So important is this realization, if productive working relations are to be developed between occupational therapists and attendants, that it is pertinent to end this section with her observation: "I understood now the amount of time it takes to keep patients and wards clean and everything in working order . . . . I was able to talk with attendants; whereas before I was an intolerant person. I had learned that many of them were able and intelligent persons who devoted their lives and their health to the patients."

EVENING ACTIVITIES

The extension of occupational therapy to the wards and the inclusion of more patients in activities for more of their leisure time, led to the development of evening activities. Evenings had been periods of dull monotony for patients, dealt with only by the poor expedient of making them retire early. As late as 1946, there were rare dances on special holidays, perhaps three or four a year. There was not even one regular evening activity, although two psychiatrists had inaugurated Thursday evening dances during the recent war so distressed were they by the boredom of the patients. The administration, supported by the department of occupational therapy and the nursing service, now decided that steps must be taken to remedy this situation.

At this point recognition of the need for a recreational director began to crystallize. Recreation was thought of as parallel in importance with more conventional occupational therapy, and like the latter, would emphasize the more wholesome use of patients' time and the broadening of their horizon. A recreational office would concern itself with further development of evening activities, plan parties, picnics, outings, sports events; arrange for plays, movies, lectures, and concerts, and so on. In a word, all that was left out of the activity program provided by occupational therapy and the hydrotherapy "spa" would be integrated within this office. A director was wanted who was capable of forming quick and workable liaisons not only with patients and staff, but with the growing volunteer program and the Auxiliary. It was hoped, furthermore, that he might interest individuals of means in the community in contributing to the Hospital.

An attendant on the male convalescent ward possessed some

of these qualifications. He had a close relationship with patients who trusted him, as well as a flair for group work and drama. However, he was outspoken, verbally aggressive in handling patients, and showed contempt for some of the "basic rules" of custodial caution, such as those normally invoked in preventing suicide or escape. He sometimes violated the rules requiring locked doors, or keeping an accurate account of razor blades; he escorted patients in a casual manner disregarding the threat of attack, or the need for "security" precautions. Yet his record of accidents, escapes, and suicidal attempts was no worse, but was even better, than that of other attendants. He had much energy, and a desire for leadership, which before his promotion showed itself only occasionally, since it had no real outlet. He liked the limelight and pulled others into it with him. He knew a great deal about the personal lives of his patients, much of it very important information, and frequently not known by their psychiatrists. He particularly knew about their talents, aspirations, and special abilities. His personal problems were sufficient to give him empathy with all kinds of patients, and he found hard work good therapy for his own troubles.

For his deviant behavior, his flouting of authority, his too intimate concern with patients' problems, he might have been "fired" by some hospitals, particularly large ones. He would have been discharged by Boston Psychopathic Hospital had it not come to believe that opportunities should be maximized for each employee, particularly those in the attendants' ranks, in relation to capacity for development. This man had drive, initiative, talent, that had been bottled up in a job too small for him. Therefore, he was promoted to the position of recreational director and given considerable leeway. His subsequent performance fully justified the choice. He sparked the whole activities program, became the leader of psychodrama when it was introduced, and helped in research projects. Through this work he has grown in maturity and responsibility, increased his understanding of patients, and acquired a helpful fund of professional knowledge. Psychodrama has been developed by him to such a degree that Mac, as Francis James MacCumber

is universally known, is today a familiar figure to countless
visitors as well as to students who attend the sessions.

With his appointment the introduction of evening activities
became a focus of attention. The Thursday night dances were
reconstituted, while bingo which was capable of interesting
even very withdrawn patients was scheduled for one evening
a week, with candy and cigarettes as prizes. Another evening
weekly was taken over by nursing students who voluntarily
offered to produce skits with the help of the patients. After a
while these skits were replaced by amateur night, for which
the patients explored their own talents, first with the help of
recreational and occupational therapists, and later by themselves. So great was their enthusiasm that they wanted to take
full responsibility for this program. Members of the staff attended as interested onlookers only.

The Auxiliary assumed responsibility for one weekly program,
when it showed movies or brought entertainers who usually
gave their time without charge. Patient Government, which will
be discussed in the next chapter, reserved one evening for its
meeting, and a Saturday night coffee hour (to be differentiated
from the interdepartmental coffee hour for personnel described
later) completed the week's program. The coffee hour, entirely
a patient innovation, began when convalescent women invited
convalescent men for coffee or tea. Return invitations started
a pattern that continued for many months, and attracted the
interest of perhaps half the persons on the two wards. During
the coffee hour patients played cards, danced, or listened to
music. Since the ban against men and women patients mixing
had been lifted much earlier, it was now the "accepted thing"
for patients from both male and female services to get together
for all sorts of social events: dances, picnics, lectures, moving
picture and television programs, shore parties, amateur night,
and so on.

With the exception of the Thursday night dances for which
members of the occupational therapy and medical staffs took
responsibility, all evening activities were carried out with no
added demands on personnel's time. Volunteers, auxiliary

workers, or other interested persons made the arrangements, always with the goal in mind of motivating patients to take over sufficient functions to give them a feeling of autonomy and control. This was visible evidence that the philosophy of giving responsibility for many aspects of the Hospital's community life to employees, volunteers, and others, for eventual transfer to patients, was being understood and acted upon.

REORGANIZATION OF MEALS FOR PURPOSES OF SOCIALIZATION

The main dining-room of the Hospital is divided into two sections. The smaller one, long known as the "doctors' dining-room," was formerly restricted to physicians, administrative and supervisory nurses, and senior psychologists and social workers, who were served their meals by waitresses. The larger section was a cafeteria used by all other hospital personnel. Because of shortage of waitresses during the war cafeteria service was extended to everyone, but otherwise status barriers were maintained. In the doctors' dining-room a table was reserved for the medical director with whom the chief medical officer, chief psychologist, and chief of research laboratories always ate. Should anyone not specifically included overstep the bounds by eating in that section, he soon learned what was expected and conformity followed. Even after the introduction of cafeteria service when administrative staff members waited in line with other persons, they received special food privileges, such as a choice of milk or coffee, a pot rather than a cup of tea, or a dessert not available to others. After filling their tray they had to walk the length of the larger section of the dining-room through two rows of tables at which sat the "lesser" personnel. This the professional "nobility" did for many years, rarely stopping to speak or eat with anyone outside their own group.

Dr. Solomon had little sympathy with such petty discriminations, and he further felt that hierarchical barriers stood in the way of his reaching personnel and patients. So he ate where he pleased, not necessarily at the same table twice, with any or all groups of staff as the fancy struck him, or according to his needs of the moment for talking to certain persons. His example was gradually followed by other professional persons; rigid boundaries broke down, and new lines of communication were formed. The meal hour became more relaxed, and no one group or individual was set above another. In this climate of deemphasis on class distinctions, special food privileges for physicians were soon abandoned.

While this bit of democracy in action was going on, a new and hard look was taken at the way patients were treated during their meal hours. Food was sent from the main kitchen by elevator to the wards. On each convalescent ward there was a dining-room with tables set by an attendant. Here patients were permitted to use knives and forks. On the two disturbed wards there were no dining-rooms. After patients had waited in line to receive their food, they stood, sat on beds, or found a chair, balancing their tray as best they could, because of inadequate table space. Food was essentially of the soft-solid variety because the only eating utensil permitted was a spoon. There were no drinking glasses, only plastic cups and dishes, all unbreakable. Nothing was permitted that could conceivably be used for the purpose of cutting or stabbing. Patients had to ask personnel for water, since no drinking fountain was available. While they ate, apart and unrelated, they were often scolded for spilling food on the floor, or hurried through meals by the few attendants left in charge of the ward. These attendants wanted to get things "cleaned up" so they could have their own meals.

If minor discriminations prevailed between the food given the administrative staff and other hospital personnel, gross differences existed between that served to patients and that served in the main dining-room. Food sent to the wards was often inferior in quality, prepared in a less palatable manner, and cold. These discriminations were hidden from direct view by the fact that patients and administrative staff had no contact with each other at meals. Practically no attention was paid to the possibility that mealtimes might provide an opportunity for patient socialization, or that socialization might increase the satisfaction of eating.

Systematic discussion of meals with patients and personnel gave new insight into the problem.[1] One patient said that he felt that good food, well cooked and well served, was important to recovery. A woman on the acute admission ward commented: "I looked forward to the supper meal the most when the family sat around and discussed the day's events. It was a leisurely meal and an enjoyable one. Holiday meals were enjoyable because of the family gatherings." Said a lady who had been returned from the convalescent to the acute ward, "I do not like the tables to be cleared before all the patients have finished eating. I enjoy discussing current topics during the meal as we did on the convalescent ward." The following excerpts characterize the comments made by ward staff when interviewed by Miss Dolan.

An attendant, who showed much awareness of the importance of meals, explained: The patients used to rush through meals and it made them irritable. When we slowed down and encouraged socializing it made them more satisfied and relaxed. I feel that good food is conducive to helping patients therapeutically, and that with supervision, the use of knives, forks, and spoons is important in giving them a sense of well-being. Personnel should stimulate socialization among the patients.

Another attendant on the acute women's ward commented as follows: I feel that eating hours for personnel are too close to the patients' meal hours, and it does not give nurses and attendants time for their own meals. Often food is served cold to the patients.

A head nurse expressed it thus: I feel that meals should be used in the patients' daily hospital routine as a therapeutic tool. Too much of the nurses' time is taken up with administration and we do not have time enough to be with the patients. I have very little contact with them at meals. I do not feel that the atmosphere around mealtime is conducive to meeting the emotional needs of patients.

A student nurse added: We do not have anything to do with

[1] Dolan, Regina, *Research Project on Meals at Boston Psychopathic Hospital,* 1951. Unpublished manuscript.

the patients at mealtimes, but from observation I feel that those concerned with the meals are anxious to get them over with. The atmosphere is noisy, confused, and hurried.

Gradually the conviction grew that psychotic patients, too, could enjoy their meals and should be given every advantage enjoyed by others; that mealtimes embodied many cultural values, which when denied to patients contributed to their sense of loss of dignity, and defeat. Slowly, changes took place that transformed the situation. Patients on all wards were provided with tables, chairs, and all customary eating utensils. Action by Patient Government solved the problem of getting hot food to the wards. Patients participated increasingly in serving the food and cleaning up afterward, and soon took over these functions entirely. They made meals more leisurely and social, added radio music for dinner, encouraged smoking by distributing cigarettes and ash trays. The efficiency motif gave way to the social motif which proclaimed the right of every person to "dawdle" after meals and enjoy conversation. Throughout this period the actual quality of the food improved and discrimination between personnel and patients disappeared almost entirely. The latest change was to have all patients from the convalescent wards go to the main dining-room for their meals. Thus, there was a chance for personnel to eat with patients if they wished and vice versa.

When we review the alterations that have been made in the life of the Hospital, we see that the formal, limited, and rather stereotyped contacts between staff and patient, such as admission, physical examinations, "rounds," and even psychotherapy have been broadened to include more spontaneous, informal relationships, like dances, picnics, and meals. Treatment personnel thus have been revealed to patients as human beings, professional defenses have been let down, and the *whole* personalities of therapists and patients now have more of a chance to interact. The impact of one person on another can therefore be greater and therapeutic interactions in the institutional community gather strength and force. In almost all of these developments that elevated the status of individuals as human beings and eventually made them happier, the new way was embraced as the better way, after a mildly stressful period during which some members of the staff protested. Often the formerly most ardent critics eventually asked themselves how it could ever have been different.

SOCIAL POTENTIALITIES OF PATIENTS AND PERSONNEL

Looking back over more than a ten-year span, the Hospital could have taken pride in the rapid progress that had been made toward facilitating the resocialization of patients, did it not realize how superficial and poorly sustained were some of the changes, and how many roads to progress that had been pointed up by its experiments had not been exploited. On the positive side, patients could have a choice of diversions both in the daytime and in the evening. Group identification had been strengthened, there was greater freedom of movement, initiative was being encouraged, barriers between patient and patient, and between men and women had been broken down, and freer intercourse between patients and personnel had been developed. Improvement in the physical environment helped to impart a homelike appearance to the wards, and the beneficial change in patient behavior created an atmosphere of hope for recovery in most instances. Meaningful group experiences, particularly in Patient Government, strengthened the feeling of the dignity and worth of the individual, and encouraged a sense of participation in the formulation of institutional policy.

On the negative side, a study, made in 1953 by Mrs. Francoise R. Morimoto and the writer to evaluate the degree to which the social capacities of patients and personnel were being utilized and developed by the sociorecreational program, revealed how small a fraction of the available talents and interests of the members of the hospital community were being called into use.[1] In this study an inventory was made of the

[1] Morimoto, Francoise R., and Milton Greenblatt, "Personnel Awareness of Patients' Socializing Capacity," *American Journal of Psychiatry*, vol. 110, December, 1953, pp. 443–447.

leisure-time interests and skills of patients prior to hospitalization by interviewing their relatives, and by observation of what interests and skills they manifested on the admission ward. Nursing students and attendants were also questioned concerning their own social capacities and proclivities, and they, too, were carefully observed as they interacted with patients and others. Furthermore, an estimate by ward-staff members of the potentialities of individual patients was obtained after the former had had several weeks' contact with the patients on their wards.

The results of this investigation indicated that personnel tend to judge capacity for social activity of patients in the light of the *lowered* responses manifested by patients on the wards during their illness. Even nurses and attendants who were fairly intimate with them were aware of only a small fraction of the actual talents and experience they possessed. Furthermore, the staff tended to look upon patients as having abilities that were socially nonrelevant; that is, that were pursued alone for self-diversion. Family members on the other hand described the patients as possessing many socially relevant assets, such as dancing. In general, personnel were least familiar with the skills of patients who had not as yet begun to interact with other persons on the ward, and most familiar with the ones possessed by those who were already showing some of their social capacities. Some nursing students did not know of any prehospitalization interests among their patients, and a graduate nurse was not aware that one of her patients had had professional training in ballet, which was in fact the latter's chief recreational interest at the time. As a consequence of lack of such knowledge, personnel were not functioning so effectively as they might in initiating social activity for the group of patients who needed it most.

Capacities remained undiscovered in the above setting, we believe, because the Hospital had not yet recognized the desirability of maximizing all the former social abilities of patients that were applicable to its community. This is not to deny that in many instances patients have reported living a fuller and more interesting life in the Hospital than in their home and neighborhood before their illness; and a few have experienced new vistas so satisfying as to make them reluctant to leave it. A married, childless woman of forty-five, for example, lived for many years with a husband who gave her little attention and too often yielded to alcoholic overindulgence. Feeling very inferior because of her marital unhappiness, this woman made few friends and sat at home wanting babies. She was given to periodic depressions, the first of which followed the death of her new-born child. Her stay at the Hospital subsequent to a particularly severe depression was characterized by participation in many occupational and recreational groups. She established warm and intimate relationships with a number of other women and enjoyed sports she had never participated in before. She regretted leaving but felt better prepared to broaden her scope of activities in the community, based upon the friendships she had made in the Hospital.

Implementation of the goal of maximum utilization of patients' social potentials involves setting up a systematic technique for obtaining information from both relatives and patients. This could be made the responsibility of the person who obtains the case history on admission. Once data were gathered about social assets, they should be transmitted to departments of occupational and recreational therapy, as well as to physicians and nurses in charge of the patient. A clearer definition of the doctor's and nurse's role and delineation of their area of responsibility would unquestionably emerge after discussions with occupational therapy and recreational workers. Education of both psychiatrist and nurse for leadership in promoting social interaction might come to be considered an important part of their training, for it must be recognized that no amount of information gathering or reliance upon other personnel can replace the earnest motivation of ward staff based upon belief in the value of social therapy and technical experience in its application. The head nurse in particular is strategically situated to organize and encourage social activities on her ward. In doing this she would need to be aware not only of the unrealized capacities of her patients, but also of the latent potentialities of nurses and aides under her command.

Assessment of staff nurses, affiliates, and attendants reveals that a situation exists which parallels that of patients. They possess many interests and talents that are unknown to ward administrators and are never brought to light in their handling of patients. Techniques for eliciting these skills and interests are lacking, much as they are in the case of the patients. Both nursing students and aides expressed eagerness to Mrs. Morimoto to apply their talents to their work but did not realize that it was expected of them or perhaps even desired. They had assumed that provision for the social life of patients was essentially the responsibility of the occupational and recreational departments. Despite the previous emphasis on social activities, they still felt a lack of knowledge and experience in how their skills could be utilized in the ward situation. They stressed the importance of administrative support, opportunities for discussion, and individualized teaching in the clinical setting.

6. Patient Government

AN AUTOCRATIC HOSPITAL SYSTEM is inimical to the best interests of patients. Behind rigid rules and multifarious regulations lies the necessity for enforcement and obedience; this in turn tends to breed punitiveness and restrictiveness, and favors the drive in many individuals for power and control. Such a system cannot readily subordinate itself to individual differences or the manifold needs and demands of patients, which, when satisfied, yield ever more needs and demands. It is too often inflexible in the face of changing requirements of patients during various phases of their illness or recovery; of the changing culture within the hospital as treatment, research, and educational philosophy grow; and of modified demands from the outer community. Finally, such a system is not sufficiently self-critical to conduct experiments for the purpose of testing basic assumptions or evaluating ingrained procedure, and to integrate fundamental lessons from either experiment or experience into a growing social structure.

How does one, then, go about modifying the hospital pattern which is almost universally autocratic to open channels of communication, spread responsibility, increase participation, and foster initiative? One successful effort at dissemination of democratic powers among mentally ill patients, as it evolved at Boston Psychopathic Hospital, is described here.

COMPLAINTS OF HOSPITALIZED PATIENTS

In an attempt to discover more about patients' attitudes toward the hospital environment, Miss Mary E. Hatch, a social worker, in 1948 interviewed 100 patients primarily from the convalescent wards.[1] This was a research effort carried out expressly with the consent and support of administrative leaders for the purpose of apprising them of any hardships, whether large or small, which patients were experiencing as a result of living together. It was hoped that this research would uncover those distresses and discomforts imposed upon patients by the rigidities and inflexibilities of the hospital system that were not easily communicated through routine channels. This hope was consistent with the assumption that any organization which emphasizes the welfare of its members must encourage these members to speak frankly, and that no administrator of a hospital or even a ward can know *a priori* what is best for all patients.

The greatest dissatisfaction with the hospital environment was found to be dormitory living. Nearly half of the patients expressed negative feeling, and some 38 mixed feelings; only nine were definitely positive. Some patients were too hot in the dormitory, others too cold. Twenty-six patients had resented being obliged to go to bed so early when they were in the admission wards, saying that it was impossible for them to sleep. Five patients declared they had to stay up too late in the convalescent wards. Practically all patients felt that 6:30 in the morning was too early to get up. Some suggested 7:30 for rising and eight o'clock for breakfast, and no disagreement with these hours was expressed.

Miss Hatch's study revealed many other dissatisfactions, only a few of which can be dealt with here. These were dissatisfactions which administrative officers had sensed were present, but which in the absence of a definitive study they were often unable to "pin down" as to prevalence and intensity. Patients referred by the courts for observation were resented by the other patients; some of the women objected to associating with "alcoholics and prostitutes," and some of the men objected to children being placed on the adult ward.

[1] Hatch, Mary E., *An Inquiry into the Attitudes of Patients Towards Their Hospital Environment.* Submitted in partial fulfillment of requirements for M.S. degree, Simmons College, 1948.

The admission wards were described as very terrifying by 18 of the 100 patients. All were glad to be on the convalescent wards and suggested that there should be a separate section on the admission wards for patients who were not "so sick," and for those who were feeling better but had to remain there until beds became available on the convalescent wards. Both men and women considered the plumbing inadequate and faulty. (It was overhauled later after specific budgetary requests had been made.) The lack of privacy in bathrooms was very disturbing to 19 women patients who felt it was "quite shocking not to have doors on toilets and to have to bathe in public," while "not enough baths" was the complaint of seven others. The men were disturbed at not having better shaving equipment: the razor blades were "no good," the shaving brushes were worn out, and the soap was unsatisfactory. A few suggested that some arrangement be made for sending out personal laundry and clothes for cleaning. Some spoke of a soap and toilet-paper shortage.

Many men and women were bothered by the noise of other patients, and especially of personnel, talking loudly, slamming doors, and rattling keys. Although a few patients enjoyed dormitory living as carried on in 1948, the intensity of negative feeling and the large number of irritating or unpleasant details mentioned were very impressive. But these were the patients' opinions concerning only one aspect of hospital life.

The general response from most of the patients concerning medical and psychiatric treatment was positive. The patients seemed to have confidence in the hospital administration and regarded the Hospital as the best institution of its kind for the treatment of mental illness. However, seven patients complained about not seeing a physician often enough; 13 said they had been given inadequate explanations about their treatment. Very strong feelings of resentment and annoyance were expressed by seven patients at being interviewed so often by graduate students and having to repeat their stories many times. Presentation at "staff"—conferences of 30 to 50 hospital personnel representing all echelons—brought bitter comments from a few patients who spoke of their embarrassment and nervousness at "appearing before so many people." Electric shock therapy was disliked and feared by 12 patients, but considered "wonderful" by five others. Psychotherapy was not always understood as a form of therapy, but some of the patients were apparently receiving great benefit, as revealed in statements such as this: "Psychotherapy has opened up a whole new way of living for me." Some of the patients suggested group psychotherapy as an aid to better understanding of the different kinds of treatment available, and their specific purposes. (This suggestion was soon put into effect.)

Comments on hospital personnel included hearty approval of physicians, nurses, and male attendants, but some criticism of women attendants. Actually, 14 of the 50 women patients interviewed complained bitterly about the female attendants. They were "squawking all the time"; they threatened to return disobedient patients to the admission ward; they pulled the blankets off the beds early in the morning to wake patients. These particular women felt that the attendants were bored, not interested in their problems, and did not approach patients with sufficient gentleness and courtesy.

The daily program came in for considerable praise, but a number of minor criticisms about lack of physical exercise and fresh air, and suggestions concerning type of movies and use of the record player were made. The chief complaint was that weekends were dull. Queries concerning the patients' religious life met generally with either neutral or positive responses. Negative feelings, however, were expressed by 14 persons to the effect that their religious needs were not being satisfied. Representatives of all faiths pointed out that provision was not made for Jewish patients comparable to that for Protestants and Catholics.

Some of Miss Hatch's conclusions are worth stating, for they indicate the type of benefit that may flow from sincere concern with patients' opinions.

1. The study demonstrated a new field of usefulness for the social worker in a mental hospital in helping to evaluate the meaning of the environment to the patient.
2. The mere process of this kind of interview was therapeutic,

permitting ventilation of feelings and later stimulating a realistic appraisal of the environment by patients in groups.

3. Reports of the patients' opinions became a teaching aid for new student groups, attendants, nurses, and all who were concerned with the care of patients, by orienting them to feelings of patients about their environment.

4. Certain social actions, unrelated to the original aim of the study, resulted. The mobilization of feelings about the Hospital stimulated the patients to cooperative action, including writing letters, voicing their opinions, and requesting changes. The original recommendations came from one woman, a patient on the convalescent ward, and included suggestions of major significance, such as a request for group psychotherapy, assignment of a head nurse to the ward, and enforcement of the rest period for all patients. These requests were forwarded to administrative officers, who with their nonauthoritarian orientation were gratified that patients were taking a hand in improvement of ward life and felt it wise to encourage their suggestions.

GROWTH OF SELF-GOVERNMENT

The assistant superintendent, Dr. Robert W. Hyde, sat down with the patients and discussed their requests in great detail. It was decided that they could best enforce their own rest periods. A nurse was assigned to the convalescent ward in question, and arrangements were made with a physician for group psychotherapy. Ward betterment meetings became a regular feature of life on this ward, under the name Patient Government. When the new nurse received her assignment, she was carefully alerted to this surge of interest and was instructed to do everything possible to cooperate with the group. She became the representative of the administration at these meetings, where she played an essentially permissive role, and the liaison between the members of Patient Government and the medical director and assistant superintendent.

Soon the patients took over all the housekeeping functions and organization of dormitory living. But at this juncture a problem developed with the attendants on the ward. Two fine older women who had been with the Hospital a long time, went to the assistant superintendent in abject misery complaining of the unscrupulous way in which they had been treated. After many years of service they were being deprived of their work, making beds, getting meals, cleaning up, even writing letters for patients. They were utterly useless. It was unfair and discriminatory to be put in that position. This posed a difficulty because of the rigidity of their attitude and because of their deeply vested interest in doing things for patients. Part of the difficulty stemmed from the fact that the administration had not foreseen the problem and had not prepared these attendants for new roles. Now their feelings were hurt; they became deeply resentful; and it was impossible to orient them to an unfamiliar supervisory role of helping patients to help themselves. They were therefore transferred to the female admission ward, where the traditional form of ward management still existed, and were replaced by new attendants who were briefed in the art of giving patients initiative in action and of functioning as group helpers.

Patient Government flourished for six months on the female convalescent ward before it spread. On one occasion the women gave a tea party for the convalescent men, who were so impressed by the improvements in the ward and by the tea party itself that they also organized themselves into a self-governing group. After several months the two groups united, then gradually the plan was extended to include all the wards of the Hospital. Regular weekly meetings were begun and in May, 1949, a constitution was drafted, which stated the following as the purposes of the organization: to provide experience and education for patients in democratic living; to improve the environment and interpatient and staff relationships; and to set up regulations for the election of officers, committees, and their functions. The high level of interest attached to the business transacted and to the social possibilities inherent in getting together, has kept this organization alive as a vital function one evening each week since its inception.

Because nursing, occupational therapy, social service, and psychology are considered the departments most closely related in function to Patient Government, they were asked by the administration of the Hospital to send one staff member in turn to the meetings. It was hoped that by this system of rotation several ends might be achieved simultaneously: The Hospital would be represented by someone who could interpret its philosophy and program; the four departments would be given a more intimate opportunity to visualize how their goals and those of the organization could be interrelated; and the likelihood of control by the staff would be minimized. Since patients have a tendency to lean on personnel, to look for too much direction, and to take orders, it was deemed essential to use extreme caution not to foster this tendency but rather to help patients toward growth through self-government.

During its early development the organization was faced with the difficult problem of learning how to adjust to the relatively rapid rate of discharge at the Hospital. The four officers, usually persons well on the road to recovery, were frequently able to serve only for very short periods, so that elections were almost a weekly affair. For a while two patients were elected to each office, in case one of them should suddenly leave. Then the device was found of increasing the number of major offices, of establishing various committees with chairmen, and of appointing a responsible representative of each ward. Thus, the size of the active nucleus became large enough to provide greater continuity.

PATTERN AND CONTENT OF MEETINGS

Like every other patient activity in the Hospital, all who are able are invited to attend the meetings. Usually between 50 and 60 are present. Those who are physically sick, too disturbed or disorganized, or under special supervision are not permitted to attend. At each meeting there are patients who are present for the first time, and others who have been at several previous meetings.

The call to order is followed by the reading of the minutes of the last meeting by the secretary, and by the report of the treasurer. Then the letter from Dr. Hyde, in response to a weekly communication to him by the secretary, is generally read and items in it discussed. Thereafter, complaints, centering chiefly around dissatisfactions with ward living and lack of repairs or inadequacies of facilities, are heard and decision is taken about their possible remedy and whether they should be reported to the assistant superintendent. Much attention is also devoted to purchases to be made or entertainment to be provided with the funds at the disposal of the group.

Since self-governing bodies everywhere have the right to raise and expend money, and since money plays so important a role in the social fabric of American life, it was early deemed essential that Patient Government be given this right as part of the Hospital's plan for resocialization. Through soliciting funds from friends and relatives, collections taken at the four large annual dances, and profits from candy and cigarette machines and the coffee shop,[1] the organization has a not inconsiderable income to spend as it sees fit. With the money obtained it has bought television sets, provided prizes for bingo and amateur night, decorations for parties, and so on. There has been no evidence of injudicious or irresponsible use of money; the judgment exercised by patients collectively would appear equal to that of normal assemblies.

Short of the reproduction from tape recordings of exactly what transpires at these meetings, copies of representative correspondence between the secretary and the assistant superintendent at least give some indication of the discussion that centers around those problems which the organization decides should be transmitted to the Hospital. The correspondence also reveals, in part, the type of relationship that exists between it and the assistant superintendent. For example, after the meeting of April 1, 1952, the following letter went to him, was subsequently published in the "Patients' Press," and was mailed

[1] The small coffee shop is a new joint undertaking of the Auxiliary and Patient Government to serve several purposes. Profits go to the latter organization in proportion to the number of patients recruited for work by it; these patients benefit from the responsibility involved in the simple running of the shop; and the availability of coffee, sandwiches, and doughnuts during the morning and lunch hours is welcomed by the staff and visitors. Not to be confused with the coffee shop is the lobby shop, long operated by the Hospital, where cigarettes, candy, and toilet articles may be bought at designated times. Profits from this shop are used for the purchase of additional facilities for the recreational program, generally for items that have been requested by Patient Government.

to a large number of interested persons many of whom had been former patients.

To: ASSISTANT SUPERINTENDENT

The Patient Government Meeting of April 1, 1952, was called to order by President D B. The Secretary's report was then read and accepted as read. Elections followed, as a result of which D H was elected vice-president, and J M was elected secretary.

A motion was made to hold a dance on April 3, but it was pointed out by President B that the usual spring dance is to be held within two weeks.

Volunteers for the OT [Occupational Therapy] Coffee Committee include W H of Ward II, B F of Ward III, and C of Ward IV.

A suggestion was made that the program schedule be returned to its former setup. The old arrangement included Motion Pictures on Sundays, and the Patient Government on Monday nights, with Tuesday being used as television night.

It was also suggested that the tennis court be repaired for spring and summer usage.

It was further suggested that movies consist of a "short" as well as the main feature.

In regard to the OT Coffee Hour, it was pointed out that a number of staff personnel have been forgetting to pay for the coffee and yet have been found to be chiseling in on the beverage.

In regard to the motion picture, it was also pointed out that the size of the film be enlarged to coincide with the size of the screen. A suggestion was made on the part of D H that the organ box be repaired for the Easter church services.

A complaint was made on the part of D H that the trays for the insulin patients are constantly being put on the elevator with the doors left open, thus preventing the use of the elevator.

The meeting came to an adjournment at 9:20 p.m.

Respectfully submitted,

SECRETARY

The Assistant Superintendent replied as follows:

To: PATIENT GOVERNMENT

In answer to the minutes of the meeting of April 1, I would say the following:

I am glad to learn that the OT coffee group is functioning so well and am very sorry to hear that the staff have been forgetting to pay for the coffee. I brought it to their attention at Monday staff meeting and hope that this will remedy the situation. I have also talked it over with Miss D [head occupational therapist], who assures me that she will make a greater effort to collect from the staff. It is indeed sad to hear that we are not fulfilling our part of the bargain.

I discussed the proposed change of moving the movies back to Sunday with the president of Patient Government. I wish to present the following points. The change to Monday was made at the request of Patient Government after a great deal of deliberation and careful polling of their desires. Then it appeared quite reasonable and I wonder if it has been given an adequate trial. They tell me that Sunday is still a good television night and that many would prefer it to the movies. There is the alternative of moving Patient Government to another night of the week, possibly changing it with bingo on Friday night, which could be tried. We are willing to change the movies back to Sunday if we are certain that is what you desire.

We are seeing whether we have any money available to resurface the tennis court. We feel that it is in such condition that resurfacing is indicated. Thanks again for bringing this to our attention.

As to the size of the movie film, perhaps you could talk that over with Mr. G [male supervisor] and see if he has any information about the size of the picture as related to the distance the projector is from the screen.

The Solovox has been repaired.

I am looking into the matter of leaving trays on the elevator and will see what action can be taken to remedy it.

RWH/ch   ASSISTANT SUPERINTENDENT

The following letter from Patient Government dated October 31, 1951, is a communication with a more peremptory tone:

ASSISTANT SUPERINTENDENT
BOSTON PSYCHOPATHIC HOSPITAL
BOSTON, MASS.
DEAR DOCTOR:

At our meeting last Monday night, the 29th, several questions about incompleted business arose, and we would like to hear from you concerning the same.

1. Approximately when will the TV set be delivered to the Hospital?

2. What action has been taken on the Patient Government Council's request to sleep later on Sundays?

3. What are the specific rules about interward visiting between open wards, such as A and Convalescent 2?

4. What, if anything, can be done to repair or replace the faulty TV antenna on Ward 2?

We realize that you have a heavy teaching and administrative schedule, but the answers to these questions would enlighten the group tremendously.

Respectfully,

PRESIDENT
PATIENT GOVERNMENT COUNCIL

To: PATIENT GOVERNMENT COUNCIL

I have received the minutes of the October 27th meeting of Patient Government and Council and your letter of October 31.

With regard to the specific questions asked, I would like to report as follows:

We have heard from the Sylvania television distributors, and they advised us that they were willing to sell us a table model which retails for $290 for $204. They were told that there was only $189 in the Patient Government and Television Funds and they are willing to let us have it for that. Will you please let me know as soon as possible whether you are interested in the above set and I will make arrangements for its prompt delivery.

Inasmuch as the purchase of a new television set was so imminent we did not have the Ward 2 TV antenna moved, because we thought it would save us a great deal of money if both could be set up at the same time.

Visiting between Wards 2 and 3 is allowed and encouraged. Patients from Ward A are allowed to visit on 2 and 3, but it does not seem advisable to establish a general policy of letting patients from 2 and 3 visit on Ward A.[1]

We have gone into the question of your request to allow patients to sleep later on Sundays. I regret to advise you that it does not seem practical at this time to make any change inasmuch as the kitchen is not prepared to serve meals any later than at present, and even if it were it would not allow the patients who attend Mass enough time to eat and get to Church at 8:15. We don't see how you can rise much later without rushing too much.

RWH/ch   ASSISTANT SUPERINTENDENT

---

[1] As then constituted, Ward A was on the ground floor, completely open to the lobby and street, and had no staff other than a social worker. It was used for women patients who had improved sufficiently to leave the convalescent ward but who, for various reasons, needed a little more time in the Hospital.

As might be expected from Miss Hatch's study which showed that patients were most dissatisfied with dormitory living, the main substance of letters to the assistant superintendent concerns improving the details of ward life. At first sight, many of the requests appear inconsequential, but as a matter of fact, they are of great importance. The patients function as an ever-alert team of inspectors who keep constant check on supplies, damages, repairs; the Hospital could never hope to do so well with paid personnel whose sensitivities to ward living are undeveloped. The patients also prevent the accumulation of annoyances which lead to a sense of confusion and despair; they are an invaluable source of creative suggestions for further improvement. They are the first to know when the washing machine needs repair, the piano needs tuning, the pool-room light and the radio knobs need replacing. Requests for metal wastebaskets, dish towels, shoe-shine box, cloth to make plastic aprons, pen and ink, bath mats, new typewriter ribbons, bridge lamp, pop-up toaster, tables—all come in a steady stream. They were the first to suggest that the lobby shop be opened a few minutes before visiting hours so that relatives who buy supplies for patients might not waste valuable visiting time; they suggested that there be setting-up exercises in the morning; that card games be held between patients and physicians; that the name of the weekly newspaper, Psycho News, be changed to Patients' Press; that the hours of electric shock treatment be altered.

Careful attention is given each request. The assistant superintendent's letters indicate what action has been taken for the satisfaction of the patients, and if no action is possible he explains in full the point of view of the Hospital. This goes far toward reducing hostility toward administrative policy, which otherwise is often interpreted as being arbitrary and impersonal. Through his letters, his representative at the meetings, or conferences with the officers, Dr. Hyde often gives gentle guidance and makes suggestions which patients are usually eager to follow. Some of his letters show genuine gratitude for specific services rendered. For example, after members of Patient Government had assisted him in his teaching of students from the Simmons School of Social Service, he sent a note of thanks and enclosed a gratuity for their services.

SIGNIFICANCE OF PATIENT GOVERNMENT

The mere fact that the Hospital recognizes and encourages Patient Government indicates to everyone that the patients are truly held in esteem, both for their ability to utilize the democratic method in a reasonable, useful, and successful way, and for their capacity to grow as individuals through the exercise of this privilege. Instead of losing during hospitalization the rights, privileges, and responsibilities which were his during his residence in the community, the patient is provided through this organization with the opportunity for exercise of democratic powers, and in a manner often more vital and realistic than he has before enjoyed. In this group experience he is able to explore every detail of hospital life, with the possibility of changing the environment to conform to his own needs. He may even try out a variety of possible new roles: that of responsible ward representative canvassing his fellow-patients and personnel for suggestions for ward betterment; that of governing officer entrusted by his own group and by the Hospital with leadership responsibilities; that of member of an active committee set up to ensure good housekeeping, evening snacks, or a coffee hour, or to raise money, conduct tours for students and visitors, and look after social activities such as picnics, plays and skits, and the "Psycho Pops"[1]; or that simply of voting member, free to speak his mind, air his "gripes," and help to decide issues.

There is little question that the patients themselves consider Patient Government a valuable experience. After interviewing many who had taken part in it, Miss Hatch stated, "It has been an effective therapeutic tool in giving patients free expression for their ideas and in allowing them to govern their own activities. It has proved to be a successful experiment in what might be termed a form of 'nondirective group therapy.'"

[1] Programs of recorded semiclassical music.

Later she noted that from remarks made by the officers it was evident that "all of them were very much pleased to be elected, and gained personal satisfaction and prestige from the jobs." Concerning those who did not necessarily have an active, responsible function to perform, her general statement would probably be applicable. "Patient Government helps the patients to relax . . . to feel free to speak their minds. It gives them confidence in the Hospital as they are all fighting for the same thing. It gets gripes out and taken care of, so that they do not continue to complain all the time and, therefore, it makes the ward livable and enjoyable for patients as well as staff."

What Miss Hatch was not in a position to explore was the therapeutic effect that the meetings may have upon individual patients. Some who have been so withdrawn as to appear incapable of social interaction will, under the excitement of a debated issue, make a motion or otherwise express strong preference. Another patient who is manic will try to manipulate the group for his own purposes until it is driven in self-protection to silencing him. This group action is sometimes so beneficial that the patient subsequently appears less excited and more considerate of others.

Potentially, Patient Government can affect relations between the Hospital and the community profoundly. The effect on students, visitors, and volunteers who have attended the meetings is frequently remarkable. Those individuals in particular, who think that mentally ill persons are necessarily robbed of rights and privileges during their illness, whose conception of intramural life is based largely upon information derived from "Snake Pit" sources, are often dramatically moved to see how much trust, freedom, and self-realization the patient can enjoy. Among the large number of persons that visit the Hospital each year whose good will and understanding are essential for its progress over the long run, there are many volunteers from the Gray Ladies, the Auxiliary, Volunteers' Service Bureau, and miscellaneous sources. In an article on Patient Government published in 1950, the authors wrote:

It became the practice to have new volunteers with special

talents introduced to the recreation committee of Patient Government so that they could work out together how the patients' needs could best be served. . . . This direct relationship proved exceedingly valuable in bringing about a smooth introduction of new volunteers to the Hospital. They had an opportunity to overcome any timidity and confusion regarding their role by these firsthand contacts. This made the volunteer program one that was sponsored by the patients from the start rather than something that was forced upon them. . . . For example, one volunteer became social adviser to the Patient Government and worked directly with it to obtain orchestras and arrange programs for special seasonal dances. These events, for which patients worked with plans, decorations, etc., became the most impressive and spirited which the Hospital has seen.[1]

Since then representatives of Patient Government have been asked increasingly to introduce the Hospital to various groups. Five members of the organization, for example, were selected to conduct a tour of the institution for some 25 graduate students from the Harvard School of Public Health. Later, when it was known that a large number of staff from the neighboring psychiatric hospitals that were cooperating in the Russell Sage Project on improvement of patient care wished to visit the wards, Patient Government was requested to assume responsibility for planning and conducting the tour. The surprised group agreed that this procedure was a distinct change from the customary one in which visitors walk the wards while patients often feel themselves the object of scrutiny and comment, like animals in a cage. In instances where patients have served as hosts and hostesses, their pride in the institution has been stimulated, and visitors have obtained exceptional and intimate glimpses of hospital life as seen through their eyes.

[1] Hyde, Robert W., and Harry C. Solomon, "Patient Government: A New Form of Group Therapy," *Digest of Neurology and Psychiatry*, vol. 18, April, 1950, pp. 207–218.

7. Development of Therapeutic Potential of Personnel

IN THE MEDICAL AND SURGICAL WARDS of the general hospital the physician examines the patient and prescribes specific treatments that he can predict with reasonable certainty will be carried out. The efficient running of the wards presupposes a high degree of cooperation between patient, nurse, and physician. While a personal relationship between the patient and members of the professional staff is desirable and often essential, this does not ordinarily imply the depth of understanding that is necessary in working with psychiatric patients before forward movement can be produced. If there are no untoward happenings, the medical or surgical patient will recover completely from his pneumonia; his cardiac condition or nephritis will greatly improve; his appendix or gall bladder will be removed quickly, smoothly, and without complications.

In the psychiatric ward conditions are different. The patients' immediate and adequate cooperation in striving for health cannot be assumed; instead, many are quite satisfied with neurotic or psychotic maladjustments. The prescription does not read "digitalis gr. III, B.I.D."—but contains subtle and immeasurable ingredients, such as understanding, acceptance, interest, sympathy, and affection. These are the factors that may promote "ventilation" of problems and desensitization of conflicts, and may provide the foundation for insight, education, and resocialization. The prescription in a word calls for mature social relationships to undo pathogenic ones from which the patient has been suffering. These ingredients cannot be ordered from a pharmacy. They are in the heart and mind of man. They may be brought forth abundantly and generously if conditions are right; if thwarted, they may become negative tensions precluding therapeutic interactions.

In our large mental hospitals physicians alone cannot reach the patients, so few are they in number and generally so far removed from the ward. If the sick are to get well they must be helped by ward personnel, in whom potentialities for therapeutic interaction have been mobilized and a sense of enthusiasm and participation in therapy cultivated. Of all personnel the great untapped reservoirs, as already indicated in the second chapter, lie in the attendants. Though most numerous they are least trained, least identified with professional aims, lowest in the social hierarchy, lowest in the wage scale. It is as though the hospital system were organized on principles calculated to guarantee defeat of its primary aims. Can anything less than a social revolution within the hospital remedy these ills?

EXTENSION OF THERAPEUTIC FUNCTIONS TO WARD PERSONNEL

To what extent can nonmedical personnel carry on therapeutic activity in the formal sense? Dr. Rudolph Kaldeck, when clinical director of Medfield State Hospital in Massachusetts, undertook pioneering experiments in the use of attendants and nurses as group therapists.[1] Faced with a small and overburdened medical staff and lack of trained group leaders, Dr. Kaldeck decided to recruit and train group psychotherapists largely from the nursing service. The support of the superintendent of the Hospital and the director of the nursing service helped to make this experiment successful. He formed 21 groups, each with 12 to 15 "back ward" patients. Twelve of these groups were conducted by attendants, two by nurses, one by a social worker, three by psychologists, and three by physicians. Where selection was possible, emotional maturity and experience in working with patients were the deciding factors. Group meetings with patients were held three times weekly. Group leaders met with Dr. Kaldeck once a week to discuss in seminar fashion problems they had encountered during the week. Thus, more than 250 chronic patients who otherwise might have been idle, out of a hospital population of 1,600, were brought into a group

[1] Kaldeck, Rudolph, "Group Psychotherapy by Nurses and Attendants," *Diseases of the Nervous System*, vol. 12, May, 1951, pp. 138–142.

experience utilizing primarily leaders from "lower level personnel." Wrote Dr. Kaldeck:

I do not hesitate to state that these seminars with the group leaders have been most rewarding. It has been fascinating to observe their growth and development stimulated by their actual work. . . . [Initially] they were mainly interested in altering reality factors; they wanted a patient's relatives to visit him more often or to have better equipment for the activities of the ward. They might suggest having patients assigned to more suitable work or transferred to another ward. These recommendations were followed up by the hospital physician in order not to discredit the attendants. However, they were made to understand that the purpose of group therapy was something else . . . an attitude of helpfulness and sincere interest was more significant. . . . The attendants soon ceased to favor patients who praised them and to resent the abusive and overcritical attitude of other patients. . . . They became increasingly aware that the seemingly senseless behavior of the psychotic had a definite meaning. . . . The attendants learned to observe the patients with new interest and increased respect.

At one group session led by an attendant, an angry male patient spoke disparagingly of his sister, claiming she always tried to steal his things. At another session he yelled at his fellow patients, demanding that they stop calling him a woman. Suddenly he became excited, dropped his trousers, and exposed his body to the group. The attendant-leader calmly told the patient that the group knew he was a man and that there was no need to prove it. The patient quieted down immediately. Many instances of this sort convinced Dr. Kaldeck that during their long hours of close contact and observation of patients, untrained personnel could develop extraordinary insight into psychotic behavior which they later utilized in an intuitive therapeutic manner. The results of this courageous experiment are described further as follows:

They [the patients] utilize the opportunities presented at the meetings to talk freely without being reprimanded and to compare their own problems with those of other patients. They learn to verbalize their anxieties instead of acting them out. . . . Three patients attending the groups, who had been in the hospital for many years have since left on indefinite visit. Several others have shown so much improvement that they are able to go out on occasional visits to their families. Others could be transferred to better wards. Only a very few patients, notably paranoiacs with systematized delusions, have refused to participate. The majority of the patients enjoy the increased attention and like to attend the group meetings.

Of equal importance is the effect on morale and attitude of attendants. Their self-esteem is heightened; they become aware that they are not working in an asylum where mere custodial care is given, but in a hospital where every effort is made to get patients well. Several desirable applicants including psychology students have applied for positions as attendants when they learned of this project. An attendant who has participated in group therapy will apply his experience to the rest of his work on the ward. This attitude is not limited to the group leaders but spreads to the other employees. In this way group therapy helps the personnel to achieve the most important factor in a mental hospital: *the therapeutic attitude.* [Editor's italics]

The implications in this report as to the extraordinary potentialities of attendants and other nonmedical personnel are further heightened when one considers the innumerable therapeutic contacts which staff make with patients in informal, unstructured relationships. The spontaneous affinities which spring up between patients and personnel may be illustrated by the relationship between an attendant, Edward Fitzgerald (a thirty-one-year-old married man and college graduate, with a strong liking for people and a vigorous interest in social psychology), and a male patient of sixteen, Albert, who was in an acute catatonic regression. This relationship was studied by Chaplain Joseph Woodson at Boston Psychopathic Hospital in the course of an inquiry into how rapport becomes established and develops between patients and members of the hospital staff.

In June, 1953, Albert was mute, withdrawn, in a typical schizophrenic retreat. Fitz [the attendant] started feeding him about the middle of July. . . . This continued for a month. The patient showed more recognition. Fitz used fatherly firmness; would pick him up and take him to the shower. Albert then began going to the shower on his own. Fitz laid out a game of cards before the patient each day for a week, and after a week the patient played with him. The same thing happened with checkers. Albert started taking his tray back to the dining-room, sweeping, and making his own bed. He drew a picture of a rose and a sketch of Fitz. He seemed much improved.

On September 11, Fitz formulated his goal in relation to the patient. "I want to take him out for a ride and over to the house for dinner in a couple of weeks. I was in OT today when he was playing pool. He interrupted his play and apologized for shots that beginners make. I showed him how to play. I feel that he wants to do well in my eyes. I smoke cigars; he wants to smoke cigars."

On September 15, Fitz said: "I have seen Albert [who had been transferred to the convalescent ward] briefly a couple of times. He shook hands with me yesterday and came near squeezing my hand off. This was in response to the way I used to try to get him to shake hands with me when he was sick. He is going out [leave the Hospital] in a couple of weeks. He is going to have dinner with me today."

The patient's feelings in this relationship were explained later to the investigator. "Fitz is a nice guy. He is the one who paid most attention to me on Ward 4. Every time he meets me he talks to me for five minutes or more. He got me to eat. I used to be shy. I used to stand in the corner. He got me out of that; snapped me out of my shyness. . . . He got other patients to talk to me. I got to talking to them. He took me to OT and we had a game of pool. He used to buy 'cokes' for me. Today I am going to meet him downstairs and have dinner with him. He is going to take me to his house one day next week to meet his wife."[1]

Later inquiry revealed that Mr. Fitzgerald's physical build, his kindness, and interest reminded Albert of a friend he called "Uncle," with whom he had been able to establish a positive rewarding relationship. Fitz, in turn, was immediately interested in the boy when they first met not only because he was the "baby" of the ward, but because his muteness and withdrawal that had defeated efforts of personnel to penetrate were a challenge which Fitz wanted to accept. Albert's muteness reminded him of his own shyness and refusal to read orally in school because of an early speech difficulty.

[1] Woodson, Joseph, Notes gathered for thesis, *The Meaning and Development of Empathy*. Submitted in partial fulfillment of requirements for Ph.D. degree, Boston University, 1954.

In some types of hospital this degree of fraternization between attendant and patient would not have been permitted, perhaps even considered dangerous. Before such a relationship can occur the attendant must be able to think of himself as playing a vital role in treatment and be moved to help the patient through use of his own resources. His rewards are the satisfaction of giving, consciousness of his power of healing, respect and affection from the patient, and recognition from the staff. To permit this type of relationship, indeed to encourage it, requires a special orientation toward personnel that emphasizes trust and belief in their interest and motivation. The conviction that patients have enormous potentialities for improvement under beneficial conditions is paralleled by the belief that personnel, too, have possibilities for growth. In order to maximize the therapeutic forces in the environment, it is necessary to maximize personnel's opportunities and capacities to play a therapeutic role. A further assumption of a system which favors a variety of personnel-patient relationships is that, in our present state of knowledge, it is difficult if not impossible to predict how or when patients will receive help. Until far more scientific assessment and evaluation of many kinds of social interactions are made, we believe it wise to experiment actively and openmindedly with varied small and large group relationships, not excluding the possibility of including all personnel in the hospital. A corollary of this concept is, that any institution which acts upon this philosophy must provide continuous training and education for many categories of personnel.

Before we discuss the instrumentalities for helping personnel to develop with which our Hospital has been experimenting, let us examine a significant instance of extension of the psychotherapeutic role to a head nurse at Boston State Hospital.[1] June Mellow, in charge of a 32-bed ward at this large public institution, was deeply moved when an attractive girl, Andrea, aged twenty-four, was admitted in great distress. Andrea had suf-

[1] Mellow, June, *An Exploratory Study of Nursing Therapy with Two Persons with Psychosis*. Submitted in partial fulfillment of requirements for M.S. degree, Boston University School of Nursing, 1953.

fered an acute psychotic attack during which she exhibited pronounced excitement and turmoil, vivid hallucinations and delusions, and unpredictable, aggressive behavior. Her delusional thinking and physical assaultiveness disrupted the plan of the ward psychiatrist for intensive psychotherapy. The patient believed him to be the man in charge of a white slave racket. Afraid, and determined to protect herself, she resorted to violence whenever he approached. She kicked him, threw things at him, and was completely unmanageable. After repeated failures to establish contact, the physician decided to let the relationship between the head nurse and the patient become the pivotal one in therapy, for although violent and abusive toward him, Andrea seemed to like this nurse and responded to her. From a supportive role, Miss Mellow now stepped in as the main therapeutic actor, in an intense dyadic relationship. She had never had experience of this kind before, and could only rely on her general knowledge and understanding of psychotic behavior, fortified by a personal psychoanalysis and weekly conferences with the doctor. Helpful environmental factors were the general permissive atmosphere that was established and maintained on this ward, and the cooperation of its personnel. In all probability, of critical significance was the personality of the nurse, who was generously endowed with emotional warmth, intelligence, and sound judgment.

How did the head nurse find time for intensive individual attention to one patient, and how did she go about promoting an environment conducive to "individual nursing therapy"? The answer lay in her attitude toward her role as ward administrator. She delegated the routine aspects of administration to a capable charge attendant, thus greatly increasing her "free" time, which was spent both with the patient and with ward personnel. Conferences with day staff were called at least once a week, and oftener when necessary, to discuss the therapeutic progress of the patient. Other conferences were held weekly to consider the emotional and interpersonal difficulties of all ward patients, including meetings with evening aides in order that therapeutic attitudes might be consistent. During conferences of the first type the aides were encouraged to express their personal feelings toward the patient, and their views regarding her ward relationships. By explaining the dynamics of the illness, by spontaneous clinical "demonstrations" and by placing emphasis on the importance of their attitude, the nurse was able to convince them of their value in the recovery of the patient. They proved to be a source of much valuable information, increasing her awareness of the impact of individual nursing therapy not only on the specific patient, but on the atmosphere of the ward. Thus, by delegation of administrative details, opening channels of communication for the sharing of knowledge among staff, and showing recognition and appreciation to aides for work well done, interest in all the patients was furthered and personnel were educated in a concrete experiential sense. Because of her intimate, lengthy contact with both patients and aides, Miss Mellow was probably in a more advantageous position than the psychiatrist to mobilize and apply constructively the skills of personnel.

Throughout the therapeutic process this nurse was placed in various roles by the patient: that of prostitute, girl friend, spy, mother, and finally her true self. Toward each fantasy person Andrea acted out weird delusions. Eventually, four months after admission, she underwent a complete restitution, was discharged from the Hospital, found an interesting job, and developed an active social life. Two years after her acute psychosis she was known to be in good mental health.

As a result of this experience, a second and third patient were assigned to Miss Mellow specifically for intensive individual psychotherapy, under the general supervision of a physician. In these instances the marked degree of spontaneous empathy which existed initially in the case of Andrea was lacking. The nurse entered consciously into the role of therapist and the relationship evolved as it might in the psychiatrist's office. Space will not permit description of the course of therapy; it is perhaps sufficient to state that these patients, too, improved clinically. May we not conclude, therefore, that under proper conditions the traditional role of the psychiatric nurse can be augmented to

include the function of individual therapist, a function hereto-
fore almost exclusively reserved for the psychiatrist?[1]

These examples of extension of the roles of ward personnel
open new vistas to thinking about ways in which the therapeutic potentialities of the hospital community may be mobilized
for the development of the abilities of personnel and hence
for the good of patients.

CONCEPTS GUIDING DEVELOPMENT OF PERSONNEL AT THE HOSPITAL

The expectation that nonmedical personnel were to assume
more initiative and responsibility for patient care, and the attempt to provide them with enough psychological support and
informal guidance to enable them to fulfill this expectation were
for this Hospital radical changes. These changes resulted from
the insistence of the medical director and his chief assistants
that concepts like the following be translated into action. To
quote Dr. Solomon's extemporaneous remarks:

> All rules of procedure are to be neglected to a large extent.
> Personnel are to be taught that they are to use intuition, imagina-
> tion, initiative, judgment, rather than be constrained by rules of
> procedure. Create a general investigative attitude, go beyond the
> formal scientific experiment, and try out devices as they are rec-
> ommended. For example, let the nurses decide whether or not
> they are to wear uniforms, and the best way to get along with
> patients. If they want a certain type of ward organization, they
> do not need special permission, unless it unavoidably collides
> with something else.
>
> We want continuing change, not by ukase, but by discussion
> and argument, perhaps continuing for months; with respect for
> the opinions of all. Issues can be decided by logical debate rather
> than direct orders. The "High Moguls" should be willing to justify
> themselves to the "Low Moguls." This will lead to a feeling among
> the staff that they are not being pushed around. Let personnel

[1] The way in which the time of psychiatric nurses, who are as yet few in
number, can be most profitably used is still an unanswered question. Should
they work primarily with individual patients, with groups of patients, or with
the members of their ward staff? Intensive work with individual patients under
the supervision of a psychiatrist perhaps seems like a wasteful extravagance
when so many other patients are greatly in need of attention. This type of
deep psychological experience, however, may be an essential step in helping
nurses achieve sufficient understanding and insight into emotions to enable
them to move closer to all patients.

and patients, rather than doctors only, use their creative imagination in developing enterprises.

Or again: Nurses are not expected to stand at attention for doctors. We want no guard-like poses. All personnel are alike insofar as our only craft is getting patients well. Look for capacities additional to those imparted by training or required by the role. Especially important are those qualities which are submerged, seeking outlet, but inhibited by rigidities in our system and in our thinking. Many persons have an interest and a drive to do more for patients than they are doing. They should be made to feel that the patients need them.

One important focus and starting point for movement are the interpersonal and group tensions to be found everywhere in our social system. We should see to it that individuals and groups are brought together with adequate opportunity for discussion of sensitive topics and exchange of ideas.

The concepts are not new, only the doing is new.

Many instrumentalities have been tried for helping personnel move in the general direction indicated above. The primary device has been the group meeting. Groups of many types consisting of either personnel or personnel and patients have sprung up over the years, some at the instigation of the administration, some suggested by staff members, others by patients. Often functions have overlapped but in general each has had a characteristic purpose not duplicated by any other. Some groups have been transient, others have remained essentially stable through the years, apparently serving ends that are relatively fixed and indispensable.

HELPING NURSING PERSONNEL DEVELOP THEIR CAPACITIES

Recognition of the drab existence of patients that came from direct observation by the administration of their lives on the ward provided the initial spark for work with various categories of personnel. It was obvious, as has been indicated in earlier chapters, that ward social interaction was at a very low ebb, that attendants and affiliate nursing students did not feel it their function to talk with patients, or did not know how. On the other hand, there was a sudden surge of spirit among the patients when the occupational therapist arrived with her games, crafts, and general knowledge of how to organize activities. The interest and energy released during the activities did not subside immediately after their end, but persisted for a longer or shorter period depending on the time interval between them and the emotional richness of the experience. Once moved out of lethargy, patients continued to show interest and anticipation for a while, but slumped back if further opportunities were not provided.

Attendants

Since attendants formed the largest category of ward staff, intensive work began with them in 1946 under the leadership of the assistant superintendent. Five years later the director of nursing assumed the responsibility. It was decided that intensive work could be done through meetings held at least once a week, at which attendance was to be voluntary. Rarely fewer than three or more than nine attendants are present at these meetings, depending upon conditions on the wards and more particularly upon their own interest. Often they come in response to immediate vexations and troublesome problems with which they want help. Because of the smallness and intimacy of the Hospital, it has been possible to reach the majority of the 50 attendants, even though some attend very infrequently. The night attendants present the most difficult problem. In the beginning the assistant superintendent experimented with seeing them in the early morning before they left the Hospital or on payday when they came to get their checks. It has now become customary for Dr. Hyde to meet regularly with them once every two weeks, even though Miss Harriet M. Kandler carries responsibility for all other attendant training. Initially the major need was so emphatically for instruction of the men attendants that the women were overlooked. Later, they were encouraged to attend the meetings. Even now, however, they are not proportionately represented, chiefly perhaps because the meeting place is more convenient to the male wards.

Initially, the meetings were designed to serve two distinctly different purposes. They were to consist of discussion of sub-

ject matter, much as in any classroom, that the assistant superintendent thought would be useful or that the attendants
wanted reviewed; they were also to provide opportunity for
discussion of current ward problems presented by the attendants for help. Subject matter included the physical, mental, and
laboratory examination of the patient upon admission to the
Hospital with explanation of technical procedures given generally by the technicians and laboratory assistants who were
doing the work. This added a teaching dimension to the usual
activities of such personnel. In addition, the following topics
were discussed in early years: the attendant's approach to the
patient; the meaning of various events in the patient's day
from rising to retiring; the meaning of the patient's symptoms;
the attendant's role in treatment; the handling of difficult patients; and, finally, problems of ward administration and interpersonal relations between various types of personnel.

The second purpose, consideration of current ward problems
suggested by the attendants themselves, has always received
much attention and since the meetings were taken over by the
director of nursing has constituted the almost exclusive goal.[1]
Essentially the problems brought up by the attendants concern
patients who are psychologically difficult to handle, who make
them anxious or somehow interfere with the pursuit of their
job as they see it. Staff frictions are also aired at great length.
Their feeling of inferiority at not being considered part of the
therapeutic team emerged so often and insistently in the early
sessions that provision, described in a previous chapter, was
made for them to attend staff conferences, join ward rounds,
and study patients' records.

In the opinion of those responsible for the meetings *appreciable learning and emotional growth have come from the opportunity furnished attendants to unburden conflicts about discharge of duties; understand the dynamics behind the behavior
of patients; realize their own relationship to individual patients
and how this relationship may create problems; achieve the*

---

[1] At present, instruction in subject matter occurs during the week of individual
orientation that each new employee receives, and major opportunities to learn
are provided during the many meetings with physicians, nurses, social workers,
and occupational and recreational therapists that they are encouraged to attend.

feeling of being more fully accepted by their peers and by authority figures; and gain satisfaction from improved motivation and effectiveness in caring for the mentally ill. The down-to-earth nature of the discussions and concentration on feelings rather than on accumulated learning have made it possible for attendants of widely divergent backgrounds, both educational and social, to speak a common language. Like the medical staff conference, where a psychiatrist presents a case history before other psychiatrists, day after day, year after year, always freshly challenged by the endless variations in human adaptation, so attendant meetings grounded in the clinical approach can continue with profit indefinitely.

At present, however, the director of nurses believes that the meetings might be improved if they were conducted at times by other members of the staff. Some of the problems presented could perhaps be more adequately considered with her administrative assistant or with the chief male supervisor. Feelings growing out of staff frictions might be expressed more readily to the assistant superintendent, for no matter how "accepting" she may be, the director of nurses is nevertheless "boss" to the attendants. Hence, it has been decided to rotate the weekly sessions so that the attendants will meet in turn with different supervisory staff members.

Earlier sections on Seclusion contained excerpts from discussions at attendant meetings. The content and procedure of such meetings are further illustrated by a typical session, where group tensions between attendants and affiliate students came to the fore and were relieved sufficiently to permit appreciable gain in insight. Disagreement had risen about attitudes toward a particular patient who, though young and good looking, was very demanding and had a bizarre, compulsive tic which interfered with his speech and threw his whole body into contortions. The men attendants had in general adopted a strict attitude toward him, while the women students were friendly and protective.[1]

---

[1] Hyde, Robert W., in collaboration with the Attendants of Boston Psychopathic Hospital, *Experiencing the Patient's Day:* A Manual for Psychiatric Hospital Personnel. G. P. Putnam's Sons, New York, 1955, pp. 208–211.

ATTENDANT W C: From my point of view the patient is a like-able chap in spite of his impulses, but his constant demands are the only way he knows to attract attention to himself. We have been ordered [by head nurse] that he is to receive no more consideration than any other patient. Neither is he to be given duties like other patients.

DR. H: How do you feel about that order?

ATTENDANT W C: I agree with it.

ATTENDANT H G: If you stand and watch him, he'll stand and sputter as long as you stay there. He'll ask favors of anyone in the ward until he gets the service he wants. He will set his dinner aside and come begging for food. Once he went into the refrigerator and stole some food. He has attacked and beaten Patient G who is much smaller than he is. Since I have been showing emphatic disapproval of his disobedience he has done much better. *Our attitudes conflict with those shown by affiliate nurses but it seems we are right.*

ATTENDANT C: He'll curse at you and he has struck other patients.

ATTENDANT G: He has struck me. . . . He uses vile and obscene language. We are not persecuting him. *The students and nurses have not developed a rational point of view toward him.* The attendants' course of action is planned to break down the ring of protection which the students have permitted to grow around him.

ATTENDANT E G: You attendants are meeting resentment with resentment. You are fighting fire with fire.

ATTENDANT E: We have to.

DR. H: You have given the opposite of the affiliates' point of view.

ATTENDANT W: Each group tries to demonstrate that its point of view is the best one. Each becomes more vehement in demonstrating to the other. The patient is a football each of you is kicking back and forth.

DR. H: You can't carry out the order as long as you are hot about it.

ATTENDANT G: I have objected to the fact that they [the students] were all clustering about him. I don't like it when one of them informs the attendant that he is being a beast. We object to the mothering of patients.

ATTENDANT C: I second all his statements.

ATTENDANT W: My feeling is that this whole discussion has not been too fruitful. It has just helped to relieve our emotions and anxieties.

DR. H: That must come first.

This conversation led to recognition of the need to clarify differences existing between attendants and students. The next day a ward "clinic" was conducted in which the patient's physician, the head nurse, three affiliates, and three attendants took part. The doctor pointed out that the patient might feel fully as disturbed by the pitying and pampering of the students as by the hostility of the attendants. Attendants W and EG saw that the patient was suffering from a clash of attitudes, sustained by the attendants' feelings that they were supporting the head nurse. The tension of weeks began to simmer down following the clinic in which all involved parties viewed the problem together. In later discussions the attendants recognized that they were jealous of the "mothering" attitude of affiliates toward the patient, and resentful at being called "some variety of beast." As a result of this experience, the teaching program for students was altered to include attendants' explanation of their roles to successive new groups.

The informed reader will recognize in this example the typical triangular situation described by Stanton and Schwartz—in which a member of the hospital community, often the patient, gets caught in a submerged tug-of-war between authority figures.[1] The victim frequently reacts to this struggle with tension, confusion, or deteriorated conduct. Years of discussions with attendants have disclosed that, although superficial discussions are often valuable in relieving emotions and anxieties, we should not underestimate the amount of work that must be done with personnel before "sick" interpersonal and intergroup relations can be fully diagnosed, the unpleasant effects thoroughly purged, and the social unit nursed back to health.

Nursing Students

The second largest group of personnel at the Hospital that have a close relationship with the patients are the nursing students, who currently come from seven hospital schools and one university school for a twelve-week affiliation in psychiatric

[1] Stanton, Alfred H., and Morris S. Schwartz, "The Management of a Type of Institutional Participation in Mental Illness," *Psychiatry*, vol. 12, February, 1949, pp. 13–26.

nursing. Hence, they are generally spoken of as affiliate nurses or affiliates. Schedules are so arranged that approximately 30 students are in residence throughout the year and, therefore, the Hospital can depend upon having part-time assistance on the wards and in occupational and recreational programs from that number as part of their clinical training. Except for the university students that arrive as one unit accompanied by a clinical instructor who seeks to make this experience an integrated part of their entire course of study, the department of nursing assumes responsibility for the objectives pursued, the curriculum offered, and the teaching and clinical supervision provided.[1]

The affiliation is designed to give the student a general introduction to the nature of mental disease, its treatment, the role of the nurse in treatment and patient management, and the degree of success that can be expected when therapy is begun early and pursued actively. It also serves to give her some knowledge of the interrelationship of physical and psychological factors in the life history of the individual person, and of the fact that the behavior patterns of the mentally ill are only gross exaggerations of behavior frequently observable in the physically ill and even in supposedly normal persons. Finally, it attempts to give her more understanding of herself and of her own motivations, attitudes, and perceptions, as the basis for understanding and working constructively with other persons.

In conformity with these broad objectives both class teaching and clinical experience have been arranged. The largest unit of time in the formal training consists of one four-hour morning each week devoted to psychiatry. Most of this course is presented clinically around specific patients whose patterns of behavior and treatment are discussed as introduction to more

[1] The reader should understand that this affiliation, like all others in psychiatric nursing, is not for the purpose of preparing specialized psychiatric nurses. Several universities in the United States offer such preparation for which graduation from a school of nursing and often a bachelor's degree are required for admission. Boston Psychopathic Hospital is used as one of the clinical facilities for those graduate nurses enrolled in Boston University who wish to become specialists in psychiatric nursing and thus eligible for supervisory, administrative, and teaching positions.

detailed consideration of plans for their nursing care. Unlike the procedure generally followed elsewhere that has often proved unsatisfactory, this course is organized and given exclusively by nurses on the assumption that it can be more efficiently and expeditiously adapted to the needs of students than if physicians were to give the customary lectures on psychiatry. Provision is made, however, for students to attend patient-centered clinics held by psychiatrists. In fact, a specified minimum of hours must be spent in attending a wide variety of conferences and staff meetings where the student can observe the dynamics of attempting to furnish patient-centered care.

The weekly clinic of one hour with Miss Ogilby, the social worker, is for the purpose of viewing the patient as a total person with family, community, and work ties, and of emphasizing the importance of environmental factors in his treatment and rehabilitation. Another hour each week is reserved for students to attend the psychodrama sessions, which will be described in the next chapter. To help the affiliate to a better understanding of her own motivations and those of others, two group therapy units of eight to fifteen students each have been conducted, one hour weekly, since 1951. Five different psychiatrists, who did not have ward responsibilities and, hence, were not seen by students on the wards, have taken charge of these sessions for varying periods of time. Although all students supposedly attended, they were not required to attend. It was found that often the very ones who needed the help most dropped out because the content discussed produced anxiety in them. Hence, attendance has recently been made obligatory, and Dr. J. Sanbourne Bockoven who has experienced marked success in working with groups is now conducting both units.

As illustration of what comes up for discussion at these sessions, we wish to present one specific problem in some detail because it not only constitutes a continuing therapeutic theme, but is a problem generic to all personnel working with psychiatric patients. It stems from the age-old principle in medicine of "equal service" for all patients. This principle does not necessarily give the student too much trouble in the general hospital, where her relationships are highly structured and less personal and where she has traditionally been expected to suppress, rather than examine, dislikes and prejudices. Upon arrival for her affiliation in psychiatric nursing, however, she is strongly encouraged to interact with patients in a far more personal and spontaneous manner. Presently it is discovered that she tends to interact with those who attract her, but to neglect all others. She can even forget the existence of patients who seem repulsive to her. Sociometric ward studies at the Hospital have revealed statistically how significant a factor is "favoritism." The frequency and duration of interaction of students with "liked" patients is far greater than with disliked patients; while the interactions with "liked" patients are more friendly and more natural than those with "disliked" persons. Although preferences for different patients vary among different students, still there is a marked tendency for the latter as a group to concentrate positive feelings upon a small proportion and to neglect or reject others. To make matters worse, it is the well-liked patient who ordinarily shows the most clinical progress and the disliked patient who lags behind.

Because this problem assumes such importance both for students in their affiliation and for all psychological care of patients, much attention is focused upon it in the group therapy sessions. Here, opportunities provided by affiliates are seized upon by the therapist to raise the question of *why* certain patients are liked, *why* others are disliked, and whether there is realization that some are not only neglected but forgotten. On the basis of repeated discussions of this kind, an attempt is made to broaden the range of positive identification of personnel with patients by continuous working through of negative feelings. Fortunately, experience suggests that many human antipathies are relatively superficial phenomena that can be altered by group therapeutic processes, such as those now being used with the students and also with attendants and graduate nurses. In addition, a powerful impetus is provided if the hospital culture rewards preeminently successful work with the sickest and most difficult psychotic patients. In another part of the book an illustration will be given of how the welfare of the "underdog" can become the *raison d'être* of personnel, when the latter have sufficient motivation.[1]

During their clinical experience other problems appear with which the affiliates need help, in addition to the nursing instruction *per se* that must be provided them. Although young and adaptable, the fact remains that those from the hospital schools have generally been trained in a fairly rigid autocratic system. They often are afraid of their superiors, and look upon psychiatrists with awe and reverence. They have been taught to take orders, be seen more than heard, carry out technical nursing procedures quickly and efficiently, and keep their personalities to themselves. However, in the psychiatric hospital their vitality, freshness, and enthusiasm, and their great potentialities for spontaneity and sympathy are the very elements that are most desirable to elicit in their relationships with patients. How to help them make this great transition in the brief period of twelve weeks is a consideration of the first magnitude. Perhaps no other group of personnel has so much to offer patients, so much to learn, and so little time as do affiliates. Unless this opportunity for growth and development can be used constructively, moreover, it can be very threatening, with traumatic consequences reaching beyond the period of their psychiatric affiliation. Explorations by Dr. Julius Levine of the initial difficulties of students in relating to patients have sharpened our awareness of the potential dangers of trauma.[2] Dr. Levine points to those difficulties that result from fear of criticism by authority figures who are seen as rather strict, or from the emphasis upon nursing techniques with suppression of self that is carried over from the general hospital training. He points more insistently to those difficulties arising from conflicts within the student that have been activated by observing "mental" cases. These conflicts produce fear of aggression from others, or of one's own aggressive feelings. Strong attractions and repulsions in rela-

---

[1] See Chapter 17.
[2] Levine, Julius, *Anxieties and Stresses of Student Nurses.* Unpublished study at Boston Psychopathic Hospital.

tions with patients may be both the effect and cause of conflict. Recognition in patients' behavior of some of her own fantasies is often disconcerting to the student, while the bandying about of psychoanalytical terminology and concepts can stir up latent neurotic trends. These anxieties, however, may be capitalized upon to the student's advantage if they are taken up and re-solved, either in individual or group conferences.

Every student is given clinical experience both on the acute and the convalescent service, but which comes first in time de-pends upon the scheduling required to provide ward coverage. In spite of the fact that there is more disturbed and bizarre behavior on the acute service, beginning students prefer it be-cause they can make greater use of the nursing procedures on which they depend for psychological support. Not until they become more comfortable as persons, do they feel at ease in a convalescent environment. At first as noted earlier, they are often anxious, even guilty and self-critical, when they sit down to talk or play, for in their medical or surgical training, they were taught that this was loafing. In psychiatric training, how-ever, especially if the hospital has been able to release their social talents, affiliates may have a satisfying experience in the mental hospital environment. They may enjoy dances, parties, picnics, evening social activities, and learn to include the patient in a natural, artless way.

An extensive study made by Miss Alice F. Behymer, a psychi-atric nurse, showed that when affiliates arrived at the Hospital the only facile exchanges of conversation were with each other and with attendants.[1] To a slight extent they talked with pa-tients, but these interactions were guarded and reserved, and mostly in connection with routine nursing procedure. They were, of course, behaving in a manner entirely consistent with their earlier training; not knowing what to do or how far to go in self-revelation, they sought concrete stereotyped patterns. Through the variety of situations in which they are placed that encourage more freedom in self-expression, most of them make

[1] Behymer, Alice F., "Interaction Patterns and Attitudes of Affiliate Students in a Psychiatric Hospital," *Nursing Outlook*, vol. 1, April, 1953, pp. 205–207.

marked and rapid gains. In one area, however, the problem has not been resolved. It is that of frequent and comfortable meeting and talking with physicians. Nothing in Miss Behymer's study was so disconcerting as her factual revelation that affiliates have almost *no* contact, to say nothing of satisfying, growth-inducing contacts, with the ward medical staff. In a series of 150 consecutive interactions carried out by six students, which she observed and charted, only two were with physicians. One occurred when a doctor, passing hurriedly through a ward, asked an affiliate for the name of a patient he wished to identify; the other occurred when a student was asked for a match, which she supplied. Doctors and nursing students scarcely know each other as human beings. Between them is an unexplored "no man's land." Can anyone estimate the potential loss to patient care that comes from such disregard of fellow personnel? This failure will not be corrected until the Hospital has found a way to make the ward medical staff an integral part of the social environment.

Head Nurses

Registered nurses were given charge of the wards when the Hospital opened in 1912, and have continued to assume responsibility for them under the general direction of the medical and nursing administration and the ward physicians. Each head nurse looks after 28 to 30 patients, a heavy load, considering the fact that the Hospital has a varied and intensive treatment program and there are no graduate staff nurses. While attendants and affiliates are in immediate contact with patients, the nurse has had the problem of not being close enough to them. This psychological and social distance was most marked prior to 1943, when she often spent a major portion of her time in her office, behind closed doors, receiving reports from her assistants, giving orders, and handling telephone calls. The punitive or restrictive practices described in Chapters 1 and 2, considered sound in their day, were carried through by her at the request of the physician. Since she was the immediate authority figure on the ward, and the apparent executive agent behind all orders, unconsciously a block developed between her and the patient, which tended to preclude therapeutic interaction. On daily rounds with the doctor she transmitted official information about the activities of the various individuals under her supervision. Thus, she was often viewed as an informer who told of misbehavior by patients and abuses by personnel. Under these conditions it was difficult for any nurse to develop a happy, comfortable ward, or to play a personal role in a treatment team. It should also be noted that the gulf between her and the attendants was also great because she was not supposed to be seen socially with them. Nurses and doctors, too, were far from being equal partners in a treatment endeavor. The Hospital was then operated according to a fairly hierarchical pattern, and the nurse was expected to carry out the physician's orders. Only he alone did "real therapy."

Changes in Role. In the last decade many changes have occurred in the nurse's role. The elimination of punitive, restrictive measures, and the reduction of disturbed, excited behavior in which she took a prominent part, slowly led to a movement away from rigid routinized practices. By no specific dictum the head nurse began to be drawn into the thinking and planning of ward activities. Focusing of attention on ward life obviously involved her, especially when the goal was to make the ward a pleasant place in which to live. Largely through her initiative, once expectations of administrative psychiatrists were stated, she did much to improve furnishings, organize painting crews or paint walls herself, clothe patients, obtain apparel and toilet articles from their relatives, prepare snacks during the day and at bedtime. Later, as she became an important influence in the developing of recreational and occupational programs, she began to think of herself as responsible for patient interaction, group activities, and ward morale.

Time-honored rituals and practices frequently went by the board as the nurse became a vital element in the treatment team. As noted before, relations with physicians became more relaxed, and the practice of jumping to attention when they entered the room was abolished. The door between the nurse's office and the ward was cut in half, Dutch style, so that she could see and be seen by patients and could communicate more often with them. Patients were permitted to come into the office, sit down and talk; many informal group discussions arose in this way, increasing both her therapeutic potential and her closeness to patients. Discussion of, and experimentation with, whether the nurse in a mental hospital should wear a uniform, led to the decision that it helped to orient patients on the acute wards and often allayed some of their anxiety and insecurity relative to admission. On the convalescent service on the other hand, uniforms were felt to be a frequent barrier to close relationships, hence the nurses vetoed their use there. Affiliates, however, seemed to need the uniform for both status and protection, and have worn it on all wards, unless taking part in work or play projects that require something more suitable.

With improvement in the physical environment, the participation of patients in social and recreational programs, and their progressive assumption of responsibility for self-care and self-government, the head nurse has been released from the unhappy, tense role of taskmaster, and three dynamic and fairly distinctive functions have emerged. First, she is the *captain of the ward team* which consists of patients, attendants, nursing students, and any graduate nurses engaged in specialized training. The psychiatrist assists, oversees, and generally directs, but he is not the on-the-job captain; the all-important morale of the ward is left very largely in her hands. She not only takes responsibility for the hygiene and cleanliness of both ward and patients and for obtaining all needed housekeeping and medical supplies, but she must attempt to provide *all* members of her team with a wholesome living and working experience. The second role of the head nurse is that of *teacher* of ward personnel, and even patients. She is responsible for the training on the ward of attendants, affiliates, volunteers, and students who come for experience from the several neighboring colleges. She also helps to orient occupational therapists to ward and patients.

Finally, she is increasingly a *group leader*. As such, she conducts many formal and informal meetings, whether of ward staff or of patients and staff, where discussion revolves around problems of living and working together on the ward and enriching its physical and social environment. She does not undertake to lead formal group psychotherapeutic sessions, nor sessions of the two-way type, where the principal focus is the unraveling of neurotic attitudes and behavior. Frequently, however, the physician delegates to her, much as to the social worker, functions of a therapeutic nature, usually indicating the goals to be sought, the nature and depth of the psychotherapy, and the techniques to be used. If it were not for the fact that the house medical staff is relatively large, the Hospital might have explored the possibility of the head nurse assuming a larger psychotherapeutic role, more nearly comparable to the sociotherapeutic one she now plays.

Among the best instrumentalities available to her as group leader are the ward meetings held at least once weekly on each ward and attended both by patients and staff. They were started early in 1948 for the specific purpose of bringing head nurses, affiliates, and attendants closer to the patients, increasing community spirit, hearing complaints and suggestions; and helping patients assume greater responsibility for ward life.

The writer recalls a recent meeting he attended. Almost everyone on the ward at the scheduled hour was present, including patients, the head nurse, one attendant, and an occupational therapist. It was rumored that Dr. Solomon was unhappy because patients were spending too much time watching television, thus retreating into passivity and avoiding occupations which encouraged movement and active participation. This rumor was in essence correct; but the patients wrongly concluded that the television sets would be removed from the wards. Every patient had something to say. An informal poll revealed that the time spent daily watching television ranged to at least ten hours, with an average of slightly more than four. Only two patients were uninterested in it, all others sang its praises. After considerable discussion in which the patients' anxieties were rather freely expressed, the group was assured that the sets were not going to be taken away, that the problem was to find the best pattern of activities for each person. The medical director's concern was interpreted to the patients as a desire to prevent its utilization for purposes of retreating from anxiety-producing social contacts. The benefits of exercise were stressed and the unhygienic effects of prolonged sitting emphasized.

Once the patients were reassured, the discussion moved to how television could be used in the evening so as not to annoy patients who wanted to retire early. Could the "early-to-bed" patients be moved to the far end of the ward where it would not be so loud? Worse than its effects, many patients complained, was the noise of the raucous buzzer and the slamming of the door by late evening visitors. Sleep was also being interfered with by the playing of records at the opposite end of the ward. Some patients preferred quiet but were caught between television and the record player. With fears concerning the loss of television neutralized, personnel were able to adopt more active roles in helping patients to judicious choice of leisure-time activities. One patient volunteered to report the discussion to the assistant superintendent, including suggestions for change. A curfew for programs was decided upon, the patients electing to assume responsibility for its enforcement. This ward meeting solved the specific problem and produced positive effects on morale beyond what had been anticipated when it began.

Continuing Education. The education of the head nurse cannot cease with her formal preparation; indeed, it is essential that her development continue throughout the period of hospital service. Her position demands a high level of skill to begin with, and it demands even higher levels as she gains in experience. Increasing maturity, manifested in better handling of her own narcissistic or neurotic trends, is one of the major requirements—and one of the rewards—of continued service. Some nurses have sought personal psychotherapy or psychoanalysis to aid them in understanding patients, as well as to resolve neurotic character traits that have interfered with or complicated their jobs.

Among the many activities in which the head nurse participates that offer opportunities for growth and development are: daily rounds with chief of service, clinical director, or ward physicians; "intake" conferences about new patients; staff conferences in which patients' problems are presented in detail by the house psychiatrists; research conferences; psychodrama; and "total treatment" staff conferences that will be described in detail in the next chapter. She also has the opportunity to learn from supervisory nursing personnel, and from the many graduate students engaged in a variety of ward observations. Perhaps the most important single learning experience comes from her own direct observation of patients' behavior as she mingles with them in social and recreational activities, works with them in occupational assignments, or watches and listens to them in various meetings.

Since August, 1952, weekly "classes" for all head nurses have been held under the leadership of the director of nursing. It was intended that these classes should provide a better channel for communication regarding all matters that relate to nursing service and for discussion of questions of administrative importance. It was also hoped that they would offer nurses the same chance to express grievances and frustrations as had been given attendants and nursing students. The first two goals have been more successfully realized than the third. The very presence of two or three persons from the administrative office has probably tended to discourage freedom of expression. Because of this fact, and also because several nurses requested opportunity to explore principles of dynamic psychiatry, group meetings with Dr. Hyde were arranged to be held once or twice weekly. At these meetings there is ample provision for discussion of involvements with personnel or patients, and conflicts with the administration, as well as attitudes toward sex, marriage, and so on.

Relation to Other Groups. Roles so complex and demanding are understandably not without many stresses and tensions, nor is it surprising that education for them is woefully inadequate. A frequent complaint is this: "Why doesn't the doctor help more?" The nurse is often in a position analogous to that of a mother who is not receiving assistance from her husband in the running of her home. No matter how able she may be, she misses the support of the psychiatrist who is the source of authority. If he concentrates all his interest on specific aspects of psychiatry such as diagnostic classification, or individual psychotherapy, teamwork and mutual aid and understanding are lacking. Many of the residents are so inexperienced and insecure when they begin their ward duties that they are unable to give support even if they wish to do so. Much of this is the failure of the Hospital to help them develop competence and empathy for acting as ward managers. Further reference will be made to this problem in the next section of this chapter.

Patients come to the head nurse with problems that lie in the realm of the social worker, such as worries about paying the rent, their children, and their job; with problems that have not been cleared with the admitting office or their therapist. Thus, she finds herself serving as mediator between patients and other professional personnel. She is also in frequent and close contact with relatives who may look to her as the primary source of aid. Unless she is skilled in handling them and has insight into her own reactions, she is likely to develop many tensions, particularly if she takes sides, when relatives and patients are at odds and are acting out their grievances against one another. To be accepting of relatives, as well as patients, and to see two sides to the patient-relative relationship sometimes requires great emotional maturity.

Because the nurse has rarely had any introduction to social therapy in her training, the transition from housekeeping and managerial duties to those of social therapist imposes much strain. She finds herself criticized if patients lie around all day, or even sit too long watching television. If the level of ward activities falls or task involvement and interpersonal interactions run down, she may be held accountable. If patients fail to move from their isolation toward group experience, this becomes a problem for correction. How does she meet all these demands? The nurse has found that the best way is through cooperation with both patients and occupational therapists. Because pa-

tients cannot be therapeutically mobilized to social activity
through punitiveness or distant commands, it becomes necessary to develop a close relationship with them. The weekly
ward meetings about which so much has already been said, are
a major instrument for this purpose. Here the nurse elicits their
interest, advice, and later actual assistance in such matters as
color of ward paintings, selection of pictures, arrangement of
beds; in fact, anything that impinges on ward activities or living
conditions. Much of her work as a social therapist involves a
variety of tasks for which occupational and recreational therapists have been trained. In this Hospital she is expected to:

> Help to accumulate and look after reading and art materials,
> games, music records and instruments;
> Keep patients creatively occupied whenever possible;
> Diagnose occupational-recreational deficiencies, and call occupa-
> tional therapists as consultants;
> Note opinions expressed by patients about the Hospital's activity
> program, and transmit these opinions to the appropriate persons;
> Instruct and supervise students and attendants in ward activities;
> Participate with patients in activities, especially dances and pic-
> nics;
> Establish cooperative relations with volunteers and relatives in
> furthering specific social goals;
> Develop and utilize her own special interests, hobbies, and talents.

Obviously, any nurse who has not had preparation for such
numerous and varied duties needs to be on the best of terms
with the department of occupational therapy. She needs to
feel quite free to call frequently upon it for personal help and
advice, as well as for the more formal consultation that it is
expected to provide to the wards.

Finally, the head nurse's most important relationships perhaps
are with her attendants and students. She must keep them on
good terms with each other; to do this, if for no other reason,
she must have the understanding and confidence of both groups.
Because she was once a student and her basic loyalty is to the
nursing profession, she is likely to ally herself psychologically
with the affiliates. But she recognizes that no matter how much
students do to brighten the wards, they come and go, whereas

the attendants constitute the regular staff. Hence, she must master any inclination to favor one group against another. At the same time she must be alive to antagonisms that easily spring up between them because of differences in age, experience, knowledge, and in their relationships to authority and to patients.

EDUCATION OF THE RESIDENT PSYCHIATRIC STAFF

One of the central functions of the Hospital, as already noted, is the education and training of physicians, through a residency program, to be psychiatrists. Although it has assumed this responsibility since its establishment, profound changes have occurred during the past decade, some of which are the reflection of the evolving outlook of, and toward, psychiatry as a whole. The most conspicuous change has been in number of residents admitted. Before World War II it did not exceed six, in 1954 it was 24. The sudden and sharp increase mirrored the growing demand for postgraduate psychiatric education which stemmed largely from the war. Many physicians had been utilized by the armed forces in the capacity of psychiatrists even though they had been trained for general practice or in other specialties. After their return to civilian life they clamored for approved residencies in psychiatric teaching hospitals in order to obtain certification, and to solidify and integrate the significant experiences they had had while in service. Paralleling this change, and contributing to it, the undergraduate teaching of psychiatry to medical students was greatly increased in scope and intensity. As a consequence, more medical students began to show an interest in a career in psychiatry, whereas their predecessors had been attracted primarily to medicine and surgery.

Consistent with the earlier essentially diagnostic functions of the Hospital, the chief preoccupation of residents had been with diagnosis, description, and disposition of cases. Their primary learning experiences came from examining a large number of essentially acute psychotic patients, under the supervision of their immediate seniors. In addition, they attended ward rounds, primarily oriented toward getting acquainted with new

patients, and care-centered staff conferences in which they presented the problems of individual patients with pertinent additional data contributed by various diagnostic laboratories or
members of the psychiatric team. These conferences provided
them with an opportunity to prepare a case in detail, discuss
it before a group, receive criticisms, and learn from formulations and judgments of mature clinicians. They also participated
in teaching nursing students, but only rarely did they assist in
the instruction of medical students. Since the treatment functions of the Hospital were comparatively minimal, patients were
not often held for intensive psychotherapy, and somatic therapy
was largely limited to neurosyphilis.

After 1943 the change in the character of the Hospital from
a diagnostic to a treatment center meant for the residents a
major shift in interest and attention. They were challenged not
to be satisfied with mere descriptive formulation of cases but
were to try to restore the patient to sound health and a place in
the community as quickly as possible, by a judicious selection
and vigorous application of all pertinent methods of treatment.
As this new responsibility was accepted, several avenues to
learning were opened. One of the first opportunities was oc-
casioned by the introduction and utilization of the somatic
treatments described earlier. Training was modified to include
a period of responsibility for electric shock and insulin therapy.
Instructed and supervised by a senior psychiatrist, the residents
learned the indications, contraindications, and complications of
these forms of therapy and gained a proper respect for the
somatic or physiological approach to psychiatry.

Part of their time was given also to the outpatient department
where they began to see patients over a period of many months,
to explore in detail the psychodynamics involved as well as the
possibilities in intensive psychotherapy. Competent instruction
and supervision were provided by the addition of experienced
psychotherapists to the staff, particularly Dr. Ives Hendrick,
who was a leading proponent of psychoanalysis and had an
established reputation as a teacher. Responsibility for treatment
in the outpatient department began to return dividends early,

for the residents could now follow their patients into the community, learn about stresses and strains encountered, and help to integrate the program of the department with community resources.

The greater utilization of a psychotherapeutic approach to the hospitalized patients seemed a natural consequence of the emphasis placed on such therapy in the outpatient department. Encouraging reports from other centers of the use of psychotherapy with 59 psychotic patients, together with the appointment as clinical director in 1952 of Dr. Elvin V. Semrad who was intensely interested in the interpersonal treatment of schizophrenia, helped further to solidify the trend. During their residency many of the young physicians were able to arrange for a personal analysis which reinforced their commitment to psychotherapy, and made them more aware of the nature and significance of details of patients' inner lives.

Further learning experiences came from greater participation in the teaching program for Harvard Medical School students, and their attendance at a variety of teaching and research conferences, as well as informal meetings with psychiatrists or specialists from related fields who visited the Hospital in an unending stream. Expansion of the research, social, and occupational programs; the introduction of psychodrama and group therapy; exploration of the use of the social environment as a therapeutic modality; reorganization and enlargement of the outpatient children's facility; and the establishment of an affiliation with Metropolitan State Hospital for experience in the management of chronic mental patients, all offered rich potentialities to residents for growth and development.

With their medical and scientific backgrounds, it was comparatively easy for them to appreciate the possibilities in somatic treatment, and they were receptive to instruction in this area. The use of intensive individual psychotherapy could be readily rationalized by recourse to the elaborate body of psychoanalytic theory that had evolved since Freud published his first articles. Group psychotherapy presented a more complex set of interactions for which an insufficient theoretical framework existed, but even here the residents could understand the formal procedures and could make some use of psychoanalytical formulations in understanding the dynamics of small groups.

It is in the inadequate comprehension of the social system of the hospital as a pertinent factor in treatment and in the management of the social environment as a therapeutic force that the major defect in resident training now lies. Like other physicians, residents have either had no undergraduate courses in the social sciences or the content of such courses has long since been forgotten. The relevance of the social sciences to medicine, moreover, has been little stressed during their medical training except in an occasional department of preventive medicine and public health. No well-formulated system of hospital sociology exists that might facilitate instruction; indeed, not so much as one satisfactory course dealing with the subject has as yet been developed. Residents are consequently much preoccupied with plumbing the intricacies of the physiological bases of disease, psychosexual development, and treatment particularly of the dyadic variety. But they are not yet able to conceive of themselves as ward managers and social therapists, in which functions, we believe, a large measure of their therapeutic potential resides.

8. Development of Therapeutic Potential of Personnel (continued)

THIS CHAPTER DESCRIBES THREE METHODS used for the training and development of personnel and for improvement of interdepartmental relations that the Hospital has found remarkably useful. They differ from previous methods discussed in not being directed toward a specific occupational or professional group, but toward increasing interrelationships. Psychodrama at Boston Psychopathic Hospital, which has undergone several modifications since its inception in 1947, has been one of the most creative and expressive tools for promoting mutual understanding between patients and personnel and for teaching nursing students. The seminar on Problems of Living that ran from 1947 to 1949 accomplished two objectives: it provided a forum in which *all* personnel could express their views, and increased cooperation between departments for the ultimate benefit of patients. The "Total Treatment" Staff Conference, a weekly feature since its beginning some six years ago, has helped markedly to develop in all categories of personnel a sense of participation in, and responsibility for, individualized care of patients, and for using the resources of the Hospital to better advantage.

PSYCHODRAMA

Several striking experiences contributed to our interest in psychodrama. Six patients and four occupational therapists were together one day in the department of occupational therapy, when someone suggested that the various methods used in trying to get a patient to do something be play-acted.[1]

[1] Doubtless Dr. Jacob L. Moreno's demonstrations of psychodrama, which had been seen and talked about by members of the staff, prompted the suggestion. The later development of psychodrama at the Hospital rests in large measure upon concepts evolved by him.

One of the patients, Mr. A, took the role of a mentally ill person who was reluctant to start on a task, and each of the four occupational therapists in turn tried to get him to work. They were surprised when he declared after they had tried their best, that their approaches were "all wrong." He said that he had felt oppressed. The five patients who had been spectators had the same fault to find, that the therapists had pushed Mr. A too hard. Apparently in trying to satisfy their own wish to obtain some kind of response, they had not considered his feelings. This demonstration that trained workers were not a success in the patients' eyes, was highly significant to all who participated. It showed clearly the folly of continuing to operate upon preconceived notions of good technique, without constant "feedback" of opinions and reactions from the patients. Mr. A was asked to play the role of occupational therapist, and he gave a remarkable performance of searching out the patient's attitudes and feelings, before coaxing, cajoling, or trying to shame the latter into activity. Then, when an occupational therapist played the part of patient, she began to see more clearly how inadequate her own method had been to obtain cooperation that was based on a satisfying personal relationship.

An extension of this role-playing technique was tried in studying how a group of new affiliate students should be introduced and oriented to a ward. A carefully planned introduction is considered important, for the first day on a ward can be traumatic for students, and perhaps "sour" them altogether on their psychiatric affiliation. One student played the part of an affiliate who had just arrived and three head nurses assumed the task of introducing her to the new clinical experience. The first head nurse spent all the allotted time being nice to the student, getting to know her as a person. The second introduced her to the geography of the ward, showing her where the linen and bathroom were, and telling her where to find things that patients would need. The third nurse asked some of the senior affiliates to play the roles of patients who were severely depressed, overactive and demanding, or paranoid and suspicious; then, accompanying the student whom she was trying to orient to the ward, she approached the difficult patients in turn and talked with them in a calm, relaxed manner.

In discussion it became obvious that each nurse was inclined to orient the student according to her own experience. The first wanted the head nurse and the affiliate to feel secure with each other, on the theory that the latter's attitude to authority held the key to a smooth introduction to psychiatry; the second was guided by the assumption that the affiliate wanted to know how to do things for the patients, and would be lost until the elementary knowledge necessary to carry out familiar nursing procedures was available; the third head nurse was evidently concerned with handling the anxiety provoked by first contacts with patients whose behavior was bizarre and perhaps unpredictable. The student vote as to which of the demonstrations was best resulted in a three-way split; each introduction had its adherents. The head nurses had given excellent illustrations of what would calm their own anxieties were they new affiliates again, but they had not attempted to individualize the orientation to meet the needs of the particular affiliate they were teaching. After prolonged group discussion it became apparent that the students would appreciate all three kinds of orientation, but with individualization, and that during the first day it should be possible to meet this triple need. Thus, play-acting demonstrated that the drama technique had great potentialities for focusing attention upon, and exploring problems of, both patients and personnel.

Another arresting incident occurred after psychodrama had become an often used device at the Hospital. A patient was asked to play herself as she had been on admission when she was distressed, preoccupied, and depressed. Several occupational therapists and students failed to bring her out of herself. Then a man patient grabbed a pack of cards, pulled up a chair, reshuffled them in an ostentatious manner, and carried on a monologue while he was apparently having an absorbing game by himself. The woman patient became more and more annoyed by his open neglect, and finally burst out, "What are you doing here?" Soon they started to play cards together. Then he put on a phonograph record and said, "Let's dance." They danced together.

Members of the staff had tried pleading, cajoling, and failed —but a patient broke through her negativism. It was an impressive, almost overpowering experience for the onlookers. Everybody saw clearly that the only person that reached the woman was another patient, who depended entirely upon intuition rather than learned procedure. The staff were thus encouraged to be freer and more intuitive in their own relationships with patients and to avoid doing only what was suggested in the textbooks. Better than any lecture was this concrete demonstration of what can be learned from the patient by listening, watching him act, and carefully considering his criticisms.

Many such instances made it clear that in psychodrama we had a flexible and powerful method for investigating interpersonal relationships. The drama gave the problem under consideration qualities which otherwise were often hard to achieve, namely, concreteness and objectivity, and at the same time it added interest and intensity. When examining stress among personnel or patients where difficulty in communication would be encountered, a dramatization of the stress-producing situation was warranted. When a discussion was leading to unjustified assumptions, resentment, or personal bias, dramatic methods confronted the discussants with a reality that could not be denied. Involvement, identification, and participation were enhanced and interpersonal frictions melted in the heat of free emotional catharsis. Role-playing could be used to anticipate events, as well as to portray those from the past. Thus, the student could see experienced members of the staff enact a scene with a difficult patient, later take one of the parts herself, and finally meet a comparable scene "in real life" with proficiency.

A great variety of situations meaningful to patients and personnel, whether of a psychological or a sociological nature, have been acted out. Leadership has been in the hands of nonmedical personnel; initially the sessions were led by a volunteer student of dramatic arts, since then by the recreational director who showed himself adept at mobilizing patients for group activities and flexible enough to assume various roles. Under his direction the procedure became a weekly function attended on a voluntary basis by patients and personnel. The topics chosen for presentation have included various aspects of the patients' hospitalization, such as admission, first day on the ward, reaction to shock treatment, seclusion, social activities. At times past experiences in family or job relationships that were critical for a patient have been brought under scrutiny. The theme of many performances has been how to handle distressed or difficult patients, especially the frightened, agitated one for whom shock has been prescribed but who dreads the experience, the one who misinterprets everything, and the desperately lonely individual. Two types that provide material for unending demonstrations before affiliates and even head nurses are the "petted patient," who receives far more than his share of attention, and the "male wolf," the seductive fellow who tries to "date" nurses. Through role-playing those major pitfalls of becoming overinvolved or of rejecting patients have been repeatedly the focus of attention. Stresses of many kinds between attendants, students, and head nurses have been portrayed. Attitudes of physicians and the ideas of the senior medical staff are consciously or unconsciously woven into many scenes, and are often the object of direct attack.

Procedure in Psychodrama

Chairs are grouped in a semicircle around the front of the auditorium. The leader invites everyone to be seated, and then explains the purpose of psychodrama: to enact scenes that are meaningful in the hospital life, encourage expression, and "see ourselves as others see us." He emphasizes that the dramatization should be as spontaneous and unstructured as possible. He then asks the audience to suggest a suitable problem to be enacted. Perhaps there has been a demanding, hostile, or resistant patient on the ward who has been a thorn in everyone's flesh. If the use of this theme is acceptable to the majority, the scene starts with members of the audience playing "patient" and "therapist," the latter being any one of a number of personnel who are in close contact with patients and are regarded as members of the treatment team. The person playing the patient acts out his difficulties as he imagines them, while the therapist attempts to establish the best relationship he can. Perhaps several therapists are asked in advance to approach the patient successively; if so, each is given a chance to do what he can without having seen the preceding demonstrations. During the interaction the leader moves to the side to observe what is transpiring. He may assume the role of "conscience," and as such make remarks of an interpretive nature that seek to reveal hidden affects covered up by the overt behavior of the participants. He represents the "conscience" that is continually at work beneath external appearances. The actors are expected to ignore him, but often they are caught unawares by penetrating insight, and coming out of character, respond directly to him.

The members of the audience form a kind of jury or discussion panel whose comments and criticisms are later elicited. They are encouraged to comment freely as this may be a crucial learning experience for each of the participants. It is naturally threatening to personnel to have their skills scrutinized, although someone usually comes to the defense of a person who has been attacked without mercy. After the participating jury have been called upon, the therapists themselves are given an opportunity to say why they did what they did, or to debate with members of the jury. Finally, the person who acted as patient may be asked to state his reaction to the various approaches of the therapists, and to discuss comments from the jury. Reversal of roles is often tried when insight into both sides of a relationship is sought.

Although it is impossible to convey by written word, which reproduces neither voice nor gestures, the subtle qualities of role-playing, we offer for their limited value parts of the transcript of two one-hour sessions, the major aim of which was instruction of new nursing students. Present were patients, nurses, attendants, students, social workers, occupational therapists, an occasional physician, and visitors to the Hospital.

MAC: (leader of psychodrama). There are new students here to learn. We are trying to teach them about psychiatry, the various things we try and hope to do. They are here to learn the technique of psychodrama or sociodrama; we use the patients as critics. . . . To have the patients tell you what is wrong with your approach is better than reading from any textbook, as they are living the experience. Please listen carefully and seriously. I am the patient and I am waiting to have electric shock treatment. Those who play the nurse will approach me and persuade me to go in and have treatment.

[Three persons are chosen to take the role of nurse: Miss O, a social worker; Miss W, a head nurse; and Miss S, an occupational therapist.]

MAC: Remember I am under treatment. I am agitated, unhappy, sick, and depressed. [He suddenly assumes the role of patient, wrings his hands, jumps up and walks around, sits down again, clasps his head in his hands.]

FIRST NURSE (MISS O): Good morning, Mr. Jones. [Soft, friendly voice.] May I join you in a smoke? [Lights a cigarette.]

MR. JONES (PATIENT, PLAYED BY MAC): Miss O, *why* do I have to have these treatments?

MISS O: Tell me a little about how you are feeling?

MR. JONES: It's terrible, terrible!

MISS O: Have you had treatments before?

MR. JONES: Yes, I've had two. They are not helping me.

MISS O: Remember how you felt afterward? Remember how you sat quietly and ate your breakfast? Two treatments aren't enough to make you all better.

MR. JONES: Miss O, I am *afraid* of them.

MISS O: Of course you are afraid, why wouldn't you be afraid? I think if you recall, that after the second treatment you felt a little more relaxed. We have helped others, we can help you.

MR. JONES: Yes, that is true.

MISS O: Why don't we walk together.

SECOND NURSE (MISS N): Good morning, John.

MR. JONES: Good morning, Miss N.

MISS N: Did the doctor talk to you about having a treatment this morning?

MR. JONES: Miss N, I don't want the treatment.

Miss N: I know you don't like them, but they do so much for you.

Mr. Jones: They just frighten me.

Miss N: Your problem is the same problem lots of other people have.

Mr. Jones: Can't I get well without them? I am trying.

Miss N: I know you are trying, but you need the treatments so you can go home soon, don't you?

Mr. Jones: 'Course I do, 'course I do.

Miss N: You and I can walk together until it is time.

Third Nurse (Miss S): Good morning, John. John, it is time for your treatment now.

Mr. Jones: Don't mention *treatment* to me!

Miss S: Why do you mind them, Jones?

Mr. Jones: Because I hate them.

Miss S: Do you remember how you felt last time, John?

Mr. Jones: I remember how I felt. I was held down last time. That room!

Miss S: I will go into the room with you. I know you don't want them, but you will feel much better afterward. Let's get it over with.

[The leader then comes out of the patient's role and asks for comments from the audience. The following are the patients' remarks.]

J B: I liked Miss O's approach best. It was kind of her to say, "Why don't we walk over together." I don't like the nurse to say, "Let's get it over with."

V S: I didn't like it when Miss N said, "Your problem is the same problem lots of people have." The ordinary depressed person is interested in himself only. I felt "To hell with the rest of them" when I was sick.

S T: When the nurse thought of putting herself in the patient's place, and said, "Let's walk together and let's talk together," I felt encouraged.

S D: I, too, liked Miss O's approach. All were helpful, but personally as a patient I have not had much help from anyone during my anxious moments waiting for treatment. I think it would be a great help to a patient to be approached in this manner, but usually there is a whole roomful of people waiting for treatment. Unless you have had one you can't conceive what it's like waiting.

S F: I like Miss O's approach best. Both her approach and her conversation afterward gave you the feeling that things were not utterly hopeless. She gave encouragement and then said, "Of course, you are afraid, why wouldn't you be afraid?" She judged the situation correctly, that the reaction was one absolutely to be expected. You felt you were a normal person, not something to go out on the ash heap. She gave you a measuring stick for your courage and it could be a pretty big one.

V D: Miss N smiled, I didn't think she should have smiled. Miss O and Miss S didn't smile. I think it is no smiling matter.

J P: I didn't have shock treatment, but I was depressed when I came in here. I liked all three approaches, and thought it was all right to smile, but I liked Miss O's approach the best, especially joining the patient in a smoke! I appreciated the statement "We have helped others, we can help you."

[Comments of the student nurses.]

A C: I liked the way Miss O spoke. She spoke to you as if she were with you.

D N: I liked the sound of Miss O's voice. I felt Miss O was the most sincere.

Of the nine persons who commented, seven made statements which singled out Miss O for praise. There was something in her manner, soft voice, ability to put herself in the patient's place, positive acceptance of his fears of shock treatment, offering of a cigarette, and suggestion to walk with him, that led the audience to favor her way of relating to the sick person. One "nurse" was criticized for smiling at a serious moment, although the smile was later defended as natural for her. Apparently, "Let's get it over with" and "Your problem is the same problem lots of people have" displeased the onlookers because these remarks tended to minimize the suffering that the patient feels.

[In the second psychodrama Mac who again is leader begins by saying:] Now we are in an occupational therapy situation. The worker is going to approach me in the Craft Room. I am a paranoid patient, having delusions of persecution; people are against me. I don't trust anybody—have a tendency toward daydreaming. This type of patient suffers terribly. Perhaps he thinks when you offer him a cigarette that there is dope in it. The job of the therapist is to reach me in some way.

FIRST THERAPIST, MISS S: [Begins to measure the window.]

PATIENT: What are you doing?

MISS S: Trying to figure out the measurements for this window box.

PATIENT: What window box?

MISS S: The window box for this room, we are going to buy flowers for it.

PATIENT: What kind of flowers?

MISS S: We haven't decided yet. Some volunteers are going to bring in some plants and bulbs.

PATIENT: I think it is dreary here.

MISS S: The light is better *here*. Are you good at figuring out measurements?

PATIENT: No, I don't want to figure measurements.

MISS S: This doesn't fit, have you any suggestions?

PATIENT: No, I have no suggestions. Can't you figure in another room, Miss S? [Patient leaves room]

SECOND THERAPIST, MISS O [Walks into room, pulls up a couple of chairs, and puts a pack of cigarettes on the table]: Good morning, John!

PATIENT: Hello.

MISS O: What are you doing?

PATIENT: I am working on a wallet.

MISS O: I'll put these cigarettes here where we both can reach them if we want one.

PATIENT: I have some of my own.

MISS O: Wouldn't you like a light?

PATIENT: I am turning a corner on this wallet. Have you ever tried to do that? What do you do here in the Hospital, Miss O?

MISS O: I do social work, Mr. Jones. You can call it anything you want; sometimes I think that I am an odd jobber. I am here if anyone wants me, if there is anything I can do to help. You seem to be enjoying yourself making that wallet.

PATIENT: I am trying to figure out how to get around this corner.

MISS O: Get the occupational therapist to help you, don't ask me. Have you ever done any work with your hands?

PATIENT: I should like to do something with my hands.

MISS O: Have you any idea what you might enjoy doing?

PATIENT: No.

MISS O: I guess hard work is something that not all of us care for.

PATIENT: What is your leg twitching for?

MISS O: That is a habit I have. I always wiggle my ankle.

PATIENT: It *annoys* me. [Leaves] I'll see you, Miss O.

THIRD THERAPIST, MISS N [Walks to window and pulls up the shade to give more light. Approaches patient]: I wonder if you would take this off the shelf for me?

PATIENT: I am not tall enough to reach it.

MISS N: Here is a chair, stand on it. I should like to have you feel that you are one of us.

PATIENT: They asked me to come upstairs, so I am here.

MISS N: Have you found anything you would like to do while you are here? We certainly can find *something*. Why don't you look around a little?

[Patients' criticisms were as follows:]

V S: I would question mentioning a window box to a patient of this type. He might feel that someone would try to push him out the window.

S T: I liked the informal way Miss O came in, drew up the chair, and put the cigarettes on the table. She took a cigarette herself, and stopped twitching her foot when it annoyed the patient. She answered all his questions, and wanted to know if there was anything she could do to help.

F T: Miss N's approach was very good in allaying all suspicion. She knew she had a paranoid case to comfort and I think she did flow comfort into that tortured mind and body with her words, because she immediately started doing things herself. She showed him that she would gladly work herself, and appealed to his valor. I think it was very important to erase all that suspicion from his mind.

S M: One thing I like very much. Miss O drew up a chair as if she were drawing you into a circle and not putting you on the spot; as though she were reaching out in a friendly manner to draw you in.

F N: I think Miss S's point about the details of the measurement seemed to be a little beyond the patient in his condition. If I felt like he did, I would not want to figure anything out. Add a little friendliness to this approach.

B O: As a paranoid, no matter what the occupational therapist did I would be suspicious. You would naturally be suspicious of someone you are not familiar with.

F R: You would say to yourself that you don't care whether they are good to you or not. But if they are nice to you, it takes that starchy feeling of crime out of everything, that ache surrounding you, the germ in the milk, the things that could happen.

This session ended with the therapists' discussing their own reactions to the patient. One felt some resentment to answers she received, another was puzzled, not knowing how much hostility the patient harbored and would express directly if irritated. The third felt a need to do everything first herself, to prove to him that there was no risk or danger. As training for students this brief play and the subsequent discussion illustrated a variety of interpretations that the paranoid patient may place upon others' behavior; his suspicion and negativism; good and bad points in several different approaches to the patient; the fallibility of the therapists; and the personal feelings which each therapist has that may stand in the way of successful rapport.

THE "PROBLEMS OF LIVING" SEMINAR

The desirability of improved interdepartmental relations became apparent from: the observed infrequency of contacts between members of the various departments and professions in the Hospital; the difficulty of obtaining spontaneous, smooth cooperation among these various groups; the realization that members of one group often made remarks indicating ignorance of the nature of the work of other groups, as well as feelings of prejudice and jealousy; and the partly observed and partly surmised need of many persons to understand better the dynamics of their own and other personalities.

The idea of a seminar on Problems of Living (that later became popularly known as the Coffee Hour because of the coffee and doughnuts served) originated in a discussion by three relative newcomers to the Hospital, who shared the conviction that interdepartmental morale could be greatly improved. It was agreed that the meetings should be social in nature and include workers from all departments; every one should have equal recognition regardless of educational level or position in the Hospital; all statements should be in nontechnical language; and subjects chosen for discussion must be of common interest and concerned with aspects of personality development. A general invitation was posted, and about 20 out of approximately 150 persons attended the first meeting. Some one-third of those present took part in the discussion of The Need for Recognition, which followed the more formal presentation by two persons. A subject was chosen for the second meeting and two new discussants appointed; at that meeting a moderator was selected, and at the end of each succeeding meeting the group suggested a new topic for discussion and asked for volunteers for moderator and discussants. After about 12 meetings it became obvious that the physicians were dominating the group; so that they decided among themselves to "take a back seat," while an executive committee elected by the membership began to exert leadership.

The Coffee Hour was held weekly in the late afternoon for more than two years. All categories of employees were represented—clerks, secretaries, head nurses, affiliates, maintenance and kitchen personnel, psychologists, psychiatrists, social workers, medical students, and occupational therapists. Also frequently present were students of theology, sociology, social work, and clinical psychology who came to the Hospital for clinical experience or for field work. Members of the group sat in a large circle, without distinction as to rank. Attendance usually averaged from 20 to 35 but at times it exceeded 60, when topics of wide interest were announced or especially colorful individuals were expected to talk. Not infrequently the Coffee Hour was extended to include half the evening, the group breaking up into smaller units which then continued informally.

Without question the Coffee Hour made an important contribution to the Hospital. It decreased personal prejudices and interdepartmental friction, provided all groups of employees with an opportunity for self-expression, gave them a feeling of dignity, and helped them have less anxiety when taking the floor. Its most important effect, perhaps, was that of decreasing the reluctance of the individual to tell about his own problems, faults, and mistakes. All persons, whether high or low in the hospital hierarchy, began to be seen as human beings sharing the same general problem of social adjustment. A supervisor who during work hours was a cheerful but authoritarian leader, spoke in the group as a family man, a serious father, and bread-winner. A nurse, who throughout the day was seen as a hard-working, self-assured technician directing an important treat-ment procedure, disclosed that she had an invalid mother and therefore felt that she could not marry. A Negro social worker, known as a cool, composed person, expressed deep antagonism and cynicism not before suspected. An attendant who had never attracted attention except for his occasional alcoholic indul-gence proved to have deep psychological insight into his con-tact with patients, and true pride in his role. Thus, there was a growing appreciation of many individuals by other indi-viduals. Physicians, for example, became acutely aware of the thoughtfulness, intelligence, and perception of many of the attendants and treated them with increased respect and recog-nition. Social workers commented that they had not previously realized that nurses had so much real understanding of patient needs. The stature of the affiliate student increased as the freshness of her perspective enlivened the meetings.

Topics had to be found that supposedly were of universal interest. Hence, an attempt was made to focus on problems that many persons had been called upon to face. Some of the meet-ings, nevertheless, evoked little interest; others produced gen-eral excitement and the topics were rediscussed in small groups throughout the Hospital for days afterward. Although The Need for Recognition appeared to be a good topic for the first meet-ing, so much of the time was monopolized by the two persons who introduced it that the group did not get the "feel" of spon-taneous participation. At the second meeting on The Need for Other People, many of the group spoke but the discussion was far from lively. Friendship, a topic that would be expected to elicit much interest, became focused on one small facet, that of how highly young people value the friendships made in private schools. The Social Use of Alcoholic Beverages seemed to have little personal relevance for most of those present. With the meeting on Anger, however, both interest and feeling ran high. The question raised was whether anger should be expressed or bottled up. The presence of a quick-tempered telephone operator whom everyone knew gave the discussion an authentic ring. A specially requested meeting on Extramarital Relationships was largely attended, as was expected. Psychosexual development, late marriages, and the double standard were covered. Considerable spontaneous expression of opinion followed, but it was obvious that many persons who were almost "bursting" to say something were afraid to do so. Eight remained afterward to discuss the question freely and at length.

How to Know the Right Man to Marry was gay and quick paced with comments from the unmarried women and with questioning married persons about how they had made their "momentous decision." The topic Responsibility to Our Parents led to consideration of the obligation of an unmarried nurse of thirty-five who was the sole support of an aged mother and who was unwilling to worry her about a prospective son-in-law. In the seminar Problems Confronting the First Child, so many members wanted to be heard it was decided that first children should speak first, then those who were second, third, and fourth in the family order, and finally those who were only children. This session was of particular interest because it appeared to provide an opportunity to voice resentments that many persons had been harboring toward siblings and parents. Other seminars explored Selfishness, Gossip, Jealousy, and Mixing Marriage and a Career. One in which the discussion was particularly intense was entitled Can Psychiatrists Get Along with Normal People? An attendant violently attacked the normality of a particular psychiatrist. Several members of the group supported his contention that physicians enter this profession in order to solve their own problems. One of the psychiatrics present maintained that they have more insight into their problems than do other people. The discussion was participated in by almost everyone, and aroused so much interest that the medical director chose the same topic for his Friday Medical Staff Conference.

The Coffee Hour taught many lessons in practical group management that have been particularly helpful in subsequent undertakings. Among the problems encountered was the tendency for professional personnel to dominate a meeting by emphasis on rank, display of academic knowledge, or doctrinaire insistence upon their particular point of view. This tendency was controlled by challenging such persons in open session, or by helping them modify their attitudes through unofficial discussions behind the scenes. A more serious problem was that of the rivalry created by the desire of persons selected to present material to outdo each other. The same problem was met later in the Total Treatment Staff Conference, as will be seen in the next section. As a consequence, we concluded that spontaneous discussions would probably be more successful in promoting self-expression and maintaining interest. Hence, the seminar was permitted to lapse, but not before the original goals set for it had been substantially achieved.

THE TOTAL TREATMENT STAFF CONFERENCE

We have described instrumentalities for the education of residents, attendants, and nurses, and for the improvement of interdepartmental morale. But we have not yet seen the nucleus of the staff most directly concerned with treatment of the patient sitting down together to find solutions to the many problems that develop when the work of at least a score of persons needs to be coordinated if the treatment is to be successful.

The Total Treatment Staff Conference began when "staff" conferences at the Hospital still meant meetings only of physicians, or clinical case presentations by psychiatrists before chiefs of service. At these conferences interest was centered upon diagnostic classification of the clinical condition presented, consideration of the patient's psychodynamics, planning the treatment program, or attempting to decide whether the patient was ready for discharge. Frequently social workers, head nurses, nursing students, psychologists, and occasionally attendants were present. Their function was primarily to be educated by listening to discussions. Occasionally, they were asked to contribute specific information, but they never held the stage themselves, and there was no completely *free* discussion among all personnel as equal contributors to the treatment process. Those who have attended medical or surgical staff conferences in general hospitals, know that case presentation is usually by younger physicians for consideration by older men. Seniority and rank decree how far participants can go without risking the stigma of bad manners. Our psychiatric staff conferences, too, were modeled after those in medical and surgical clinics. Although auxiliary personnel were heard from, seniority and rank largely determined who spoke and how much.

If patient care was to be improved, it was obvious that attendants, nurses, and other groups of personnel would have to be pushed forward to more self-expression and initiative, and to group consideration of those problems where dovetailing of effort was essential. Consequently, one day a week, formerly devoted to the conventional medical presentation, was set aside for a staff conference on so-called "total treatment." At first, it took the form of presentation by psychologists, occupational therapists, physiotherapists, and nurses or attendants, in rotation, of a case or activity in which their particular group was interested. Physicians were not included in the list of those making presentations, although they attended when "the spirit moved them." They understood that this was *one* staff conference that was not to be doctor oriented. Competition sprang up between this total treatment conference and the psychiatrists' clinical staff conferences, and was fostered both by expressed and unexpressed attitudes of some of the leaders of the total treatment staff. For a long time physicians did not feel entirely welcome at the meetings. Perhaps because of this fact they responded, when they came, by being dominating, over-clinical, haggling about a diagnosis, and generally showing resistance to acceptance of the social-environmental approach to patient care which is the *raison d'être* of the total treatment staff. Even now the medical house staff is reluctant to examine fully the therapeutic potential of sociological factors and of the coordinated efforts of many persons. Acceptance of this potential would mean modification of the time-honored concept of the doctor-patient relationship, sanctioned by medical training prior to residency in psychiatry and reinforced during psychiatric specialization by psychoanalytic theories and by pressures of work and lack of time.

Early meetings of the total treatment group were highly successful, but held within them the seeds of their own destruction. Competition and rivalry appeared much as in the Coffee Hour, with each group striving to outdo the other in excellence of presentation of human interest problems. Finally, the child psychologist reached the zenith when she brought three babies from the adoption clinic of the outpatient department to a session, and proceeded to demonstrate her skill in administering psychological tests. The conference room was packed to overflowing. The delightful babies, the engrossing problems involved in their adoption, and the recognition of the talent possessed by the psychologist, not before generally known to the Hospital personnel, were so dramatic and compelling that all later presentations seemed anticlimactic. Interest in the total treatment program became perfunctory for a time, and it was decided to reorganize the meetings along lines which minimized competition. As a result, they were made more informal and problem centered rather than program centered.

At present 20 to 40 of the staff meet each week, without any formal agenda but with the knowledge that initiative both for introducing and sustaining the discussion must be taken by them. The session is opened by a leader, usually the assistant superintendent who simply asks, "What is the problem of the day?" or "What has happened that we want to talk about?" Very quickly a problem is presented that, more often than not, is of general concern. If so, the discussion is permitted to continue as long as the group wishes. Often the entire hour is utilized and not infrequently a particular problem that has sorely tried many of the staff is brought up again at later meetings. Should the topic presented be of interest, in the opinion of the leader, to only a limited number or should it be used to avoid consideration of another subject that had produced deep anxiety, a request is made for other problems to be stated.

Probably the greatest total amount of time at these meetings is spent on aspects of patient management and the reactions of the staff to specific patients. An illustration of severe exacerbation of staff feelings by one patient will indicate the nature and purpose of the discussion at such sessions. An attorney, who knew how to manipulate social structure for his own purposes, had played various categories of personnel against one another until he had produced hostility, resentment, or withdrawal in nearly every member of the staff with whom he had come in contact. In an extraordinary way he was first able to ingratiate himself with personnel and then, when favors or privileges were denied, turn against them, telling others about their outrageous, inhuman treatment of him. Had his methods been less artful, his behavior would have been quickly labeled extremely paranoid, but this man was a clever lawyer, skilled in argument. He was used frequently in teaching sessions and enthralled many an audience with his dramatic descriptions of psychiatric syndromes; thus, he became a favorite with some of the instructors.

Perhaps no other patient in recent hospital history has been so outstanding in his ability to divide personnel from each other, or the object of so much strong ambivalent feeling. No fewer than four meetings in the space of two or three months were devoted primarily to expression of these feelings. Much communication between various members of the staff was necessary, and cross-checking of each person's information with that of others, before it began to be clear to what extent the Hospital had been manipulated in a destructive fashion by this patient. It also began to be seen that he was much sicker than previously supposed, the gravity of this disorder being more evident in the long-term social consequences of his behavior than in any gross deviation of conduct or immediately visible chain of symptoms. With ventilation of feelings and greater understanding of the effects of his psychopathology, the staff were able to draw closer together and to plan a unified approach, with the result that he improved greatly in behavior and gradually ceased to trouble them. In addition, they became sensitive to this disruptive pattern in other patients and were largely able to anticipate, ward off, or minimize similar problems thereafter.

Besides patient management a large variety of subjects of a more sociological kind concerning use of the physical and social resources of the Hospital are considered, sometimes over a period of several months before any effort is made to reach a majority decision. Questions of increasing visiting hours, exchange of acute and convalescent wards in behalf of giving the sickest persons the more pleasant setting, better utilization of hospital space, planning of large social events, opening of Club 105 in a neighboring house at 105 Fenwood Road which was available to convalescent patients and those in the out-patient department, and collaboration of the staff of Boston Psychopathic Hospital with other hospitals—these are illustrative of the breadth of subjects that are brought to the meetings.

In looking back at the experience of the Total Treatment Staff Conference, it seems even more important now than it did in 1948 that there be an instrumentality flexible enough to include all individuals in the Hospital who are vitally related to problems both of patient care and of utilization of the social environment, and free enough to permit expression of deep feelings, positive or negative. This conference has come closer to realizing these needs than any other yet arranged. Subjects have been brought up for consideration that would never have received adequate attention in the medical case conferences, and discussions have generally been much more controversial and heated than those of the physicians. The tolerance of the group for negative or hostile feelings appears remarkable to most outside observers. The meetings have become the crucible in which interpersonal and interdepartmental tensions, so important to the patients' welfare, could be worked out. They began where the Coffee Hour left off, but with much greater spontaneity and immediate relevance to the primary function of the Hospital. The group has now arrived at a point in its development where it feels able to challenge some of the judgments of the physicians concerning patient management. After months of questioning the wisdom of psychiatric decisions about discharging or not discharging specific patients, it recently made the suggestion that its opinion be sought in controversial cases. The group maintained that the desire of many residents to continue individual psychotherapeutic treatments had undoubtedly biased their judgment about the degree of benefit patients could or could not receive in the Hospital short of prolonged stay; it maintained, furthermore, that its members had an opportunity to see so many facets of each patient's adjustment that its opinion could not wisely be ignored. This suggestion, which received approval from the administration, is evidence of the fact that the nonmedical personnel consider themselves increasingly a significant part of total treatment.

9. Improvement of Patient Care Through Teaching and Research

THE IMPACT OF TEACHING AND RESEARCH upon the care of the mentally ill is often indirect, but nevertheless powerful. An earlier chapter has described the instruction of nursing students and psychiatric residents who constitute important segments of the hospital staff. Now attention will be focused upon other teaching programs less directly connected with preparation of personnel, and also upon research. In both instances emphasis will be placed on those aspects that relate most directly to better care for patients.

DEVELOPMENT OF TEACHING

Let us begin with the teaching of medical students. After World War II the curriculum of the Harvard Medical School was reorganized and psychiatry was elevated to a place approaching medicine and surgery in importance. Recognition of the necessity for studying the whole person rather than organs, and an increasing awareness that sociocultural forces shaped the individual both in sickness and health were changing the outlook of leaders of medical education, and were shifting the center of gravity more toward psychiatry and social science disciplines. As a consequence, the teaching of psychiatry to Harvard medical students was expanded sevenfold, and the few lectures that had been given primarily in the second year were supplanted by a variety of instructional methods that were introduced throughout the four-year curriculum. Clinical case teaching, formerly limited to eleven sessions in the third year, was begun in the second year when the student had his first contact with patients. As part of the course in physical diagnosis, psychiatrist and internist sat down together with small groups of students to explore how the patient's environment and social situation related to his illness, helped or hindered his adjustment to hospitalization, and influenced treatment. In the third year clinical instruction was intensified and made more dynamic, although without increase in the number of hours allotted to psychiatry. During the fourth year a new program of clinical clerkship was instituted in which the student spent one full month at the Hospital, studying cases intensively, taking a great deal of supervised responsibility for treatment, and being absorbed into the atmosphere of the hospital community.

Students not only received several hundred more hours of instruction than had been given earlier, but the effects were far more pervasive than might have been expected from a magnified teacher-student relationship alone. Teaching was spread broadly to include as many as possible of the hospital staff who might engage in mutually rewarding relations with students. Some were called upon to participate who had never before taught anything. This involved eventually all the members of both senior and junior medical staffs, some social workers, nurses, psychologists, occupational therapists, attendants, social scientists, and diverse research personnel. Whoever was involved in working with patients was asked at one time or another to explain his place in the treatment community, and how his activities affected patients. Thus, head nurses told of the importance of their roles as group leaders, supervisors of ward morale, initiators of ward activities, responsible parties in the maintenance of hygiene, and instructors of nursing students and attendants in the handling of patients. Psychologists explained their part in the diagnostic team, how they assessed personality assets and liabilities through the use of projective tests, or obtained clues as to brain damage by tests of concept formation.

Social workers discussed the importance of the home and community environment in determining stresses leading to admission and critical problems posed during hospitalization; they also supervised home visits of fourth-year medical students.

Sociologists further analyzed the sociocultural stresses in the environment and attempted to draw attention to aspects of the hospital system that might enhance or retard the patient's progress toward recovery. The departments of recreation and occupational therapy were frequently called upon to outline programs in which the student's patient might take part, or to demonstrate psychodrama (with students perhaps in various roles) as an important research and treatment tool. Thus, the teaching body extended far beyond the instructors listed in the Medical School catalogue as the specialized experience, preparation, and talent of many persons other than psychiatrists were recognized, and treatment was acknowledged as an endeavor of the total hospital community.

Those who participated in the training of medical students gained a feeling of greater prestige, were stimulated to do a better daily job, and enjoyed their work more. Apart from improvement in morale, the necessity for formulating and reformulating their ideas for presentation to keen, alert, and often critical students was a stimulus to intellectual development. This constant rethinking of concepts about one's place in mental health did much to prevent hardening of theories and rigidity of practice which might otherwise have led to sclerosis in hospital care.

In the last analysis, patients reaped benefits directly from attentions given them by the students, and indirectly from the raising of staff morale and the inspiration toward creative thinking. The major portion of the students' time was spent in working with, talking to, and trying to understand the patients. Their interest was intense and their efforts far from superficial. They saw their patients in the evenings, as well as during school hours, interviewed relatives, and sometimes made home visits. The ramifications of a case history were followed up by consultation with laboratories, social workers, occupational and recreational personnel, or by joining in play activities with the patients. Sometimes long after the student had supposedly left his psychiatric affiliation, he was still visiting his patient, exploring to the utmost under specially arranged supervision the therapeutic and learning possibilities provided by continued contact. For many patients the student relationship represented their most important human contact, and upon discharge some gave credit chiefly to medical students for the benefits derived from hospitalization.

Patients benefited because students possess in abundance qualities that may be therapeutic: a fresh point of view, an accepting spirit, eagerness to understand the patients' dilemmas; furthermore, they reinforced and dignified the place of the nonmedical staff on the therapeutic team. On the other hand, students, particularly in their fourth-year work, were brought face to face with the dynamic realities of the patients' inner lives. They began to appreciate how the struggle of a person to adapt to life conditions may affect his whole being, even making him vulnerable to medical and surgical disease, determine the pattern of his illness, and influence the choice of treatment or rehabilitation methods. Their eyes were opened to the broader significance to health of psychiatric and social factors; they took this message back to instructors in other departments so that major reverberations were produced throughout the Medical School.

The marked emphasis in the teaching on the importance of the individual had profound effects upon the attitude of the student toward himself. Without the insights gained from his psychiatric experience he would have been inclined to view his undergraduate function as principally that of accumulating knowledge and developing technical skills. With intensification of psychiatric instruction in the broadest sense he began to see the relevance of many other factors including particularly his own personality. His reaction to the patient became fully as important as the patient's reaction to him. This new introceptiveness had been almost impossible to awaken in him in the days when psychiatry was a minor specialty; but the increased depth of contact of student with both instructors and patients gradually enabled him to turn his light inward.

The movement toward the mentally ill patient initiated by the Medical School was joined by a host of graduate and undergraduate students from other institutions in and around Boston. Prospective clinical psychologists, social scientists, social

TABLE 3. TEACHING PROGRAM OF BOSTON PSYCHOPATHIC HOSPITAL[a]

Field of study, affiliation, and student group	Number of students	Period	Type of instruction
Medicine			
Boston Psychopathic Hospital			
Psychiatric residents	24	1 to 4 years	Lectures, case conferences, group therapy experience, instruction and supervision in psychotherapy and somatic therapy
Harvard University, Medical School			
4th year students	80	1 month	} Clinical, case supervision
3rd year students	145	11 half-days	}
2nd year students	120	10 hours	Lectures, demonstrations
Tufts College, Medical School			
3rd year students	110	2⅔ hours	Case discussions
Nursing			
Boston University, School of Nursing			
Candidates for M.S. in psychiatric nursing, Group I	4	7⅔ weeks	Supervised clinical experience, thesis work
Group II	10	12 weeks	Seminar in group psychology
Five collegiate schools of nursing			
Candidates for B.S. in psychiatric nursing, Group I	20	7⅔ weeks	} Supervised clinical experience, group
Group II	12	15 weeks	} discussions
Boston University, School of Nursing			
Candidates for B.S. in basic program	10	12 weeks	} Lectures, demonstrations, group discussions, case study and supervised
Seven hospital schools			ward practice
Candidates for diploma in nursing	114	12 weeks	} Lectures, supervised clinical experi-
Foreign fellowship students	2 or 3	12 weeks	} ence

	Number	Duration	Method
Social work			
Boston University, School of Social Work 1st year students	75 to 100	16 hours	⎱
Simmons College, School of Social Work 1st year students	50	30 hours	Lectures, demonstrations
Boston College, School of Social Work 1st year students	55	30 hours	
Four other schools of social work Field work students	7	8¾ months, 3 to 5 hours weekly	Thesis, supervised casework
Psychology and social relations			
Harvard University Graduate students	9	45 hours	Lectures, group discussion, supervised case study
Graduate students	6 to 8	96 hours	Group discussion, research projects
Boston University Graduate students	8 to 10	24 hours	Lectures, demonstrations
Occupational therapy			
Boston School of Occupational Therapy Candidates for B.S. or diploma	50	30 hours	Lectures, demonstrations
Theology			
Boston University, School of Theology Candidates for S.T.B.	10	6 weeks	Field work, group therapy, research projects
Physiotherapy			
Simmons College Candidates for B.S. or certificate	12	16 hours	Lectures, demonstrations
Other schools Undergraduates	2 or 3	2 or 3 weeks	Field work
Forensic psychiatry			
Harvard University, Law School Candidates for LL.B.	50	3 hours	Lectures, demonstrations

ª Data are for a representative recent year. The table does not include occasional students doing research for Ph.D. dissertation in clinical psychology or social relations, or for advanced degree in business administration or electrical engineering. Field workers in occupational therapy and trainees in electroencephalography have also been omitted.

workers, ministers, occupational therapists, physiotherapists, nurses, physiologists, engineers, business administrators, lawyers, and others came to the Hospital for field training in pursuit of academic degrees, for lectures and demonstrations, or for research work. Their stay varied from a few hours to months of intensive study and work with patients. An approximate picture of the flow of students through the Hospital during one year, together with the several disciplines represented, is shown in the accompanying table. So large and diverse a group involved a major commitment of time for the staff, increased greatly the daily personal contacts of patients, and led to extensive use of patients in lectures, demonstrations, and research. As a rule, those who were a special focus of interest did not object to being interviewed by several different students, nor did they resist being demonstrated before groups in lectures. Two factors contributed to their acceptance of these attentions: first, they were carefully selected for teaching purposes and, second, the teaching culture had so permeated the Hospital that a patient who was not receiving additional attention from students often felt neglected. It was also clear that only rarely did students through inexperience activate disturbing anxieties in patients, or interfere with or unduly complicate existing relationships between them and staff psychiatrists.

Not infrequently, neurotic problems of students were uncovered in the course of their work with patients. These were dealt with in brief psychotherapeutic sessions by members of the instructing staff, or if they required further help were referred for more careful study elsewhere. The impression was that in these instances personal problems had been faced or precipitated, and that their early recognition and treatment were desirable, both for the student's further instruction and for his maturation as an individual.

EXPANSION OF RESEARCH

The original concepts giving rise to small psychopathic hospitals emphasized three functions: treatment of acutely ill mental patients, teaching of professional workers, and research.

We have seen in preceding chapters how the goal of treatment at our institution was conceived in ever-broadening terms which finally came to rest upon the idea of a *therapeutic community*. The teaching function of the Hospital, too, was interpreted in an expanded sense to include the intellectual and emotional learning that took place bilaterally when a large group of students representing many disciplines interacted freely with staff members, and particularly with patients. There remained essentially the problem of how the goals of research were to be defined and implemented.

Prior to 1943 the fields of systematic investigation embraced primarily neurosyphilis, biochemistry, and electroencephalography. In other words, there was a biological or "organic" bias in the structured experiments, although published reports, especially those written by the medical director, showed great concern with clinical or psychodynamic formulations and attempted to delineate new syndromes. The overall problem of mental illness was considered so complex, particularly by mature psychiatrists in the hospital setting, that often little hope was held out for the possibility of developing significant research designs in areas other than the biological. We were sometimes told that tools for research in schizophrenia, for example, were inadequate, and one must await further discoveries before moving on.

In 1943, although no additional facilities were immediately available, the new medical director expressed his desire to spread research interest and elicit more of the creativity inherent in all personnel, whether or not they occupied one of the limited number of research positions. Dr. Solomon then appointed as director of laboratories and research a psychiatrist who, he felt, was able to foment ideas, help others get started, function as a nodal point of communication, and coordinate activities. The research director's range and freedom were practically unlimited, and he received no specific directions as to how to run his job. His formal training in clinical psychiatry prepared him to consider the problems of psychiatric patients and to communicate with psychiatrists, whereas previous investigation in physiology and electroencephalography gave him additional foundations on which to begin. He had no intention, however, of limiting either himself or his department to physiobiological experimentation.

A critical appraisal of the place of research in the Hospital revealed the following severe limitations. Several departments which, through research, might have added significantly to the fund of general knowledge, stimulated personnel, and enriched their experience, were doing nothing at all. Clinical psychology was inadequately represented at the research round table; no work was being carried on in sociology, social anthropology, occupational therapy, nursing, or pastoral counseling; and social work studies were practically limited to students' theses. The relatively large outpatient department was almost entirely devoted to service, and was undertaking little in the nature of systematic self-evaluation worthy of the name of research, let alone tackling any fundamental hypotheses or theories.

Except for neurosyphilis, the evaluation of therapies then in use was essentially at a standstill. Exploration of newer forms of treatment was scarcely undertaken. The general attitude seemed to be "Let's see if they are accepted by the psychiatric profession before trying them out," rather than employing the Hospital as a tribunal where claims could be given fair and honest hearing and careful experimental testing.

The few who were doing research attended largely to the problems at hand; they took little definitive responsibility for inspiring younger men on the clinical staff, and not enough for engaging the interest of persons outside the Hospital. As a consequence, research was not attracting, in anything like the numbers it might, graduate students concerned with human relations from colleges and universities in the Boston area, although the number of such students was legion and the problems of mental health and disease were potentially fascinating. Effective liaison between the research laboratory and other groups in the community had not been worked out. Interdisciplinary possibilities of collaboration were therefore at a minimum, and coordinated group research was undeveloped. Little cooperation existed between service and research functions. Although reporting of experimental progress to the service staff occurred at intervals and interest was thereby stimulated, gains were mostly in the nature of increased technical knowledge, as, for example, how the electroencephalogram could sharpen diagnostic acumen regarding brain damage.

There was little research that tended to increase self-awareness: understanding of the manner in which each individual in the hospital setting was functioning, how he was contributing to therapeutic goals, and how his contribution might be implemented further. Therefore, although a few things within the hospital system were well studied, the system itself escaped notice, and research was not an integral part of the system. Many factors could be held accountable for this state of affairs, but space does not permit their detailed analysis. Certain it was, however, that the hospital culture failed to put a high enough value upon research inquiry and enterprise. In the early stages of the unfolding of the enlarged research program it became apparent that the very critical and rigid attitudes of some of the staff members would have to be overcome if the ardor of younger aspirants was not to be dampened.

One of these attitudes was that research could be done only by the most highly trained and intellectual members of the hierarchy. A definitive line of academic development was envisaged for the average research worker—undergraduate training, plus an advanced degree that included considerable preparation in research design, statistics, and formulation or testing of hypotheses. Investigation without this equipment by personnel, whose training fitted them primarily for practical work with patients, was frowned upon. How could a nurse or an occupational therapist, for example, do research without statistical competence? Unfortunately, the specialization implicit in the training of the well-equipped research worker, together with the abstract intellectual processes it encouraged, kept such persons remote from patients and practical everyday problems crying for solution. Instead, they concerned themselves with ever tighter experimental studies that might withstand the critique of members of the most "scientific" societies. Had we waited until they turned their attention to the complex problems confronting the nurse, for instance, we should still be waiting. It appeared unlikely, moreover, that they would possess the motivation, sensitivity, and discernment of the nurses themselves who clearly had more to gain from a better understanding of their jobs than did anyone else.

Research Serves Goal of Patient Care

Thus it was that efforts were bent toward mobilizing the creative forces in the total hospital community, much as effort had been exerted to develop the therapeutic forces. Especially in the postwar period the research program was aided by the return of veterans to undergraduate and graduate study, the request of the social sciences for a place in the mental health field, and the greater availability of funds from both federal and private sources. Contacts established with Harvard University, Boston University, Massachusetts Institute of Technology, and many other institutions brought graduate students and sometimes faculty from many disciplines. Nor were volunteers or undergraduates of little experience turned away before an attempt was made to find some place for them within the organization.

As research expanded and involved more people, it soon became apparent that this type of activity served the goals of patient care in many ways. Aside from providing intellectual stimulation for the Hospital and adding to the fund of general knowledge, the enthusiasm and motivation of the personnel often grew by leaps and bounds when they found their own activities worthy of scientific investigation. Upon being permitted to join in group investigative effort or present their findings before student groups or clinical conferences, they experienced the same rise in self-esteem as in teaching medical students. As their sense of personal significance increased, suggestions and ideas began to flow upward toward hospital administrators. Besides the growth of those individuals who shared in the studies, patients received a great deal of additional interest and attention. Even the most esoteric research could be encouraged with the almost certain knowledge that patients would eventually benefit, for either the research would tend to move closer to the patient who was always at the center of the hospital program, or the research worker would be seduced by the therapeutic enthusiasm of those around him. By coming directly into contact with patients in order to obtain data for these studies, by taking over service functions (such as music therapy) related to what they might be investigating, by volunteering their services, apart from research, to fill in gaps in the patients' lives, or by turning up new facets of ward care, they added to the variety and richness of the patients' hospital life.

New Professional Groups Included

Within the hospital community research was eventually broadened to include those professional groups that had been more or less excluded from participation: social workers, nurses, occupational therapists, and ministers. Social workers had some tradition of research based upon a professional curriculum that required a thesis as partial fulfillment for the master's degree. For years their affiliation as students with the Hospital had combined field work with investigation and they had explored a vast number of subjects, some with great practical bearing. However, after graduation they became essentially service personnel and rarely applied their talents to systematic examination of a problem. In fact, they seemed to suffer for want of scientific standing in comparison with other graduate students, especially those from departments of social science; and leaders in social work were frank to admit that the discipline lacked a body of knowledge based on rigorous experimentation and that its theory was undeveloped. As the research laboratory grew, social workers were included as members of multidisciplinary teams, and later, as their research skills developed, they embarked upon projects of their own with progressively less supervision required.[1] Some of them have shown outstanding promise; if opportunities were provided, they could unquestionably work out better theory and practice for the application of their efforts to mental health. They would be especially suited to clinical research, particularly in collaboration with psychiatrists investigating case problems.

Interest in developing the social environment of the Hospital as a specific therapeutic factor and the participation of occupational therapists in this effort were closely related to the work of Dr. Robert W. Hyde, who became assistant superintendent in 1945. Dr. Hyde's appointment, more than any other made by Dr. Solomon, illustrates how little attention was paid to conventional qualifications and how much to the creative potentialities of the man. Dr. Hyde had been a general practitioner in Vermont for five years, then entered military service to become assistant medical director of the Boston Recruiting and Induction Center, which was known as one of the most efficient in the country. In the organization of the induction procedure, the handling of many civilian psychiatrists who served the Center, and particularly in the broad sociocultural investigation of factors contributing to acceptance or rejection of selectees, he displayed originality and administrative ability that made him desirable as an executive of a mental hospital. The fact that he had not then had any formal training as a psychiatrist, and did not become a diplomate of the American Board of Psychiatry until some years later, was of little moment. The important qualifications were his energy and enthusiasm and his interest in finding answers to questions of how best to treat patients. Unusual was the fact that he was permitted to delegate most of his executive functions to his assistants, and that he was given both the time and the liberty to indulge his intellectual curiosity.

[1] In lobotomy investigations the following social workers made important contributions: Beatrice Talbot, Mildred Broffman, Anne P. Ogilby, Emily Robertson, Marie Wingate, Gladys Madoff, Sanford Friedman, Julian Carrick, Barbara Schwartz. In follow-up studies of community adjustment of committed cases Anna R. Pandiscio gave major assistance to Dr. J. Sanbourne Bockoven over a period of years. Georgina D. Hotchkiss explored systematically interactions of relatives with personnel and patients, and then joined the study of Hospital Ideology under Dr. Daniel J. Levinson.

The interest in social psychiatry that he had developed at the Induction Center could now be furthered by studying psychotic patients and the mental hospital itself. Employing methods of participant and nonparticipant observation, he spent many months examining ward life in an attempt to construct a picture of it, and to understand how the institutional community was perceived and experienced by each new arrival. From this early investigation he went on to an increasingly wider study of every aspect of hospital living and of the role of all categories of staff, actual and potential, in improving living conditions for the patients. Simultaneously he was evolving theories of patient care that have advanced thinking greatly about ways whereby the hospital environment may be used as a therapeutic instrument. Early in his work he brought occupational therapists into the research since they possessed skill in manipulating the environment. They were able to make remarkable improvements in ward life based on definitive investigations, although they were originally untrained in research methods, possessed no tools for observation, and had no broad view of their potentialities as social architects.

Nurses began to function in the research area, largely through the stimulus provided by development of graduate work in nursing. Advanced students came to the Hospital chiefly from Boston University for clinical specialization and preparation of theses under the guidance of the senior staff. During the course of their investigations some nurses showed particular promise. When one of them, Miss Harriet Kandler, was appointed in 1950 director of nursing, the possibility emerged of utilizing such persons for studies of a more complex nature. Of critical importance was the action of the American Nurses' Association in raising money for research from its own members. Grants from the Association permitted the Hospital to obtain the services of graduate nurses to study in more controlled situations what the nurse was doing on her job, how she related to patients, and how her role might be improved.[1]

[1] Miss Alice Behymer and Mrs. Francoise R. Morimoto were the first nurses employed under this arrangement. They made significant contributions to our understanding of the nurse's function on the ward.

Divinity students found their way to the Hospital chiefly through the efforts of Dr. Paul Johnson of Boston University, who felt that they could derive important insights into human behavior from observing patients at close range and noting the effects of life's vicissitudes. During his brief residency each student was expected to investigate a problem of special interest. The result of these critical inquiries was the realization of how little was known concerning appropriate activities for chaplains of various faiths, who were customarily attached to the mental hospitals in the Commonwealth and who were more or less accepted as part of the therapeutic staff. The only logical approach could be careful and systematic research by ministers themselves.[1]

Research and Changes in Ward Care

The investigation of major problems involved the assembling of interdisciplinary research teams. The Hospital watched these teams in action and learned the value of coordinated work. It learned also that the research workers omitted no group of personnel but valued information obtained from all. One of the primary lessons was that much of the important information about patients was in the hands of attendants and nurses. This was particularly true in those large mental hospitals, visited by teams of research workers to follow up patients after specific procedures like brain surgery that had been performed at Boston Psychopathic Hospital. The workers often found a patient "lost" in back wards as far as hospital psychiatrists and administrators were concerned.

Sometimes investigation of functions and particularly staff attitudes was taken as an invasion of personal zones of action or thinking and feeling; the research worker was not infrequently scorned as a meddler. A gradual breakdown in the resistance to being studied, however, occurred *pari passu* with the extension of research to more and more professional workers until formerly resistant personnel began to initiate studies of

---

[1] Such investigation was undertaken especially by Chaplains Robert C. Leslie and Joseph F. Woodson, under the supervision of Dr. R. W. Hyde.

their own functions. Over the course of ten years there has been a marked spread of research culture into all parts of the Hospital. Recently even the process of psychotherapy, formerly an inviolate and sacrosanct aspect of the psychiatrist's work, has been subjected to analysis by the simultaneous recording of physiological, psychological, and sociological data relating to the interview process.

Most of the advances in ward care were based upon systematic observations. Observations of interaction on the ward led to an appreciation of the generally low level of human intercourse, the marked psychological and social distance between personnel and patient, the gratifying effectiveness of occupational and recreational therapists with their special skills, the necessity for continued changing of activities to prevent slumps, the importance of music, the high potential of patients for engaging in games and arts and crafts if the equipment and materials were available. Studies of factors in rapport led to an appreciation of how various traits in patients attract or repel personnel, and this knowledge led in turn to emphasis upon the forgotten patient and eventually to resolution of antipathies through group therapeutic sessions with personnel. Studies of ward society gave insight into patient leaders, satellites, and isolates, and the potential importance of "place" in that society. Analysis of skills and interests of patients and personnel revealed great untapped reservoirs for further healthy interaction. Concern with the effect of the approach by different staff members to patients led gradually to experimentation with various forms of psychodrama. The inventory by a social worker of the complaints of patients resulted, as we have seen, in the formation of a patients' club that eventually developed the organization for patient government, which has proved one of the greatest liberating influences. Observations of patients and relatives in interaction during the visiting hour gave cause for considerable positive thinking about the role of relatives in treatment and smoothed the way for longer visiting hours.

Specific somatic treatments were either discarded, modified, or intensified depending on research findings. Intravenous ether therapy, for example, was discarded as of no greater value than ordinary intravenous saline in the care of patients. Electric shock therapy was progressively improved through both bio-physical and social studies. Various drugs like sodium amytal, methyl desoxyephedrine (pervitin), and so on were carefully explored for their value in promoting catharsis and resolution of defensive mechanisms by a single rapid intravenous injection. Transient psychological changes, induced by administering ly-sergic acid to members of the staff and students who volunteered for the investigation, were explored as adjuncts in teaching per-sonnel to empathize with and relate to patients.

This partial list of studies with consequences for practical action suffices to show the very close relationship between seri-ous inquiry and improvement in the care of the sick. From these studies has come the realization shared increasingly by the Hos-pital and the institutions of higher learning in the area that a mental hospital provides a potential center for research of in-estimable importance. For the university the opportunity to study many facets of human relations and test hypotheses of individual and group behavior is of the first order. For the hos-pital the stimulus furnished by students' inquiries opens new doors to exploration of the many manifestations of mental ill-ness and its more perceptive treatment.

10. Relation of the Hospital to the Community

THE REPUTATION OF THE MENTAL HOSPITAL in the community determines in large measure the tensions and anxieties of patients and relatives who come to it for help, their willingness to cooperate with the hospital program, the nature and amount of the community's contribution to its welfare, and the generosity of legislators in granting it an adequate budget with which to do its job.

Through their numerous contacts with the community the personnel of the hospital are among the chief ambassadors of good will. Each member of the staff, if properly educated, can become an interpreter to some part of the community of the goals and aspirations of the patient treatment program. The more frequent and intensive the contacts, the more likely are personnel to make a significant impression upon their friends. Experience indicates that lectures, radio, and television broadcasts have comparatively little effect. Real knowledge about mental illness cannot be transmitted, or significant changes in attitudes and prejudices accomplished by a few lectures in the course of a year. Close association and continuous emotional involvement with the institution, on the other hand, can produce profound change. Ideally these can be best achieved through direct work with disturbed persons plus continuous training related closely to work with patients. But before members of the community can overcome their fear of mental illness to the point that they are willing to meet patients, much education must be carried out.

For many years attendants, nurses, residents, and other personnel lived in Boston Psychopathic Hospital. Their quarters took up valuable space that could have been used to better advantage for patients. Their extramural contacts became limited and they tended to be isolated from the outer world. The living-in arrangement encouraged a kind of social retreat similar in type, though not in extent, to the social withdrawal of the patients. Hospital positions became a haven for persons who were themselves uneasy about human contacts, and increased the tendency for attendants and others to be ashamed of their jobs and to think of their work as menial and insignificant. Efforts were made to reverse this trend by repeatedly pointing out to the staff that it would be better for them and for the patients, as well as the community, if they lived normal lives like other workers. They would avoid narrowness and provincialism, learn more about the problems of adaptation of patients to the community, and as they won a place for themselves in a circle of friends, increase interest in the mentally ill. They were encouraged to invite their friends and acquaintances to come to the Hospital to meet their co-workers and learn about treatment at first hand. Frequently administrative psychiatrists personally helped in orienting these visitors to the concept that mental illness is rather like other illnesses, can be treated, and in general carries a hopeful prognosis, and that patients are not inhuman or degraded.

The open-door policy resulted in many community groups requesting permission to visit the Hospital and learn about its work. Requests came from schools, colleges, churches, parent-teacher associations, women's clubs, and other organizations. Visitors were initially taken on staff-conducted tours. The practice still obtains particularly when a group is small. Increasingly, however, provision has been made for large groups to be subdivided and for these several units to be shown the institution by members of Patient Government, or for a clinic conducted largely by patients to be organized for the instruction of guests. Not infrequently individual visitors with altruistic interests have seen opportunities to help and have offered their services as volunteers.

STAFF PARTICIPATION IN PANEL DISCUSSIONS

Recently the staff have taken a more active part in educating the public by holding panel discussions of mental illness and its institutional care. These discussions arose from the work of Miss Anne P. Ogilby, executive social worker, who in 1948 conducted a series of group sessions with relatives described later in this chapter. After the sessions came to an end she began to receive requests, mostly from the former members, to talk to groups in the community. She based her talks upon the actual hospital experiences of specific unnamed patients. Since this seemed to meet the needs of her audiences exceedingly well, other persons were soon invited to tell of their part in the treatment program, increasing the dramatic appeal and authenticity of the report. A panel finally was made up of representatives of five different hospital departments: psychiatrist, social worker, nurse, occupational therapist, and volunteer.

Individual programs are unrehearsed, and differ according to the audience being addressed and the case discussed. The story starts in the admission room with an account of events leading up to hospitalization, and procedure in handling the patient. The nurse then describes taking the sick person to the ward, and pictures what the ward environment is like and her role in making him comfortable. Details of the medical and psychiatric background, and treatment program during hospitalization are presented by the physician. The home situation is discussed by the social worker who shows the relevance of family attitudes to severity of illness and response to treatment. Social and recreational aspects of treatment are described by the occupational therapist. Finally, the volunteer indicates from personal experience how a friendly person from the outside world can help the patient. By the time the story has progressed to where the patient leaves the institution to return to the community, a fairly complete picture of the Hospital and its functions has been given.

The panel has appeared before many church groups, women's clubs, parent-teacher associations, community fund committees, and hospital associations with considerable effectiveness, we believe. At least three significant results have been noted. First, persons in the audiences in need of psychiatric help have been encouraged to seek it; second, many individuals have come to the Hospital to "see for themselves," or have contributed gifts or volunteered time and services; and, third, personnel who have participated in panel presentations have seen their relationship to the community as a most significant factor in their ability to bring aid to the mentally ill.

VOLUNTEERS AS AUXILIARY PERSONNEL

Where the needs of mentally ill patients for social interaction and kindly care are so great, hospitals throughout the country woefully understaffed, and the tradition of voluntary participation in community affairs so much a part of our democracy, how is it, one asks, that psychiatric hospitals have not directed greater efforts toward inaugurating and expanding volunteer services?[1] Part of the reason is to be found in the attitudes of fear and prejudice held by the outside community toward the mentally ill. Some of the difficulty arises from hospital administrators who are afraid that the volunteer may get into difficulties for which they will be held responsible. They cannot exert control over the volunteer in the same sense as over the paid employee. A rigid hierarchical organization dedicated to staying out of trouble cannot have the flexibility necessary to integrate volunteers of varying talents, capacities, interests, and time schedules into the already complex hospital organization. Unfortunately, no well-defined general philosophy or body of rules and regulations exists to guide administrators in their use. Resistance to volunteers often comes also from the staff of the hospital. They may be distrustful of the motives of the volunteer, too "busy" to train him, or fearful that he will make a salaried job unnecessary. Half-hearted acceptance either by ad-

[1] We are indebted to Dr. Hyde, Mrs. Lovett Morse, formerly president of the Boston Psychopathic Hospital Auxiliary, and Mrs. Edward Boulter, director of volunteers, Metropolitan State Hospital, for help in developing this section. See Hyde, Robert W., and Catherine F. Hurley, "Volunteers in Mental Hospitals," *Psychiatric Quarterly Supplement*, vol. 24, 1950, part 2, pp. 233–249.

ministration or by personnel quickly discourages any volunteer program.

Some of the early mental hospitals, such as the York Retreat in England, Bloomfield in Dublin, and the Friends' Hospital in Frankford, Pennsylvania, were founded by the Society of Friends, which contributed greatly by its volunteer services to the care of the insane. In recent times, however, volunteer work has been developed largely in the military services and in the Veterans Administration, although an occasional state hospital such as Central Louisiana State Hospital has made extensive use of it. In the Massachusetts state hospital system little was done until 1944, when the medical director of Boston Psychopathic Hospital made arrangements with the American Red Cross for its Gray Ladies to participate in the patient care program. A total of 61 took part. They worked in crafts and recreational activities, assisted in serving food, fed patients, arranged special social events, and in every way functioned as auxiliary personnel.

The next year, it will be recalled, the Boston Psychopathic Hospital Auxiliary was started, consisting originally of trustees' wives and staff psychiatrists, and later expanded to include many interested friends of the institution.[1] As the Auxiliary evolved, one branch undertook to assist in recruiting, selecting, orienting, and placing volunteers in various departments of the Hospital. The volunteers come from schools, colleges, churches, the Junior League, social agencies; some are referred by physicians, some are employees or would-be employees who wish further training and experience, and some are former patients who are deeply appreciative of the Hospital's efforts on their behalf and wish to do something in return. Former patients have been fully as helpful as nonpatients, often showing greater sensitivity and understanding as a result of their own suffering. Experience has indicated that many types of people may find a useful place in the hospital community; hence, rigorous methods of selection are not applied.

After an initial interview prospective volunteers are intro-

[1] See Chapter 3 for a list of the functions of the Auxiliary.

duced to the heads of the departments in which they will work, and thereafter interpretation, training, and supervision are the responsibility of the individual departments. The volunteers, however, are encouraged to join in all hospital activities, to attend conferences and lectures. Not infrequently, members of Patient Government are consulted about suggestions for placement before the initial interview. If either volunteers or department heads indicate a desire for a change or rotation of service, this is arranged insofar as possible.

Six years after the initiation of the Auxiliary, a survey revealed that a total of 236 volunteers had served the Hospital. More than half had worked in the occupational therapy department, where it is easiest to meet patients and to test one's skills with crafts, arts, and games; roughly a fifth had been assigned to nursing service; and a wide variety of tasks had occupied the remainder. A review of their undertakings during the decade since they began shows that they have conducted pottery classes three days each week; assisted Patient Government in plans for all large social events; conducted or supervised cooking classes, home-nursing classes, book discussion groups, beginning and advanced art classes, textile painting, dancing, spontaneity theater, regular drama, outdoor sports, and tournaments. Those who have not worked directly with patients have contributed in the capacity of secretaries, research assistants, receptionists, shoppers, gardeners, and so on.

Even in a Hospital fortunate enough to have a relatively large staff the assistance of volunteers is felt, as has been remarked earlier, to be almost indispensable in bringing patient care to its present level. For the very reason that they are not bound by rigid routines they can fill in the interstices between specific job descriptions. In hospitals with low staff-patient ratios they represent the most immediately available source of auxiliary nursing service.

It is gratifying to note that in 1950 the Massachusetts Commissioner for Mental Health, the Massachusetts Association for Mental Health, and volunteer leaders from the five state hospitals that had instituted volunteer programs following the early

experiments at Boston Psychopathic Hospital, together sponsored a Committee on Volunteers. This group held meetings
for the better part of one year and compiled a valuable *Guide
for Organization of Volunteer Service in Mental Hospitals,*
which is recommended to institutions interested in developing
such service.[1]

THE RELATIVES' ROLE

When one member is admitted to a mental hospital, others
in the family are beset by anxieties, fears, guilt, and uncertainty.
Are they doing the right thing in inviting the stigma of hospitalization or in signing commitment papers that abrogate civil
rights? Should they permit electric shock, insulin coma therapy,
or brain surgery with its admitted risks to life? The illness is
mysterious and terrifying. What should they tell their friends?
How will the community judge them? Is there a family taint? To
what extent do they share the blame for the patient's illness?
What are the implications for themselves and their children?

The first visit to the ward is also painful and disquieting. For
most relatives this is their initial contact with hospitalized mental patients, and the bizarre behavior often seen and the bare-
ness of the physical environment may be shocking to them. Perhaps most stressful of all are the pleadings and entreaties of
the sick person they have come to visit, who may be openly
hostile to the hospital, personnel, and even to them. He often
unloads a heavy weight of complaints and irritations, pressing
them for a quick solution of vexations and demanding immediate release. The brunt of such a tragic visit is borne by the relatives themselves; the ward staff may be absent from the scene,
too busy to be reached, or unequal to the task of allaying their
anxieties. It is easy to understand that following such a traumatic occurrence, relatives find it difficult to return to the side
of the patient, no matter how much they think they may be
needed.

[1] Kimball, Jay, in cooperation with the Committee on Volunteers, *Guide for
Organization of Volunteer Service in Mental Hospitals.* Massachusetts Association for Mental Health, Boston, 1950.

Just as in the psychiatric treatment of children it is necessary to bring parents into the therapeutic orbit, so in the treatment of the hospitalized adult, relatives may be a critical influence. The nurse or attendant, however, often sees them as persons who get in the way of treatment, leave the patient disturbed, or pester her for relief of his complaints. Some relatives exercise undue pressure on ward staff to give special attention to the particular patient. They sometimes offer bribes, which if accepted undermine the self-esteem of personnel, or increase difficulties with other patients who are as a rule extraordinarily sensitive to any favoritism shown. When their fear that the patient will be abused or neglected is reinforced by their own guilt, they often begin to attack the hospital and demand to see the "doctor in charge." Little provision is made for help from that source. So few physicians are available, particularly on Sunday which is generally the busiest visiting day, that both relatives and doctors are likely to experience only acute frustration.

Thus, the psychiatric hospital finds itself in the sorry plight of having no well-defined theories about the desirability of integrating relatives into the treatment program, and recognizing them as controlling factors in the patient's attitudes and his strongest link with the outside world. And if theories about this important subject are largely lacking, even less emphasis is placed upon making studies of how such integration could be accomplished, or upon conducting experimental programs of education designed to help relatives at least with the more superficial aspects of their role. The average mental hospital is so involved with the care of patients that it pays little attention to the great flow of relatives, although from many standpoints the patient-relative dyad may be considered two aspects of unity, inseparable in health and disease. Thus, except in the occasional institution that is attempting to do something for them, relatives are provided with no planned assistance in handling their own problems in relation to those of the patient. Simultaneously, the hospital is losing a significant opportunity to create good will for itself and to educate a large segment of the population. When such a considerable fraction of the community comes into contact with the mental hospital at one time or another, it is a fair question whether the slow pace of enlightenment about psychological sickness and the needs of these hospitals is not the result in large measure of the neglect of visitors.

Group Meetings with Relatives

Growing awareness of this problem led Boston Psychopathic Hospital to give more attention to relatives after the war. The executive social worker, who had long listened to the major share of their complaints and irritations, organized discussion groups for them that were viewed as frankly experimental and hence had no rigid objectives. It was believed, however, that from such sessions much might be learned about the needs of relatives; the groups might provide mutually supporting experiences for the members; and the time of physicians and social workers might be more economically used.

During the 15 weekly meetings, covering a period of four months, 100 relatives were in attendance, representing 60 patients.[1] Since 310 patients passed through the Hospital during this period, roughly one-fifth of all families were reached by this method. Speakers were invited about once a month to tell of various phases of hospital work. Generally, however, the sessions were informal for the express purpose of encouraging maximum participation and ventilation of feelings by the relatives themselves. Only one major limitation was imposed, and that not always successfully: attention was to be centered in the group upon topics of general interest, and individual problems were to be taken up with the patient's psychiatrist or an assigned social worker. Relatives usually wanted to know the minute details of a treatment procedure and the patients' reaction to it. The following questions are representative of those raised in the meetings. It will be noted that they often revealed considerable apprehension about the mysterious methods of psychiatry.

[1] Steele, Muriel H., *Group Meetings for Relatives of Mental Hospital Patients.* Thesis submitted in partial fulfillment of requirements for degree of Master of Social Work, Smith College, 1948.

Concerning Treatment:

If the hospital decides on a particular treatment, is the recommendation ever changed?

How soon after admission is treatment begun?

Would a negative attitude on the part of the patient affect the result?

Concerning Electroshock Treatment:

Could electric shock cause heart trouble?

Can it be given repeatedly without damage to a patient?

What happens to a patient's mind?

How long does the current pass through the body?

For how long is the patient's memory impaired?

Does he remember this treatment?

Can he become dependent on electroshock?

Concerning Insulin Therapy:

Does a person have to be very sick to be given insulin therapy?

Is it all right to bring sweets to a patient receiving insulin?

Is that tired feeling normal?

How many comas are induced?

Does the patient talk under insulin coma?

Can a patient having subshock treatment go home for the weekend?

Concerning Lobotomy:

Does the operation take long?

Is especial care required afterward?

Is it normal to be very quiet after the operation?

Do old symptoms recur later?

Does the patient slip back?

Why does Mr. X want to fight all the time now?

Concerning Psychotherapy:

How can the doctor get the patient to talk?

Can the patient tell what has been troubling him?

Concerning the Relatives' Role in Handling Patients:

What should one talk about during a visit?

Should one always agree with the patient?

What do you say to a person who is hearing voices?

Should a patient be encouraged to talk about the cause of his illness?

Should you humor him?

To what extent may the relative take the doctor's role?

When the patient comes home, should you invite other people to the house?

Should you cross the patient?
Should you discipline him?
Should you protect him?

Some of the statements made in the group meetings revealed anxiety and shame about mental sickness; others showed concern about what happened to the patient as the result of hospitalization; still others illustrated fear of social opprobrium. Typical statements were these:

> I had a great fear of mental illness.
> I didn't feel ashamed until I went to court to sign commitment papers, and the word "insanity" bothered me.
> My husband's family wants his illness kept secret.
> I thought that the other boys on the ward were a bad influence on my son.
> They say that state hospitals are easy to get into but hard to get out of.
> Are all these people going to be social outcasts when they go home?
> How will the patient be treated when he goes back to school?

Over and over again members of the groups sought for the cause of psychological illness. One would inquire if overwork produces mental breakdown; another would ask if a person could brood himself into mental illness. "Is there a change in a boy's system during adolescence that causes it?" "Is it hereditary?" To appreciate the fact that there might be many and complex factors that together precipitated the psychotic break seemed very difficult for the discussants. And when explanations were offered that seemed to imply that they themselves had had a part in the patient's conflicts, such enormous guilt was engendered that there was a tendency to reject the explanations.

The questions raised give but a glimpse of the themes that preoccupied relatives, and suggest why they need time and attention for coming to accept mental illness more nearly as they would accept physical sickness. The group method was found to have distinct advantages both in reaching a large number of relatives and in promoting greater understanding. Most of the persons who attended the meetings spoke of the beneficial effect, saying that they had gained practical information, emotional repose, mutual comfort, or support from knowing that there were others who were facing the same problems and that many had solved them.

Visiting Patterns on the Ward

If visits to the patient are to be molded toward a therapeutic end, it is important not only to deal with the attitudes and beliefs of relatives and try to allay their anxieties, but to see that the visit occurs under the most favorable conditions. We need information as to the precise pattern of the visiting experience and its effect upon the patient, to guide us in improving it. Toward this end, Mrs. Georgina Hotchkiss, an experienced social worker, began direct observation of conditions and interactions on the women's acute ward of the Hospital during the visiting hour.[1] Two of her observations will serve to give the reader some knowledge of what she saw and sometimes overheard.

A Withdrawn Rejecting Patient and a Corrective Critical Visitor: The visit took place with both the young patient, Sophie, and her mother sitting on her bed. It began in an apparently social and friendly manner, the mother appearing quite affectionate in her questioning of the patient and the latter responding. The character of the visit changed after a few minutes when the mother told Sophie that she considered the doctor inefficient. The patient protested, became very tense, and "clammed up." The mother continued, "I consider her inefficient because she doesn't make you put your clothes on and stop smoking." The mother asked if the physician had talked to the patient or given her any tests. Sophie did not respond but left in tears. When she returned, the mother offered her food. The patient refused, saying, "I don't want to eat," and told her mother to go home. When the mother started to go, Sophie asked when she could go home. The mother sat down again and said, "That's what I wanted to talk to you about today. If you'll stop smoking all those butts, get dressed, put on lipstick, set your hair, clean your nails, I'll take you home." There was no response from the patient.

[1] Hotchkiss, Georgina D., and F. L. Wells, *Patterns of Visits to Women Patients on the Acute Ward of a Mental Hospital.* Unpublished manuscript.

Discrediting the physician or other members of the staff, as in the example given above, may do much toward undermining the mental health of a patient who is faced with adjustment to opposing expectations set by authority figures. Psychotic patients tolerate this situation of divided loyalty very poorly; perhaps because it has existed in the family during their early years and they have become sensitized to it. In Sophie we see withdrawal and intensification of psychotic symptoms as soon as she is forced to make the difficult choice between mother and doctor. It is safe to say that if the administration had discovered any member of the hospital personnel undermining the efforts of the psychiatrist in this manner, something would have been done promptly to remedy the situation.

Another case is cited to illustrate how important the *conditions* of visiting may be.

Demanding, Accusing Patient and Corrective, Critical Visitor: The dining-room on the ward is used for the visit. Ruth, a girl about seventeen years old, is stating to her mother and father in a querulous voice that becomes more excited and demanding that she does not want any further shock treatments. At this point a "roving" patient enters the room, stands near the doorway, and delivers a tirade to the parents telling them not to sign for that dreadful treatment, to "take their beautiful little girl home," and that "she doesn't eat here." For some ten minutes, Ruth, the parents, and another patient and visitor in the room sit transfixed by the performance, neither making an effort to move away nor attempting to ignore the tirade. Following the roving patient's departure the mother picks up the subject, asking Ruth why she doesn't eat and telling her that she must. The patient returns to the subject of shock, begging and demanding that her mother go immediately to inform the doctor that she should not have the treatments. The mother and father both tell the patient that if she eats she will not need shock treatments, and this argument develops into a crescendo. The mother angrily berates Ruth for having messy hair, for "flopping around" in a dirty bathrobe. "I certainly won't ask to have the shock stopped if you won't eat, dress, or fix your hair." Ruth swears at her mother and the latter threatens, "If that's the way you treat me I won't visit you. Such awful language! Is that the kind of company you keep here?" The mother leaves abruptly.

Behavior of other patients, particularly those without callers, is a considerable factor in the success of a visit. One patient at the Hospital, for example, took the part of "official greeter," going to speak to all guests. If the visitor *is* actually at a loss for things to talk about, the interruption of the roving patient may relieve the tension. If, on the other hand, he monopolizes the situation, makes objectionable remarks, or asks questions of a deeply personal nature, both visitor and patient may become disturbed and the whole purpose of the visit may be lost.

If the visiting experience is to be improved, the physical conditions under which it occurs must frequently be altered. Mrs. Hotchkiss discovered that slightly more than half of the visits took place on the patients' beds on the ward. The remainder were in the small dining-room or on the porch. Little or no privacy obtains under these circumstances. Regarding this matter, as well as the role of the staff in helping relatives with their visits, and provision for therapeutic assistance to those most destructive in their relationships with patients, Mrs. Hotchkiss made the following suggestions:

Specific places should be designated as visiting areas and properly supplied with furniture. Personnel should introduce visitors to the ward at the time of their first visit, pointing out the visiting area, and offering help with any visiting problem. They should keep close track of the visit, with more and earlier participation aimed at obviating and redirecting visiting situations rather than open interference. Special difficulties might be reported to social workers who could get in touch with the visitors and interpret to them the meaning of the patient's behavior, discuss possible changes in the visiting procedure, and perhaps even discourage coming for a time. Intensive work with relatives that present particular problems in their relationship with patients may be necessary in some cases. Such work may be pursued on either an individual or group basis.

Increasing Visiting Time

At Boston Psychopathic Hospital interest in visitors has been reflected not only in the increasing attention paid to relatives during the admission procedure, individual and group meetings, and research projects, but by extending the amount of time allotted to visiting. Two hours each day, including Sunday, were originally considered generous. In 1952 a suggestion from the administration began to be considered for increasing the time. Although a general and a veterans' hospital in the Boston area reported satisfaction with such changes, the personnel at Boston Psychopathic Hospital discussed this experiment for nearly a year. Then a strong recommendation from Patient Government finally precipitated the change, and in 1953 visiting hours were extended from two to roughly seven hours a day. It is interesting to note that personnel were reluctant to introduce such a change on their own initiative, yet were unwilling to deny a recommendation put forth by the patients. When the change finally came, everyone seemed committed to making it a success.

A nearly fourfold increase in the time allotted did not increase the amount of visiting, or cause congestion on the wards by callers getting in the way. Instead, it led to a number of desirable consequences, not all of which had been anticipated. The traffic jam of visitors that had occurred daily between one and two o'clock and again between six and seven in the evening was eliminated. Visitors felt free to stay for longer or shorter periods than an hour, and many of them reduced the time, knowing that they could return almost at will. The length of the visit was governed by more natural determinants, such as interest, cooperativeness of the patient, rapport, or ward activities, rather than by dutiful compulsion to fill the allotted period or compete with other visitors. With callers coming and going sporadically throughout the day, those patients who had none did not seem so conspicuous.

The new arrangement conveyed to patients, relatives, and staff the feeling that relatives are important to the patient. Those who spent longer periods on the wards learned more about the inner workings of the Hospital, understood the patient's environment better, and transmitted a greater feeling of confidence that persons in the outside community were interested in the patients and the institution. Personnel were presented with more opportunities to observe the relative-patient relationship in action, and subsequently to reorient their handling of patients in the light of this greater knowledge. Some visitors fell naturally into the role of auxiliary personnel, taking over simple functions such as escorting patients to and from occupational therapy, introducing them to social activities, and joining in games and sports. As the participation of relatives increased, it appeared that the contribution of the hospital experience to their education was greater. In the long run this should have a significant effect on community attitudes toward the mentally ill.

Change in Psychiatric Attitude Toward Visitors

In 1863 the eminent American psychiatrist, Isaac Ray, wrote as follows concerning the prevailing view of mental treatment:

> In the hospital, the patient is withdrawn from the countless adverse incidents to which he is elsewhere exposed. He is saved from the advice of good-natured friends, oftener pernicious than salutary, because founded on very imperfect notions of insanity; he is saved from hearing or seeing something every hour calculated to maintain the morbid process which is nourished by what might seem to be the most harmless material; he is saved from all those disagreeable associations between the morbid thoughts and emotions, and the scenes, persons, and objects around him, which serve, in the strongest manner, to perpetuate the mental disturbance. . . . *It is now a well-settled principle, that, to treat the insane with the highest degree of success, the surroundings of the patient should be entirely changed so that he shall see no face nor other object familiar to him in the previous stage of his disease.*[1] [Writer's italics]

This insistence upon a complete break of the patient with his old environment and his contacts with the community is followed by a warning against giving in to the first signs of his desire to return to customary haunts, and by emphasis upon the danger of early release from the hospital. Not only should the patient be given the opportunity to forget all former ties and connections, but said Dr. Ray:

Another duty incumbent on the friends is, to refrain from all

---

[1] Ray, Isaac, *Mental Hygiene*. Ticknor and Fields, Boston, 1863, pp. 322–323.

interference with the medical or moral management of the patient. This should be entrusted without reserve to the physician, and a thorough compliance with his wishes will best promote the desired object. Many a person who would never think of questioning the correctness of the medical treatment, will insist on following his own judgment rather than the physician's, in respect to that most important part of all moral management, the intercourse of the patient with his friends. . . . It is hard to believe, no doubt, that those who are nearly related to the sufferer should refrain from visiting him when he seems to be in most need of comfort and consolation; but a little reflection on the subject will show, that what would be a sacred duty under ordinary circumstances, may be a source of serious mischief here.[1]

Early American psychiatrists saw no therapeutic role for the relatives of mentally ill patients. Conflicts and strains in interpersonal relationships were best left untouched, therapeutic reliance being placed on distraction, formation of new habit patterns, and emotional rest. If the individual's troublesome feelings were not stirred, they would eventually subside and more wholesome emotions would take their place. A pleasant environment and humane contacts would provide the best climate for such healing.

Although many of Ray's ideas have persisted to the present and there is admittedly an insufficient body of factual knowledge on which to build, the trend of child psychiatry with its emphasis on treating child-parent relationships as unity, the opening of the modern mental hospital to public influences, the emphasis upon early discharge and handling of patients as far as possible through outpatient clinics, and the recognition of the therapeutic values of the family, permit us to think more dynamically concerning greater use of relatives both as aids in treatment of the patient and as recipients of treatment efforts. Such a view, drawing upon basic concepts of dynamic psychiatry, emphasizes the importance of disturbed *interpersonal* relationships in the etiology of mental disorders, and the necessity of focusing attention upon the conflicts and strains in such relationships. The touchstone of the modern approach is the

[1] *Ibid.*, pp. 332–333.

"working through" of conflicts rather than their avoidance. The therapeutic process requires in particular the understanding of relationships between patients and relatives, and reeducation of the attitudes of each toward the other. This cannot take place in a vacuum. The emotions and excitations produced by relatives' visits become grist for the therapeutic mill; thus, in the modern hospital it is reasonable according to present conceptions to encourage visiting, to study visitors, and to accept the challenge of the problems of both visitors and patients. In accepting responsibility for the treatment of mentally ill patients we have, in effect, accepted responsibility for education of the family members.

11. Treatment Results

WHAT RESULTS CAN BE EXPECTED from treatment methods such as have been described in this report?[1] Is mental illness an ominous condition that leads to a lifetime of disablement? Or are there remissions and recoveries such as those familiar to medicine and surgery? The spectacle of many large hospitals throughout the country overcrowded with chronic patients, together with the unending pressures for construction of more buildings, leads the public to believe that mental illness is something like cancer but without the blessing of early death. Persons who are psychiatric failures stand out like sore thumbs: they accumulate in custodial hospitals where they live on, in a veritable state of vegetation, their tendency toward chronicity being greatly exaggerated by enforced idleness. Those who are medical failures, on the other hand, often die or go home and are lost to public sight. However, we are beginning to learn that these so-called psychiatric failures are in reality often failures of the custodial system to provide a proper therapeutic environment. Many experienced psychiatrists appreciate the fact that a significant proportion of "chronic" cases could be rehabilitated if the conditions were right. Just how many could respond is not yet known.

One subtle and pernicious factor that has contributed to the pessimistic view of psychiatric illness has been a curious method of reporting hospital statistics. For decades discharges have been reported as a fraction of the total number of patients "in residence" during the course of the year, rather than in relation to the total number of patients admitted each year. In other words, the backlog of under-the-conditions-irrecoverable cases

[1] We gratefully acknowledge the help of Dr. J. Sanbourne Bockoven in preparation of this chapter, which is largely based on his research.

235

has been used again and again to depress the favorable results being obtained in acute cases. Thus, if 170 persons were discharged during the course of a year out of a population of 1,000, the outcome for psychotic illness was considered to be "17 per cent discharges"; whereas the true situation might have been that 170 were discharged out of perhaps 270 admitted, which gives a discharge rate of 63 per cent—a totally different matter. The latter is no idle figure, for we know from Dr. Bockoven's study of the history of mental hospitals that many early institutions, depending essentially on a therapeutic environment and without the advantages of modern somatic treatments, discharged some 60 to 75 per cent of their acute psychotic admissions.

ENCOURAGING RESULTS OF VARIED THERAPEUTIC EFFORTS

When Boston Psychopathic Hospital was largely an institution for rapid diagnosis and disposal of cases, the yearly flow of patients was about 2,400 and the average duration of stay was from ten to twenty days. Figures show that in the 1920's and 1930's committed psychotic patients were discharged to the community at the rate of about 35 for each 100 admitted; the others were sent to the state hospitals for chronic patients. In 1943 began the sharp upward swing of care and treatment, described in earlier chapters, which has continued without interruption. We have seen that during this period physiological treatments, such as electric and insulin shock, lobotomy, and the use of various therapeutic drugs, were intensified. Psychological modes of treatment (psychotherapy, narcoanalysis, and so on) permitted detailed exploration of every facet of the patient's life experience. Recently emphasis on ward improvement has greatly increased with the realization of the potential effect of social factors and of the hospital social system on recovery. Twelve years ago the interest of the medical staff was mostly in the art of refined diagnosis and classification—"learned lucubrations upon symptomatological minutiae," as someone has aptly said. Now a dynamic element has been introduced, that of managing the social milieu as well as the psychological and physiological, with all personnel participating in the process.

What has been the statistical result? In 1953 the yearly flow of patients was around 900 and the average duration of their stay in the Hospital between eighty and ninety days. Intensive treatment had necessitated longer stay and fewer cases; yet more patients were treated, more improved, and more were discharged than before. The trend toward rapidly increasing discharges became noticeable as early as 1947 when the intense therapeutic efforts began to pay dividends. By 1953 the rate of discharge to the community had risen to between 80 and 85 per cent. Significant, moreover, is the fact that discharges had gone up in all diagnostic categories—affective, schizophrenic, and organic—suggesting that no diagnostic label necessarily indicated that a patient had a black future. So great has been the pessimism about mental illness both within the medical profession and among the laity that even many psychiatric colleagues viewed this discharge rate of 80 to 85 per cent, based on less than three months of hospitalization, with amazement or skepticism. Often they declared that the persons admitted must have been less ill than many other mental patients or were permitted to leave before any large degree of recovery had been achieved.

Catatonia Fades Away

These figures for discharges do not tell the whole story of treatment efforts. Hence, before following the patients into the community we wish to pause for a moment to look at their improved behavior within the Hospital as the physical and social aspects of the ward were improved. Reference has been made earlier to the fact that episodes of explosive violence and outbursts of hyperkinetic activity, the so-called schizophrenic "acting out," began to disappear with the elimination of ward "evils" and the substitution of social programs. As the environment fostered less preoccupation with psychotic anxieties and fantasies and more communication with the external world, we noticed a most remarkable change in the patients. The clinical condition, catatonia, was fading away! This extraordinary occurrence deserves a word of explanation.

Catatonic schizophrenia denotes a set of symptoms characterized by immobility, bizarre posturing, or repetitive motor
behavior, that not infrequently alternates with episodes of cha-
otic excitement. Those patients who pose for long hours or lie
on the floor rolled up like a ball, who hop endlessly upon one
leg, or push a broom monotonously up and down the corridor,
are usually diagnosed as catatonic. They often have mute, uncommunicative periods lasting for weeks and months during
which, however, they may be sharply appreciative of what is
going on around them. A kind of plastic obedience is sometimes
observed in which the patient can be molded passively from
one posture to another; this is called "cerea flexibilitas" or waxy
flexibility.

We believe that such patients are especially sensitive to the
interpersonal atmosphere of the ward. There is much to suggest
that muteness and repetitive behavior are defenses against a
"threatening" environment. Their immobile, cataleptic states
may be considered "frozen fear." Making the admission procedure more humane; doing away with seclusion, packs, and
tubs; bringing the patient as soon as possible into an active,
interesting social milieu; and constantly striving to increase his
satisfactions and security, all probably helped to reduce the
trend toward catatonia. If the condition is a social reaction to
the environment, as we now consider likely, the changed attitudes of the ward staffs may have been of the utmost importance. As personnel became more aware of their own hostilities
and fears that prevented their knowing and liking patients, and
as tensions created by these hostilities and fears were resolved,
it may be assumed that the patients found less necessity for
displaying catatonic characteristics.

Relationship of Hospital to Community

When the treatment results became known and patient behavior was obviously improved, the entire staff of the Hospital
reacted with enthusiasm, and through them both relatives and
patients began to feel the spark of success. Formerly the dark
cloud of chronicity had hung over the heads of everyone when

the vast majority of patients were being transferred to large "custodial" or "continued treatment" hospitals. Now there was the challenge to bring every patient during his hospitalization up to the level where he could, somehow, be managed in the community.

Closer ties were established with the community through a more active department of social service, and particularly through a subtle change in attitude of the physicians. The latter began to look upon the home environment as frequently therapeutic in itself, and, being more inclined than formerly to trust the capacity of patients to respond to a therapeutic setting, they often permitted an earlier return to the community. Since patients behaved better in the Hospital and therefore appeared to be less socially deviant, barriers were lowered and they were occasionally allowed to go outside the Hospital, just as they were given more freedom inside it. The staff members began to question the finality of their own judgment in the matter of readiness for discharge. When relatives or friends pleaded for the release of a patient, provided there were fairly adequate facilities for his care, he was given a chance to try the outer environment. Numerous instructive examples came to our attention of patients who were expected to do poorly in the community or to get into trouble, but proved able to adjust and to develop in a wholesome direction. They indicated that the psychiatrist was not necessarily the best judge of patients' rehabilitation potential in the community setting. The lines between the Hospital and the community began to be slightly less clearly drawn, and movement became freer and easier in both directions.

Attempts made to establish greater rapport between home and Hospital have already been mentioned, especially the extension of visiting hours, and the developing conception of relatives as a possible part of the therapeutic team. The large increase in facilities for outpatient care that took place during this period made it possible to follow discharged patients in a more careful and orderly manner. This culminated in 1952 in dividing the outpatient department into a "community clinic" for the care and treatment of persons who had once been committed to the Hospital, and a general outpatient department, the Southard Clinic, for patients who were not sick enough to require hospitalization. This enabled further concentration upon problems of early and smooth return to the community, and mobilization of community resources to help released patients to remain there. Patients were offered the opportunity of joining group therapy classes before discharge, and afterward they could continue to be treated in the same group under the guidance of a psychiatrist in the community clinic. If the patient was not ready for complete return to the community but gave evidence of being able to adjust to some areas of normal living, a flexible plan was adopted of permitting him to work during the day and sleep in the Hospital at night; or if sleeping facilities were adequate in the community but the steadying influence of the hospital environment appeared necessary, he could return for a prescribed number of hours to take part in the Hospital Day Program. These arrangements have worked well in many cases, and are recommended as helpful variations in the traditional system of discharge which is often much too rigid and inflexible to fit the needs of all patients.

During hospitalization considerable attention was given to a work program for each patient. It was not enough for him to become free of psychotic symptoms and to learn to get along better with others, or even to begin to enjoy the numerous social activities at hand. The set goal was for each person to develop his "work muscles," so that as soon as possible he might become a contributing, earning member of society's industrial team. Too often the patient was brought by intensive efforts to a point of being psychologically symptom-free, only to find that after the many weeks of hospitalization it was very difficult to adapt suddenly to an eight-hour workday. In other cases he had spent his time at relaxing diversions, without turning his hand to the trade which was to be his job. These considerations, which would have been obvious to any rehabilitation expert, had to be built painfully into our treatment program. The resources of the various departments were surveyed to make available jobs that might be similar to the patient's own occupation. This meant trusting patients to supervision by the hospital personnel of the laboratory, research area, record room, carpentry and painting shops, electrician's shop, and so on, who would otherwise be remote from treatment. Both personnel and patients were instructed in the philosophy that work is therapy —a necessary conception since, in the absence of pay, work may be viewed as an unfair imposition upon patients during their period of loss of civil rights. It was emphasized that work therapy must be encouraged by some reward system; that there should be tangible evidence that work was increased, decreased, or changed on a therapeutic basis; and that the patient should not be subordinated to the convenience or needs of the Hospital.

LONG-TERM PROGNOSIS OF ACUTE PSYCHOTIC PATIENTS

A five-year study by Dr. Bockoven of what happened to the first 100 patients committed to Boston Psychopathic Hospital after June 30, 1946, gives much needed information on the long-term prognosis of psychiatric illness.[1] As soon as possible after admission intensive treatment was instituted, individualized for each patient. The outcome of this treatment was that 70 were discharged to the community and 29 were transferred to other mental hospitals for continued care. One patient died. The average hospital stay was seventy-five days. Follow-up at the end of the first year, as seen from the accompanying table, revealed that 72 of the original 100 persons were in the community and 20 were in a Massachusetts hospital. Four had left Massachusetts and hence were not studied further. Four had died. At the end of the second year the number in the community was 76, and that figure remained substantially unchanged at the end of the three succeeding years. The statistics further reveal that 45 of the original group were not readmitted to a hospital during the five-year period. The study shows, therefore, that the long-term prognosis for acute psychotic patients who received treat-

[1] Bockoven, J. Sanbourne, and Harry C. Solomon, "Five Year Follow-up Study of One Hundred Patients Committed to the Boston Psychopathic Hospital," *New England Journal of Medicine*, vol. 251, July 15, 1954, pp. 81–85.

TABLE 4. STATUS AT END OF FIVE SUCCESSIVE YEARS OF THE
FIRST 100 PATIENTS COMMITTED TO BOSTON PSYCHO-
PATHIC HOSPITAL AFTER JUNE 30, 1946

	At end of				
Status of patient	1 year	2 years	3 years	4 years	5 years
Out of state	4	4	4	4	4
Dead	4	7	8	8	8
Living and in Massachusetts	92	89	88	88	88
Total	100	100	100	100	100
Of those living and in Massachusetts: In hospital:					
Not discharged	7	5	3	3	2
Discharged and readmitted	13	8	9	8	10
	20	13	12	11	12
In community:					
Discharged and not readmitted	54	51	49	46	45
Discharged after readmission	18	25	27	31	31
	72	76	76	77	76
Per cent in community	78	85	86	88	86

ment was relatively good in 1946. We believe it would be better
now.

Another fact shown by this survey was that although the patients spent an average of 18 per cent of their time during the
five years in a mental hospital, most of it was accumulated by a
small group of 10 or 12, who formed the hard core of "irrecover-
able" cases.[1] They had relatively few remissions or remained
improved for only brief periods.

Particularly interesting is the difference in the length of hospitalization for women and men. The former spent an average
of 27 out of a possible 260 weeks in a hospital; the latter an
average of 70 weeks. At the five-year mark 81 per cent of the
women were in the community and 70 per cent of the men.
These figures may reflect dissimilarity in recovery potential, but

[1] Considerable progress has been made recently in identifying early in their
clinical course the "malignant" cases that resist treatment, thus clearing the
way for intensive research and therapeutic effort upon this least hopeful group.
Experience indicates that 30 to 40 per cent of such chronic cases may be returned to the community following proper surgical procedures on the frontal
lobes of the brain, and that long-term rehabilitation can do much for the happi-
ness of the remainder.

we think it more likely that they reflect differences in social role and hence level of performance expected of men and women before discharge is contemplated. Society has cast men in the role of breadwinner and head of the family; women, on the other hand, are more readily acceptable in dependent roles unless they have responsibility for young children or are obliged to contribute significantly to the family budget.

LEVEL OF ADJUSTMENT OF DISCHARGED PATIENTS

The preceding discussion is based upon the simplest test of change in the patient's status, namely, whether he is in the hospital or in the community. We should, however, like to know a good deal more; for example, whether he is a burden to family members or is self-sustaining, whether his adjustment is a source of satisfaction to himself and his relatives, and so on. Much detailed evaluation of the patient's life in the community is necessary in order to appraise properly the contribution of the hospital to his welfare. Dr. Bockoven and Miss Pandiscio have made a fruitful beginning with a study of the social adjustment of 106 patients who were in the community three years after commitment to Boston Psychopathic Hospital.[1] They have paid especial attention to the level of satisfaction expressed by the patient and his family in regard to his occupational adjustment, family life, and community activities. According to their method of evaluation, if a patient was considered "satisfactory" in any of these three areas, it was likely that in it he was living up to the average expectations of his economic and social group.

Surprisingly, both patients and their families generally felt that occupational adjustment was "satisfactory." Eighty per cent of the former patients were working, a large majority full time, and 74 per cent were financially self-sustaining or nearly so. Although "satisfied" with the jobs, the respondents on the whole were dissatisfied with the patients' economic situation,

[1] Bockoven, J. Sanbourne, Anna R. Pandiscio, and Harry C. Solomon, *Social Adjustment of Patients in the Community Three Years After Commitment to the Boston Psychopathic Hospital,* unpublished manuscript; Barrabee, Paul, Edna Barrabee, and Jacob E. Finesinger, "A Normative Social Adjustment Scale," in preparation for publication in *American Journal of Psychiatry.*

for during their hospitalization they had incurred debts that now had to be paid. The longer the hospitalization, the larger the debt faced upon discharge and consequently the greater the economic stress. This underlines once again the necessity for prompt and intensive treatment directed toward early discharge from the hospital; anything less inevitably adds to the patient's financial burden and retards his rehabilitation in many ways.

Although occupational adjustment was "satisfactory," family adjustment was considered on the whole "barely adequate" and community adjustment was generally regarded as "almost unsatisfactory." The differences in satisfaction expressed in these three areas reflect in large measure the way in which Boston Psychopathic Hospital is now organized for service. An extensive amount of social work assistance is given the patient in relation to occupational needs. Preparations made for his return to the community, begun on admission and continued until discharge, include attempts to retrain him in particular job skills or to find new skills; counseling in job placement; and freedom to look for or undertake work in the community prior to release. Psychological support provided him by the outpatient department after he leaves the Hospital is frequently an additional important factor in his finding and holding a job.

Family problems also now come in for intensive scrutiny by psychiatrists and social workers as part of the analysis of interpersonal tensions which is so much the focus of psychiatric service today. Not infrequently, a pattern of interlocking difficulties involving several members of the family is found, and domestic discord may be handled by referring other members of the family for outpatient therapy during the time of the patient's hospitalization. When he is discharged, psychiatrists continue to work on the family problems as a necessary aspect of any enduring solution of psychological conflicts. Perhaps if more intensive and extensive outpatient help could be provided beyond that which is presently given, this area of the patient's life would improve to the "satisfactory" level.

"Community adjustment," as used in the study, refers to the patient's ability to relate himself to persons outside the family, make use of public and private facilities, and participate in neighborhood organizations and activities. The "almost unsatisfactory" adjustment to the community reported by patients and their families seems to be correlated in part with the failure of the hospital to emphasize the need for patients' improvement in their community relationships, and reflects the relative lack of outpatient resources for such an undertaking.

A typical pattern of mental illness is often withdrawal from recreational and social activities, followed by occupational difficulties and cessation of work, followed in turn by exacerbation of family tensions. These, added to economic problems, may culminate in commitment to a psychiatric hospital. On the other hand, the process of rehabilitation begins with cementing of family ties, tested by the patient's weekend visits to his home. It continues by his finding a job for which he has already geared himself through work in the hospital, showing improvement in his economic condition, and finally making a reentry into social and recreational activities in the community. The last step toward complete recovery appears to be the most crucial and difficult.

Hostility toward and mistrust of the mentally sick individual whom many persons do not accept as a full-fledged member of society, and the residues of his illness that make it difficult for the average patient to form closer alliances with his neighbors, are important factors which contribute to poor community integration. Another large factor, however, is undoubtedly the hospital's lack of resources and techniques for preparing patients as effectively for community relations as for occupational and family adjustments. One of the major challenges of the future, as Boston Psychopathic Hospital sees it, will be to provide the patient with continuity between a varied and stimulating social and recreational life in the institution, and a similar type of experience in the community. Collaboration between many kinds of "half-way homes," ex-patient clubs, and community organizations and the personnel and facilities of the hospital will be a necessary element in helping the patient develop deeper roots in society.

PART TWO

EXPERIMENTS IN WARD PATIENT CARE
AT BEDFORD VETERANS ADMINISTRATION HOSPITAL

RICHARD H. YORK, Ph.D.

12. History and Postwar Changes

BEDFORD V.A. HOSPITAL, it will be recalled, had already made appreciable changes before it was invited by the Russell Sage Project to join the experiment in improvement of patient care. As a consequence, the Project was integrated with what had been begun to such a degree that it was not always possible later to differentiate between gains attributable to policies of the Hospital and to the special undertaking. The experiment should be viewed, therefore, as a dynamic process growing out of changes already instituted and, although focused upon certain selected wards, affecting further changes on those wards and to a lesser extent in other parts of the Hospital. In order to view this interplay between administrative policies and Project decisions and the resulting action, some detailed examination is first essential of the early history of Bedford, its reorganization after 1945 with the accompanying stresses of transition, and the resulting social structure.[1]

DEVELOPMENTS PRIOR TO 1945

Direct hospital care of disabled veterans began in this country in 1919 when those institutions that had lately been used by the War Department were placed temporarily under the charge of the United States Public Health Service. Four years afterward the Veterans Bureau (which became the Veterans Administration in 1930) assumed medical responsibility for

[1] Because Boston Psychopathic Hospital was not requested to undertake specific experiments of its own as part of the Project, the foregoing presentation by Dr. Greenblatt has been primarily a historical report of developments in that institution since 1943. Parts II and III are different in purpose and nature. Their purpose is to analyze the experiments undertaken, the methods used, and the results achieved in improving patient care. Only such historical material is presented as appears essential for the reader to understand the setting in which these experiments were initiated.

men with specific disabilities that had been established as incurred during war service. In 1924 the Congress enacted legislation to make provision for treatment for veterans of all wars, and also for other than service-connected disabilities provided that beds were available in government hospitals and the veterans were unable to pay for private service. This enactment necessitated the building of many more hospitals, among them the one at Bedford opened in 1928. It was to be an exclusively neuropsychiatric institution the principal function of which, like that of almost all mental hospitals of the time, was to provide custodial and protective care. Ten buildings had been constructed around a large oval. Every building consisted of four wards, each of which was designed to accommodate 45 to 80 patients.

Between the time when the federal government assumed responsibility for the hospitalization of former service men and America's entrance into World War II, the Veterans Administration attempted to institute more active treatment for its psychiatric patients. Medical schools, for example, were requested to participate in programs of teaching and patient care. However, the patients were increasing in age and chronicity and the commonly held psychiatric opinion prevailed that such persons were essentially untreatable since their illness was thought irreversible. As a consequence, the medical schools concluded that the neuropsychiatric hospitals did not provide the variety of clinical conditions necessary for residency training. Not only was this philosophy of defeat widespread, but only a negligible number of psychiatrists had been trained in the new somatic treatments that began in the late 1930's to prove successful in acute psychosis.

During the war the difficulties seemed almost insurmountable in the veterans' hospitals. Besides losing personnel of all categories to the service, Bedford received increasing numbers of psychiatric casualties directly from the armed forces. At times the Hospital had more than 200 patients in excess of its capacity; they had to be provided with beds in corridors and day rooms. Soldiers were sent to act as attendants. Although they were a help, many intensely disliked the assignment and the skeleton staff that worked twelve hours a day only to do the most essential tasks had little time to give them either attention or training. Often they slept on duty or otherwise broke rules and regulations that did not leave them open to court martial, but that they hoped would result in their being transferred to assignments not involving contact with psychiatric patients.

Just at this time articles "exposing" such conditions in the V.A. hospitals began to appear throughout the country. Since the full background of this grave emergency was rarely presented, these articles were unfair and the criticisms were not entirely constructive. They did, however, arouse the public and the Congress to action. National interest in service to veterans was greatly enlarged, and federal legislation and increased appropriations permitted extensive reorganization and expansion both of the Veterans Administration and of its hospitals. As a consequence, this federal agency has been able to provide notable leadership to the postwar trend of modernizing and vitalizing hospital psychiatry.

ADMINISTRATIVE ASPECTS OF INSTITUTIONAL CHANGE

One of the most immediate benefits of an enlarged budget and planning for expansion and improvement on a nationwide scale by the Veterans Administration was the provision made for increase of all categories of personnel at Bedford. Between 1945 and 1952 the staff of the Hospital more than doubled, as shown by the accompanying table. The greatest numerical growth was in the nurses and psychiatric aides, which permitted adequate coverage of the wards for the first time in the institution's history. Quite as significant, however, was the upbuilding of those services often designated the ancillary therapies. Occupational, recreational, corrective, manual arts, and educational therapy, along with social work and clinical psychology, were given potentially much larger roles than they had had formerly. Even volunteers from interested community groups were encouraged to participate in larger numbers in "special services" which foster or bring to the Hospital every kind of

TABLE 5. PROFESSIONAL PERSONNEL OF BEDFORD VETERANS ADMINISTRATION HOSPITAL IN 1945 AND 1952

	1945	1952
Administrative and staff physicians	14ᵃ	24
Physicians in residency programs	—	8
Consulting physicians	2	36
Graduate nurses	58	100
Nursing students	—	37
Ward psychiatric aides	226ᵃ	404
Social workers	5	11
Clinical psychologists	1	3
Psychology students	—	11
Occupational therapists	1	6
Occupational therapy aides	5	11
Physical therapists	2	4
Physical therapy aides	4	4
Corrective, manual arts, and educational therapists	1	10
Staff of special servicesᵇ	6	10
Total	325	679

ᵃ In 1945 seven physicians and 78 psychiatric aides were army personnel assigned to the Hospital.
ᵇ Special services had also 11 volunteer workers in 1945 and 235 in 1952.

recreation and entertainment from motion pictures, picnics, and baseball to Christmas parties, and which supply the institution with many amenities such as games, soft drinks, candy, and cigarettes. The salaried staff of special services was increased, moreover, to facilitate planning and supervision of these wide-flung activities.

Equally important probably in the improvement of patient care was the introduction of teaching programs at Bedford. Under the aegis of a "deans' committee," composed of representatives of the three medical schools in the Boston area, the Hospital was made a center for the training of resident psychiatrists. The director of the newly created position of educational services concerned himself not only with their preparation, but also with programs of lectures, obtaining of medical consultants, and introduction of research designed to stimulate interest and maintain high professional standards. Similarly in nursing, an educational director was appointed who, with her assistants, was responsible for the training of attendants and affiliate nursing students and for continuing in-service preparation of graduate nurses. Clinical psychology, too, became a teaching specialty and a group of graduate students were assigned to the Hospital for part of their training.

In addition to these encouraging developments was the return of Dr. Winthrop Adams, the manager (or superintendent or director as he would be called in other than V.A. hospitals), and the appointment of Dr. Jay L. Hoffman as chief of professional services. Unfortunately, Dr. Adams had had to be away from Bedford during the last years of the war when conditions were most difficult, and when various members of the staff found themselves scapegoats for unfortunate occurrences that should have been attributed to the almost insuperable problems encountered. With his return and the arrival of Dr. Hoffman morale rose perceptibly, according to reports of staff members. One of the first tasks of the chief of professional services was to attempt to allay the extreme sensitivity of hospital personnel to criticism by relatives and organized veterans' groups. Many of the criticisms were leveled against the older custodial system that had been widely publicized. Some relatives, however, were opposed to the very changes in policy designed to improve that system, so accustomed had they become to the former hospital practices. "It seemed at times," commented Dr. Hoffman, "as if the wishes of these two groups— misguided though they might be—did more to determine hospital policy than the true needs of the patients. Here it became necessary to listen to all criticism, to accept that which was justified, but to support the staff firmly in the face of criticism which was not justified." Happily it was discovered that these groups were surprisingly responsive to a new policy "when it was explained to them with self-assurance, without hostility, and without rancor."

To reduce negative pressures from outside the Hospital required this straightforward administrative leadership. The most significant factor that enabled the manager and chief of professional services to take a confident, definite stand was the simultaneous development within the institution of a constructive, forward-looking program around which to reorient the feelings and reintegrate the interests of the community. The growing reputation of the V.A. Medical Service, supported as it was by local medical schools and distinguished consultants, did much at Bedford, as elsewhere, to win acceptance and support from relatives and the public.

Another early task of the administration was the effort to alleviate one of the principal causes of stress among ward personnel, which had resided in prewar practices and been intensified during the war. This cause was the harsh inquiry instituted for the purpose of establishing the blame of some member or members of the staff whenever any unusual incident occurred such as a patient "elopement" (escape), suicide, or serious fight. Speaking for himself and the manager, Dr. Hoffman described the new administrative attitude and its consequences as follows:

> It was first necessary to convey our attitude to the staff: that we were not exclusively concerned with establishing *culpability*, that we were concerned with establishing *responsibility* without incrimination, that frequently there was no culpability although there was always responsibility. By establishing responsibility we hoped to avoid unnecessary recurrences of undesirable events and this was of more importance to us than punishing the culpable ones. It was not easy to get this point across to the staff. They heard the words, but it was not until the administration had repeatedly demonstrated in action that they meant them, that the staff believed the words. When such belief did take place, there was evident a critical change in hospital practice.

Because attendants were closest to patients by virtue of their ward duties and were the personal instrument of custody and protection, they had been the most frequent scapegoats when unfortunate incidents took place, even though such incidents were usually beyond their control. In order to avoid reprimand, they had sometimes used harsh measures to keep patients in line, as will be illustrated in the next section of this chapter. Nevertheless, the chief of professional services found little evidence of physical abuse upon his arrival in 1946. Whenever such abuse did become known, Dr. Hoffman has said that "the reaction of administration was prompt, firm, and uncompromising." The few stupid, uninterested, and potentially sadistic members of the ward staff were promptly dismissed. More emphasis was placed, however, upon retention of good personnel; the careful screening of new employees; and the attempt to help ward staff to *understand* the questionable behavior of their patients, thus greatly reducing any tendency they might have to punish or intimidate them.

The postwar decision of the Veterans Administration to give far more autonomy than formerly to their hospitals in administrative matters and policy-making, proved to be highly important in fostering developments at Bedford. Inherent in the operation of custodial-protective institutions had been a hierarchy of authority that had sharply limited local decisions and also initiative. The modification of this hierarchical structure to further the therapeutic goals of active treatment was responsible for much of the success that the Hospital was to experience. In summarizing the process, the chief of professional services noted that "the increased authority given the local administration was gradually reflected in the delegation of greater authority to ward personnel and encouragement of their active participation in the management of their own wards." Eventually freed from a multitude of rules and regulations, they could exercise initiative "with extraordinary effectiveness," under the immediate direction of the ward psychiatrist, in the organization of the ward's social structure. "Great strides were taken in the integration of the several groups of ward personnel, and each group could be encouraged to participate without the sometimes stifling effect of the vested interests of the ward and hospital hierarchy."

CHANGES IN PATIENT MANAGEMENT AND TREATMENT METHODS

As in virtually every other mental hospital, Bedford had been accustomed to use routinely many devices to restrain, sedate, and guard patients in order to keep them from injuring themselves, other persons, or property. Because Dr. Greenblatt has written about such devices at length in Part I of this book, it is sufficient to note here that in 1946 they included at Bedford sheet and camisole restraints, seclusion, drugs, hydrotherapy tubs, and constant, individualized supervision known as "specialing" a patient. In that year the total number of hours spent by patients in physical restraints was 11,665. Between 1948 and 1950 their use was sharply reduced, until in the middle of the latter year the chief of professional services ordered all mechanical restraints removed from the wards except the surgical, but suggested that one camisole be kept in the chief nurse's office. In 1951 only 135 hours were spent in restraints, and those were almost entirely in instances of preparation for, or recovery from, surgery where impulsive moves could have serious consequences.

Particularly significant was the solution of the problem of management of "suicidal" patients, since they had been thought to present a particularly difficult problem. When Dr. David M. Banen joined the staff in 1947 he found two entire wards with a bed capacity of 200 assigned to patients who were considered to be suicidally inclined.[1] "Every patient who looked dejected, cried unaccountably, put his fists through a pane of glass, or said that he didn't care whether he lived or died," wrote Dr. Banen, was transferred to one of these two wards. Some 60 of these 200 patients were under special and very restrictive precautions in three dormitories set aside for them exclusively, and many were physically restrained. In one dormitory of 35 beds four attendants were constantly on duty. Under the leadership of the chief of professional services and with a staff that was encouraged to try new procedures, Dr. Banen closed one dormitory, then a second, and finally the third. Thereafter these patients were cared for like all others on the two wards. It is interesting to note that when the question of more humane management of this group was first discussed, the consensus of the staff was that architectural alterations in the ward would have to be made. The change was accomplished without them.

A detailed analysis was made of 23 suicides that had occurred in the past quarter of a century. Eleven were by patients in the

---

[1] "Suicide by Psychotics," *Bedford Research*, vol. 4, November, 1953, pp. 1–8.

Hospital and 12 by those on the one-year "trial visit" that is required before a patient is officially discharged. As yet, in Dr. Banen's opinion, there are no reliable indications for predicting suicide in psychotic patients. Hence, although the frequent placing of patients on formalized suicidal precautions was abolished, there was no lessening of the precautions themselves. What was emphasized was "the universality of the suicidal potential in any patient."

Aside from seclusion, the use of which was not attacked until 1952 when it was dramatically and almost completely wiped out, the most pronounced negative aspects of patient care were eliminated. No one should conclude, as Dr. Greenblatt has emphasized in connection with similar events at Boston Psychopathic Hospital, that any such drastic changes can be accomplished without much preparation of ward staff and without the administration giving them wholehearted support. Specific steps taken at Bedford to provide such preparation and support will be described later. It should be noted here, however, that more careful examination of the nature and meaning of patients' acts indicated that much of the grossly disturbed and disturbing behavior was more a manner of participating in an excessively restrictive and depriving hospital environment than an inherent part of psychotic illness. Most emotional outbursts appeared to be temporary, impulsive reactions of fear, anger, or overactivity, and were essentially self-limited when not aggravated by intervention of personnel. Attendants had been so afraid of incurring criticism for any injury or damage done during such flare-ups that they had tried to minimize the chances of reprimand by restraining patients who showed any likelihood of an outburst. Once the administration ceased to blame personnel for incidents, and instead emphasized understanding the situational context in which incidents occurred, the process of eliminating restraints was greatly facilitated.

While the process was under way, sedative medication was heavily relied on supposedly to keep patients quiet. This use of sedation was later considered by the medical staff to have been more of a supportive aid for the personnel involved in the change than for the patients, since the latter were found in most instances not to have needed it for long.

Among the positive undertakings initiated was a marked increase in active medical treatment. Insulin and electric shock were reintroduced and used extensively. Interestingly enough both had been begun in 1938 and 1941 respectively, when two of the psychiatrists had completed courses in the administration of these somatic therapies. Because the patients were almost exclusively the older group from World War I, however, contraindications were so numerous that these treatments were discontinued. With many of the younger, more acute patients from the second war the results were highly successful. Psychotherapy had attracted the interest of most of the psychiatrists and residents who joined the staff after 1946, and they were encouraged to use it with individual patients who were most likely to benefit. Among the consultants visiting the Hospital was Dr. Elvin V. Semrad, a specialist in group psychotherapy, who focused attention upon it as a particularly promising therapeutic technique for reaching more patients numerically than could be reached by individual psychotherapy.

Reference has been made to the growth in personnel associated with the ancillary therapies that were subsequently to play an increasingly important role. Most readers will be acquainted with the vital functions served by social service and clinical psychology in psychiatric hospitals. But many persons are probably unacquainted with the variety and wealth of other services contributing to treatment that are provided by the Veterans Administration to its neuropsychiatric, and also with some modification to its general hospitals. Hence, a brief description must be given of the five sections of occupational, physical, educational, corrective, and manual arts therapy that comprise the Department of Physical Medicine and Rehabilitation (hereafter referred to as the rehabilitation department). The general objective of all sections is the same, but the units differ in specialized techniques and media through which they work with the patient. The predominant goal of these therapies is socialization or resocialization: helping patients develop self-esteem and personal expression, with mastery of those social skills required for a more mature, satisfying life in society. Various levels or areas of socialization are the concern of different sections. A mute, muscularly tense, frightened patient, for example, will be helped by a corrective therapist through relaxing exercises and sympathetic personal relationships to develop initial trust in others. At a later stage this same patient will learn to work with other persons perhaps through a group project in occupational therapy, or he may learn a trade in manual arts therapy. Any of these sections, moreover, may be used to stimulate underactive or attempt to quiet overactive patients.

Another function of the rehabilitation department that is shared by every unit is helping patients with problems of daily living, including personal hygiene and appearance as well as more general aspects of behavior. Emphasis is placed upon assisting the individual to become aware of the effect of his own appearance and behavior on others as well as their evaluation of him. In whatever activity he is engaged he learns to understand acceptable limits of social participation.

Each section has its own special facilities and methods for achieving these goals. In occupational therapy major and minor crafts and the encouragement of individualistic creative expression are the focus of attention. Pottery-making, leather work, and drawing are found to engage many patients. At Bedford occupational therapy has the further responsibility of placing those men in hospital "industries," such as farm, laundry, kitchen, engineering and maintenance, who will supposedly benefit from work and work habits more nearly resembling those of the community. They are followed and their success periodically evaluated. For the specialized crafts and trades that manual arts therapy represents, there are woodworking, machine, tailoring, shoe-repairing, upholstery, and printing shops, and individuals may learn as highly skilled work as jewelry-making or watch repair. This section is primarily concerned with preparing patients for jobs outside the hospital and with helping them develop responsible attitudes toward such jobs. Educational therapy, as its name indicates, is concerned with general education and the development of intellectual and vocational interests. Teaching begins on as elementary a level as reading, writing, and arithmetic; includes such vocational skills as typewriting; and at its highest level makes provision for work that will receive college credit. Through the instrumentality of this section large numbers of veterans have received grammar or high school diplomas from the public school system.

Physical therapy includes hydrotherapy, which at Bedford now relies heavily on the warm water swimming pool for relaxing and quieting disturbed patients. Various heat treatments are also available. The section concentrates its attention primarily on specific disabilities of parts of the body. It is supplied with instruments for testing nerves and muscles, it retrains patients in the use of muscles, and teaches them the use of supportive devices such as crutches and braces. The section of corrective therapy emphasizes gymnasium activities and utilizes much equipment, including a rowing machine, punching bag, stationary bicycle, and medicine ball.

With the increase from 13 to 35 therapists and their assistants between 1945 and 1952, the rehabilitation department was considered to have sufficient personnel to extend individual or group activities to approximately a thousand patients. However, many and serious difficulties, which will be noted in Chapter 16, were involved in integrating the efforts of the department with those of others that were also concerned with therapy and patient care.

13. The Changing Social Structure of the Hospital

THE FOLLOWING CHAPTERS about Bedford V.A. Hospital are concerned in considerable part with the social structure of that institution and its effect upon patient care. The Russell Sage Project focused major attention on possible structural changes that could be made for the purpose of benefiting patients. A more systematic examination of what needed to be done plus the motivation created by the "action research" resulted in many modifications that will be reported in Chapters 15 and 16. No evaluation of their significance is possible, however, unless one is acquainted with the pattern that existed in its early years or with the profound changes that were achieved after 1946. These alterations laid the base that permitted further significant advances in early 1952, which in turn were built upon by the two-year ward experiments that began almost immediately.

SOCIAL STRUCTURE PRIOR TO 1946

Like almost all other large psychiatric hospitals, whether state or federal, the social structure of Bedford was long static and rigidly autocratic. Perhaps it had the added disadvantage, which state hospitals escaped, of having inherited elements of autocracy from the army out of which the Veterans Administration grew. During World War II it was directly subjected to military influence when the army assigned both physicians and attendants to the Hospital to supplement gravely depleted staffs. Before describing the structural pattern that existed from 1928 to 1946, and that appears in retrospect to have been extremely restrictive in its rigidity, it should be recalled that the social structure of any institution is largely implicit. Fundamental standards, attitudes, and practices prevailing at any one time are generally accepted uncritically with little awareness of the degree to which they may limit creativity in ideas or spontaneity in action. Just as years hence we shall find that many now favored practices were barriers to patient welfare and staff efficiency, so in reviewing this brief statement of Bedford, we need to bear in mind that it sincerely believed it was striving to give the best care available to patients.

For nearly twenty years a sharply defined hierarchy of staff and staff-patient relationships prevailed, built of almost universally understood, unchanging, and unchangeable ordering of custodial and protective care. Authority for all administrative and clinical matters was exclusively vested in the "top management," with specific responsibilities and roles prescribed for each successive level: physician, nurse, attendant, patient. At each level members of the staff were responsible and subordinate to those on the next higher level, while simultaneously enforcing rules and procedures applicable to those on the next lower level. Since patients were at the bottom of the hierarchical structure, they were in a position to fare very badly unless extenuating circumstances improved their lot. Communications moved in one direction—orders, decisions, and "the word" went from the top down. Major regulations governing patient management and staff relations were fixed, and could not be questioned by ward personnel or patients because these two largest groups had least status within the power structure.

Physicians were relatively few in number, and they were excessively involved in rules and procedures and unending paper work. They were the only persons considered capable of taking responsibility for such varied administrative details as receiving money from relatives for patients or signing affidavits for patients' belongings kept in the possession of the Hospital. As one physician summarized this former aspect of his work, "Anything considered to require an I.Q. of over 80 had to be done by a doctor." Sunday medical duty was described as a "nightmare," since only one physician was available on the day when most relatives came to Bedford. Often a hundred persons wished to see him about administrative matters, obtain information about the patient visited, or complain about the care provided. Responsibility even for simple decisions weighed heavily on the medical staff and much time was spent in reaching a conclusion. The question of transferring a patient to another ward involved as much deliberation then as does a decision concerning brain surgery or discharging a patient now. All the physicians would meet to ponder the desirability of moving one person. Generally unanimous agreement was required. Paradoxically, the professional group with highest status and authority in the Hospital themselves had little leeway or independence in exercising individual judgment.

Practices designed to assure security and allow patients little range of movement or selfmanagement consumed the hours on duty of the nurses. They supervised the attendants, recorded the frequent counts of patients, checked to make sure doors were locked and patients quiet. The greater part of their time was spent merely in preventing "incidents," close guarding and management of patients in various restraints, and doing everything for patients that the latter were considered incapable of doing safely. Although responsible for the administration of the wards, head nurses were not in a position to ask questions of, or make suggestions to, a physician. One nurse said of this climate of opinion, "If you once asked a doctor to clarify a question about a patient or dared make a suggestion, you got such a glance in response that you knew better than to try again." This resulted in part from the fact that the individual physician himself did not have sufficient authority to make decisions. In turn his superiors, the hospital's administrators, had been given little leeway by the Veterans Administration, and they had almost no support from the community or professional opinion in changing procedures and attitudes. Thus, the circuit was completely closed and the situation stabilized, as in practically all other large psychiatric hospitals at that time.

The role of the attendant was succinctly described by a man who had held such a position at Bedford for many years. "He was the keeper, looked on as such by his patients. He reported only unusual, disturbed or destructive behavior, and expected the nurse to prescribe things for him to do. He was told little about the patients, though he would have liked to know more." Since only "pathological" patient behavior was reported upward from the ward, constructive expressions were neglected and all behavior tended to be assessed from a negative perspective. Almost no one conceived of the possibility that there were aspects of deviant behavior that represented positive strivings or reasonable protests. The "good" patient was one who did not diverge from his narrowly prescribed, dependent part in the ward routine. As has been indicated, attendants were the primary, immediate instrument of the Hospital for enforcing the standards of this social system on the ward. Physical and psychological restraints at their disposal and fear of blame largely guaranteed their compliance with the role of keeper. The effect this role had upon them is suggested by the remark made years later by one attendant, "That continuous observation, worrying about something happening and severe reprimand if it did, kept us on pins and needles all the time. When I think of that hell-hole, Building Four, with all the supposedly suicidal and other disturbed patients! It was a nightmare."

This is the disheartening picture of the formal social structure as it existed prior to 1946. It does not, however, take into consideration more informal relationships. Even the strongest sanctions and methods of obtaining conformity to a social system never completely succeed in excluding some expression of conflicting values. Rigid and psychologically penalizing both to patients and staff as was this organizational pattern at Bedford, there was a measure of amelioration in the continuing personal consideration of Dr. Adams and Miss Mary Dawson, the chief nurse; the affectionate interest of the physicians in the fate of some individual patients; brief periods of friendly association between attendants and patients; occasional fun at ward parties; and momentary deeper insights into the meaning of patients' actions. The record of a medical staff meeting, for example, shows a physician's concern about transferring a patient who had "gone down hill" soon after arrival, from the admission ward to another "where he'd have no chance and get more discouraged from being with the untidy patients there." Many attendants report having let two patients settle an argument between themselves or having released restraints a little. "I was gentle with him, because I knew he was more scared than mean." "We'd break the rules when no one was looking and there was no chance of getting caught." Evidence of this kind is sufficient to suggest that there is probably no "new" idea or procedure being experimented with at present that was not thought of or tried by the "old-timers." The tragedy lay in the fact that organizational rigidity and the psychiatric values of the day precluded opportunity for ideas and attempts to be translated into acceptable programs of action of any considerable size.

CHANGES IN SOCIAL STRUCTURE BETWEEN 1946 AND 1952

With the reorganization of the Veterans Administration, provision was made for extensive recasting of roles in its neuropsychiatric hospitals. This provision was reflected at Bedford by assigning much of the administrative work formerly done by physicians to the registrar's office and the nursing service. The status of the latter two groups was raised by assuming larger responsibility for patients' affairs, while the medical staff were more free to devote themselves to the somatic and psychological therapies that were increasingly emphasized by the administration and the consultants. With the potential contribution to diagnosis and treatment of enlarged and better-trained staffs of psychologists, social workers, and rehabilitation therapists, physicians were obliged to give greater attention to the making of integrated teams of workers if they were to profit from the more comprehensive case "workups," the deeper understanding of the illness of each patient, and the therapeutic facilities within the rehabilitation department.

The ward nurse in turn was relieved of many kinds of paper work by the introduction of ward secretaries, elimination of much record-keeping that the use of restraints had involved, increase in the functions of nurse supervisors, and allowing the psychiatric aides (as the attendants were now called) to take responsibility for certain records. Although she still spent about one-third of her time in purely administrative work, the ward nurse was able to give more supervision to the growing number of aides and to devote some attention to patients.[1] The elimination of physical restraints and the content of the in-service training provided led her and also the aides to reconsider many aspects of overall ward management as it related to patient needs.

The psychiatric aide was more carefully selected, better paid, and given far more training and supervision. His primary function was still that of guarding patients but in a less restrictive manner. Some custodial functions were simplified by clerical and mechanical innovations, and others were removed from ward personnel. The many hours formerly spent in shaving patients were greatly reduced by the introduction of the self-locking razor that made it possible for most patients to shave themselves. The storing and assignment of patients' clothing was managed by specialized personnel. These were all time-saving changes for the aide.[2] His strategic position of continued closeness to patients in everyday ward living began to be utilized for more positive ends. Instead of being expected to note only unusual and disturbed behavior, he was recognized as an observer of various significant aspects of patient life. He was expected to assess the interests and capacities of patients, had access to their medical records, took down parts of case histories, and attended the psychiatric staff meetings if he desired.

SOURCES OF STRESS

The increasing two-way communication and interaction among groups of personnel tended to decrease the formerly extreme social distance between them, and the more flexible

---

[1] Although the nurses are predominantly women, it is significant to note that Bedford has had as many as 12 registered men nurses at one time occupying positions of head nurses or supervisors, and a man is currently the assistant chief nurse.

[2] These changes were not made easily, however, for they upset long-established habits. The response of a patient to the new shaving procedure was, "For twenty years you said I couldn't shave myself. Now you want me to. Who's crazy anyhow?"

extension of roles raised the prestige and morale of each group. Although this six-year period was one of rapid transition, the assimilation of change and the integration of an entire institution around new goals is at best a slow process. As a consequence, a number of interrelated sources of stress had developed by 1951. Wide differences in attitudes and expectations were held about the potential capacity of patients and what activities they should engage in. To implement the new concepts of total treatment in a large hospital where custodial and security aims had become embedded through habituation, was anything but easy. The very increase in number and specialization of personnel, together with altered functions, made for lack of clarity and conflict between groups regarding areas of responsibility. Channels of communication became complex and often cumbersome.

With more time available for getting better acquainted with his patients, the aide was still reluctant to initiate active, friendly relations. He would have liked to sit down and talk informally with them. But although the older prohibitions had been eased, they had not been replaced by positive support and the systematic expectation that he was to assume such a role. Although he informed the physician and nurse about individual patients, he remained inactive in the central sphere of regularly participating with the patients, and in reporting, evaluating, and modifying his own social relationships with them for therapeutic goals.

Ambivalence existed on both sides of physician-nurse relationships. The psychiatrist worked with patients individually. Although assumed to have medical responsibility for all patients as well as awareness of the impact of ward group living upon them, he did not conceive of himself as responsible for ward management, nor did the overall situation favor his assuming this task. Instead, the administration had extended to him more autonomy and authority for individual therapy, and had simultaneously strengthened the nursing service through giving it greater autonomy for overall ward management in which it was experienced by tradition and training. But even work with

patients individually was far from satisfactory to the psychiatrist, since many of them were frequently transferred to other
wards with which he was not associated. For example, disturbed
or problem patients would be sent from various parts of the
Hospital to the intensive treatment building, and from thence
they would be assigned to other buildings. Newly admitted patients would be transferred from the admission ward to the
shock treatment ward and thence perhaps to other buildings.
It should incidentally be noted that the practice of "buck passing" was facilitated by such circumstances. As one physician
said, "It is easy to get rid of a problem patient on a ward, who
may have become disturbed through some difficulty in nursing
care or with your own inability to understand him. I know, I
have done it myself."

The head nurse was responsible for arranging, scheduling,
and supervising the everyday living of the patients on the
ward. With postwar developments she sensed more opportunity
for utilizing the social environment of the ward for therapeutic
purposes, but was limited by two considerations. Nursing service had increased to a size where procedures tended to be uni-
formly established and prescribed for the entire Hospital, thus
taking initiative from her and occupying her supervisor with
administrative problems. Second, she needed the leadership
and support of the psychiatrist, which he was not in a favorable
position to give.

Under these circumstances both groups of personnel were
frustrated: the physician in obtaining consideration for individual patients when they might be moved or when nursing
procedures were not suited to their specific needs; the nurse
in obtaining encouragement to initiate changes that she felt
would benefit all patients on her ward. Both groups were increasingly aware of an interrelationship between their two
perspectives, but were unable to meet on a common ground to
integrate their efforts and settle their differences. The following
instance illustrates how resentments between them could easily
arise and be sustained. A psychiatrist noticed that one of his
patients who had not been eating or dressing well had begun

to improve. On talking with the ward aide he found a friendly relationship had been established between the aide and the patient. The doctor supported and guided this relationship with further improvement in the patient's condition. Then the time arrived for the aide to be assigned to another ward in accordance with the plan for staff rotation. This plan had been devised after careful consideration of how to minimize the amount of night duty expected of individual aides and nurses, and also meet the requirements of sick leave and vacations for so large a group of personnel.[1]

The physician requested that the aide working therapeutically with his patient be kept on the same ward, thus skipping the rotation. The supervising nurses, who frequently find themselves in the awkward position of trying to make compromises between the planning of doctors and of ward nursing staff, decided in this instance that it would be unfair to disrupt the prearranged schedule. If the one change were permitted, a considerable number of other aides would have to readjust their personal plans made in conformity with the scheduled rotation. In the opinion of the supervisors this would lead to poorer morale and be reflected, if only temporarily, in poorer patient care. So the aide went to another ward as scheduled, but the doctor was upset and bitter.

In many such instances, conflicting spheres of responsibility and interest, which in themselves sustained older intergroup tensions, necessitated requests and explanations going through long and often parallel lines of communication if problems were to be settled. One line of communication went from the ward via the doctor to the physician who was chief of the particular service, and from him to the chief of professional services; another went via the head nurse, through the supervising nurse to the chief nurse, and thence to the chief of professional services. Different lines of communication were required when

[1] This plan was a considerable improvement over the two extremes often met in psychiatric hospitals: one, where ward personnel are reassigned almost every day or week; the other, where they keep their assignments for years. The first leads to unstable patient-staff relationship, the latter to personnel getting in a rut.

another department was involved, such as rehabilitation with its many specialized services. When information about a particular problem upon which decision had to be based finally reached the chief of professional services, it was so modified through being passed on by several persons that the nature of the original problem was frequently altered. Thus, the eventual decision was often inappropriate to the actual situation, or the situation had changed enough during the time consumed that opportunity and initiative were lost on the ward.

REORGANIZATION OF BUILDING FOR ACTIVE TREATMENT

The administration at Bedford was well aware of these stresses in the social structure of the Hospital. It had been considering how they might be alleviated and the resulting action made part of a long-range plan for improvement, when it decided to participate in the Russell Sage Project. This fact provided stimulus for somewhat more immediate action, and in February, 1952, Bedford began the extensive reorganization of Building Four, which produced several significant changes not only in it but in other parts of the Hospital. Although it had been designated the "acute-intensive treatment" building and had one large ward set aside for patients receiving somatic therapy, it did not include the admission service, and the two wards that had formerly struggled with the large numbers of "suicidal" patients, as well as the disturbed ward, had won the opprobrium of being among the worst in the Hospital. From many parts of the institution men were sent to this building whenever they became disturbed. Those who improved were transferred to other buildings. To and from its wards was a continuing flow of patients. Its system of staff rotation, moreover, had militated against nurses and attendants working with patients in any prolonged or intimate way.

The primary purpose of the reorganization was the more effective intensive treatment of a much larger number of persons. Hence, those considered most amenable to therapy, primarily the younger men, were to be assigned to specific wards in this building where they were to remain with relative permanence until they were able to be discharged. Patients that had been there previously who were incontinent, untidy, or seemed fixed in their regressive symptoms were to be sent to other parts of the institution, chiefly to Building Six which was considered intermediate between acute treatment and long chronicity and which later became an experimental area for the Project. Since four wards constructed to care for some 275 patients were available in Building Four, one was designated for the admission of new cases and the former admission ward elsewhere was reassigned. The second was retained for patients receiving somatic therapy. The third, which became another experimental ward and will therefore receive detailed attention in a subsequent chapter, consisted of patients sufficiently disturbed to require special management including seclusion. The fourth was composed of those who did not fit into any of the customary classifications and hence did not belong on other wards in the Hospital, but were deemed more amenable to treatment than the patients in the chronic buildings.

Such an extensive reorganization necessitated the transfer of several hundred patients among several buildings. Only those parts of Bedford assigned to convalescents, patients on parole or working in hospital industries, and women patients were not directly involved.[1] Even the medical building was affected to the extent of losing the admission service. When this great moving ended, the ward social structure of the Hospital was largely stabilized by the firm decision that not only interward and interbuilding transfer of patients would be kept at an absolute minimum, but physicians, nurses, and attendants were to receive permanent assignments to specific wards. Thus, the ward staff would have continuous association with each other, and would be in a position to act as a unit in caring for the same group of patients over a longer period of time. The concept was established that a patient could progress through various stages of recovery on *any* ward and with the help of its

[1] One building at some distance from the others is used for about 80 women veterans hospitalized at Bedford. Because it was considered too unrepresentative to be included in the Project, no further reference will be made to it or to women patients.

permanent staff and of associated departments. This concept had a powerful effect on morale because only a few wards in the Hospital had been identified as places to which improved patients were assigned and from which they returned to the community. All other wards were known as places where patients did not improve or only began to improve before being transferred to wards for the better patients. Now opportunity and impetus were provided for the staff of each ward to strive to be identified with patient progress.

Simultaneously with this stabilization of patients and personnel, the Hospital arranged for decentralization of administrative authority by granting a large measure of autonomy to each ward unit. Physicians were given responsibility for specific wards, and other duties including the care of patients elsewhere in the institution were sharply reduced if not eliminated. Staff assigned to Building Four were those who had "demonstrated their ability and competence to carry on a modern psychiatric treatment program." When the staffing was completed there was not only one physician for each ward, but there was one head nurse for each ward and one attendant for roughly every 10 patients from seven in the morning until three-thirty in the afternoon. From then until eleven o'clock one nurse covered two wards and there was one attendant for some 20 or 25 patients. During the night a nurse assisted by a supervisory aide had responsibility for all patients in the building and three aides were on duty on each ward.

Under such favorable circumstances, the ward physicians were in a position to develop long-range plans, depend on the continuing participation and emotional commitment of a regular staff, and organize a program to meet patient needs. Within the ward structure communication could be simplified, and decisions could be made without the delay of having requests move through several intermediaries to the chief of professional services. In addition, the ward physician and his staff had considerably more freedom than formerly for experimenting with new procedures in patient care. All these measures decreased the social distance between professional groups, and provided the basis in fact for the exploration of the positive, therapeutic potential that now appeared to reside in ward and hospital social living. Several steps had already been planned to promote socialization before the Project furnished additional impetus. One step was the moving of the nurse's station or charge desk from an inaccessible place to a small room adjacent to the day room, where patients spend almost all of their time when on the ward, except for sleeping. By removing one wall and installing unbreakable glass panels with open space between them, it was possible to provide the nurse with an office from which she could see almost the entire day room and be seen by patients and aides, and she could talk with anyone who came to the window. Ward groups for recreation and specific therapeutic activity were increased. Ten aides were especially selected and assigned to these groups, and nursing service was directed not to assign them elsewhere when shortages of personnel occurred because of sickness, vacations, or other reasons. This policy had the incidental effect of stabilizing the ward staff still further by making some members directly responsible to special groups of patients. The new ward organization, furthermore, provided a more constant and simplified unit with which the rehabilitation department, special services, and specialized therapists could plan their programs for the benefit of groups or of individual patients.

14. Collaboration Between Russell Sage Project and the Hospital

IN APRIL, 1952, THE WRITER assumed the dual role of liaison representative between the cooperating hospitals, and assistant to Bedford in defining and initiating experiments in the improvement of patient care.[1] Early discussions with various members of the staff indicated that although the goal of more effective treatment through utilization of the ward social environment was strongly supported by many persons, progress in achieving it was being impeded.

STRESS IN THE STRUCTURE OF CONFIDENCE

Two major sources of tension and confusion within the social structure of the Hospital as a whole appeared responsible for the impediment. One source of stress was a residue of prejudice and rivalries between departments or groups of personnel that had been carried over from the frictions existing before the reorganization of the acute treatment service. Conflicting opinions and social distance between physicians and administrative nurses,[2] between ward doctors and management, and even between the wards themselves appeared so imbedded in past experience that they continued to be the basis for interpreting intent in the new alignment of functions and authority. In what directions the wards would move and how group relationships would evolve was not yet clear. It appeared that this aspect of the social climate would persist until whatever advantages there were in reorganization could be demonstrated.

---

[1] He assumed a similar role at Metropolitan State Hospital, which will be discussed in Part III.

[2] Administrative nurses, as used in reference to Bedford, include those in supervision, administration, and also in nursing education since the last group have been particularly active in the Project and subsequent developments.

The second source of stress and confusion was a concomitant of change itself. The structure of confidence within any social organization rests upon mutual understanding and congruent mutual expectations among the personnel and their trust in each other's willingness and capacity to contribute to the accomplishment of daily tasks and institutional goals.[1] In a period of marked change, when previous values and attitudes are being revised or challenged, this structure of confidence is often shaky. If evidence accumulates, however, that the new values produce specific achievements, personal satisfactions, or group recognition, they are likely not only to be accepted but confidence begins to be strengthened. In the psychiatric hospital the degree of confidence held by administrators in ward staff and the morale of all personnel depend to a great extent upon accomplishments on the ward as the basic "production" unit. But the capacity of these units to progress toward a defined goal is dependent on the nature and degree of psychological support given by management and of professional help provided by the allied departments.

Reference could be made to few precedents in hospital psychiatry for systematically delegating so much responsibility to, and permitting such individual initiative by, ward personnel as had occurred at Bedford. It still remained to be seen how ward staffs would react and how associated groups would adapt their work to the new organizational pattern. Moreover, confidence resides in the last analysis in the opinion of the staff about capabilities of patients for improvement including capacity to enter into a therapeutic relationship, as well as in a clear conception of what constitutes progress on the part of the patient. Here again, as in psychiatric hospitals generally, conflicting professional opinions existed concerning the nature and social pathology of the psychotic and especially the schizophrenic patient. And clinical evidence could be cited to support each viewpoint.

[1] The role of confidence in social structure is analyzed by Robert K. Merton in *Social Theory and Social Structure: Toward the Codification of Theory and Research*, The Free Press, Glencoe, Ill., 1949. See especially Chapter 7.

Some of the uncertainty and the strains between groups obviously needed to be reduced if the Project and the Hospital were to develop an effective collaboration. Since it was scarcely possible to work collectively with groups that had difficulty in working with each other, the writer sought methods for assisting in the reduction of social tension. The very fact that the experimental undertaking was initiated by Boston Psychopathic Hospital was of help, inasmuch as that institution carries some authoritative weight in Massachusetts in matters of social management of psychotic patients. Another source of support was the monthly interhospital meetings among the four cooperating institutions, which had already begun to foster a sense of solidarity and forward movement in connection with patient care. But an instrumentality was needed to help Bedford more directly "over the hump." Broadly based group participation in a series of task-oriented meetings on ward care appeared to be a means for increasing communication between groups and strengthening the structure of confidence. These meetings could also be used, as we shall see later, for advancing the goals of the experiment.

While they were getting under way, the writer discovered an opportunity to offer more direct service, inasmuch as the Hospital had requested his assistance in evaluating the results of its reorganization. He initiated conferences with the medical administration, the physicians on the wards being considered for experimental purposes, and the small steering committee that had been formed to plan Project demonstrations. Through these conferences he was able to reinforce the confidence of one group in another, and report to them objective information about specific problems and progress. On this basis the subsequent meetings built with increasing effectiveness. Although many tensions continued and new ones arose, those immediately blocking the development of ward experiments could generally be disposed of without great delay by group discussions, further extension of representation in the meetings, or opening other channels of communication. Less severe tensions, such as jealousies and resentments between services or categories of personnel, could often be redirected into wholesome competition. Unfortunately, the subject of confidence cannot be discussed at greater length but much of what follows, particularly the summary of the work of the group that replaced the steering committee, indirectly indicates how greatly the foundations at Bedford came to be strengthened.

SELECTION OF WARDS

It will be recalled from Dr. Brown's introductory chapter that the basic question to which the Project sought answers was: How can the ward social environment be managed to meet more adequately the emotional needs of patients, and thus help them to develop greater personal competence in coping with environmental factors? From a therapeutic standpoint this question emphasized modifying the environment to accommodate the individual, as contrasted with modifying the behavior of the patient to conform to static situational requirements.[1] The basic assumption on which the Project rested was that standards, procedures, attitudes, and human relationships that provide the framework of the patient's daily living either impede or facilitate his constructive social participation and integration, and hence his recovery.

From the time it was decided not to transplant experiments in social action that had been successful in the small and amply staffed Boston Psychopathic Hospital but to encourage Bedford and Metropolitan to define through steering committees what they wished to undertake, the fact was unavoidable that the Project would be more broadly exploratory than had been anticipated. Instead of setting up experiments where selected wards were used as a scientific laboratory with variable factors sufficiently controlled to determine which of them constituted socially therapeutic procedures, methods had to be devised of a developmental and situational nature appropriate to this type of investigation. Experience proved that flexibility and

---

[1] Differences in these two therapeutic approaches in institutional settings are analyzed in an article by Dallas Pratt, "Making the Environment Respond to Basic Emotional Needs," *Psychiatry*, vol. 15, May, 1952, pp. 179–188.

successive reorientations of method were essential. Specific dimensions of ward care and requirements for its improvement, we found, could only gradually be filtered out of a multitude of experiences, ideas, and circumstances that were part of the ongoing work of personnel with patients. Likewise, establishing cooperative relationships between the hospitals for the purpose of assessing patient care came to be emphasized rather than uniform quantitative measurement of variables. This allowed greater leeway for local concepts and practices and called for minimum bias in the form of specific hypothesis. Much reliance was placed upon the examination of existing ward situations from new or forgotten points of view, sharpened by observational techniques from the behavior sciences, and upon the attempt to obtain consensus from current experience.

In spite of general recognition that the Project would need to be exploratory, it was assumed for some weeks that experimental wards would be matched by control wards. Hence, the steering committees at Bedford and Metropolitan, assisted by the writer and Miss Penelope Lambros, collected extensive data about patients on certain wards such as age, length of stay in hospital, diagnosis, and clinical assessment. Data were also gathered on staffing patterns, level of ward socialization, and type of patient-staff interaction. On the basis of these data two wards, one for acute and one for chronic patients, were selected at both hospitals where experiments in improvement of patient care were to be instituted, and two roughly comparable control wards were also designated. Developments on the experimental wards at Bedford will be described in the next two chapters, and those at Metropolitan in the section of the book relating to that institution.

No sooner, however, had ward programs begun than it became increasingly clear that the control wards could not be maintained as such. Planning had been too hurried and the reasons for the failure of controls had not been foreseen, although in retrospect many of them were obvious and some were deeply moving in their implications. At Metropolitan, for example, patients could go downstairs from the experimental to

the control area, since the door to the staircase was left unlocked. They carried ideas and materials back and forth and
proved to be the instigators of competition between the two
units. When the experimental ward received a piano, patients
on the control ward became envious and begged to have a
piano too. An attendant could not resist their insistence and
succeeded in obtaining one. To block such a spontaneous development could scarcely be justified by any professional ethics.
Supervisory nurses and aides who had responsibility for several
wards were found to be passing on information about new techniques, procedures, and facilities in an experimental area, which
was detrimental to maintaining a controlled situation but often
proved valuable in bettering patient care and stimulating ward
staffs.

What turned out to be the greatest asset to Bedford and also
to the Project so far as its broader goals were concerned was
fatal to the continuance of the control wards. That asset was
psychological readiness for further alterations, eagerness for
new ideas, and willingness to engage in objective self-examina-
tion. These characteristics had been fostered by the extensive
changes made since 1946 and proved stronger than inadequacies in mutual confidence and trust that still existed. The
reorganization of the acute treatment building and the concomitant partial reorganizations elsewhere, moreover, had progressed to the point where several ward physicians were already
formulating new plans not as yet divulged. Finally, the monthly
interhospital meetings had already stimulated many of the staff
to focus fresh interest on ward care.

The following brief description of the situations found to
exist in May, 1952, on the four selected wards at Bedford will
indicate specifically why the plan for control areas had to be
dismissed; it will indicate more importantly how dynamic was
the overall situation. The ward for acute patients selected for
experimentation was the intensive treatment unit in Building
Four, where the somatic therapies were used. Although the staff
were planning some changes, it was relatively stabilized in
its procedures, had one of the highest levels of patient social-

ization in the Hospital, with affiliate nurses and volunteers active there, and was discharging significant numbers of patients.[1] The disturbed ward in the same building was chosen for a control. The administration had just recommended that the doors of the seclusion rooms be gradually removed. The ward physician and nurses accepted this recommendation as a challenge and prepared to take patients out of seclusion much faster than was expected. To achieve this end a host of other problems had to be solved, such as drastically redefining the role of the attendant and improving the poor morale. As a consequence, a ward that had been long static became quickly very active. Obviously, neither it nor the intensive treatment ward could be used as a control for the other. Hence, the decision was finally made to concentrate study, so far as acute patients were concerned, upon the disturbed ward, since the Project was thus provided with a splendid opportunity for observing and participating in a radically changing social situation.

The chronic ward to be used experimentally was in Building Six, to which a physician previously on the acute service had been assigned during the recent reorganization. Although he was in the process of formulating and revising plans for the entire building, he had been reluctant to make that fact known. What was apparent was his initial attempt to focus for practical purposes on a single ward, which was not the one selected by the steering committee. He became very much concerned about this discrepancy and justifiably resentful that he had not been consulted to a greater extent. What resulted, as reported later, was the spectacular upgrading of all four wards in the building. The second chronic ward, designated for control purposes, was in a separate building not so immediately touched by the re-

[1] Funkenstein, D. H., and collaborators, "Exploratory Phase of a Rehabilitation Project," *Bedford Bulletin*, vol. 2, May, 1953, pp. 27–28. This statistical study, which includes 213 patients admitted to the Hospital between February 12, 1951, and February 12, 1952, reveals that 107 were discharged within six months and 168, or 79 per cent, within eighteen months of their admission. While some of these patients were undoubtedly discharged from the admission ward, a large proportion are known to have been on the intensive treatment ward. Note should be made parenthetically that these results amazed hospital personnel who were unaware that discharge rates were so high, and greatly raised the morale of staff on the two wards.

organization. Its physician had been there for some time and was contemplating no changes. During the first few weeks it appeared to remain stable. Shortly, however, the staff perceived the effects of change in Building Six and the head nurse began to react positively to the new climate of initiative and exploration throughout the Hospital. As a consequence, she instituted marked improvements and she and other personnel enjoyed competing with the neighboring building.

Quite unanticipated by the administration, medical staff, ward personnel, steering committee, and writer were the speed and extensiveness of movement that manifested themselves on the wards in subsequent months. In retrospect, they can be understood only as the result of the interaction of forces released by the Hospital, and those stimulated by the Project which happened in addition to provide encouragement and support at a strategic moment. So far as "action research" is concerned, the steering committee, including the social scientist, relearned the following old and perhaps obvious lessons: (1) A human institution is so organized that significant changes in one part affect all others. (2) Motives—be they aspirations or desperations, inhibiting resentment or constructive competition—cannot be arbitrarily varied or held constant in the conventional tradition of scientific research. (3) Evidence of interest in any human endeavor, accompanied by the aim of studying or changing it, motivates those connected with that endeavor to evaluate their situation and to welcome or resist change. As one nurse noted, "There has been research in schizophrenia before at this Hospital, but there has never been research on the ward itself.[1] The interest and feeling aroused show how much it is needed." (4) The effectiveness of research and/or administrative planning depend on detailed systematic consultation with, and participation by, those who would be affected by it.

[1] As has been well documented by many previous experiments with social groups, heightened morale leading to more effective interpersonal relations and task performance came about in the cooperating hospitals as personnel responded to the interest of the research workers and became involved in a special experimental effort. See Roethlisberger, F. J., and W. J. Dickson, *Management and the Worker*, Harvard University Press, Cambridge, 1939.

It should not be inferred that there can be no scientific research in human relations, but the foregoing items do indicate the necessity for developing concepts and methods that will permit orderly change and careful evaluation through participation of the persons concerned.[1] The Project sacrificed the obtaining of refined data on each specific dimension of ward patient care and treatment. However, the flexible methodology that was instituted with its large element of group participation made possible more comprehensive understanding and delineation of the interaction of the many significant variables involved; it also made for more effectiveness by enhancing the process of social change.

SPECIFIC METHODS INCLUDING PARTICIPANT OBSERVATION

A variety of methods were employed by the Project for the purpose of obtaining data; working with ward staffs, the steering committee, and the subsequently enlarged committee; and measuring change in patient resocialization, as well as in attitudes of personnel toward patient care. As indicated in the introductory chapter, we shall not reproduce the technical instruments of measurement or discuss their use at length. Instead, we wish to indicate in the few pages available, ways in which all the methods employed were made to contribute dynamically to finding answers to *how* patient care can be improved with the methods themselves directly forwarding that improvement. Although the following description refers specifically to Bedford, approximately the same methods were used at Metropolitan State Hospital.

Interviewing was extensively utilized. In order to understand the history and social organization of the Hospital, the writer early began interviews, which were recorded, with persons in the departments of nursing and rehabilitation and on various levels of administrative responsibility. Data thus obtained supplemented those from group discussions at many types of meet-

---

[1] The nearest approximation of our exploratory method and its inherent problems is discussed by Nelson N. Foote and Leonard S. Cottrell, Jr., in *Identity and Interpersonal Competence*, University of Chicago Press, 1955.

ings called to plan and evaluate the Project. It was presently discovered that even interviewing with such a supposedly limited function served additional ends. Personnel often began to talk freely about goals of, and barriers to, patient care from their point of view or that of the group of which they were members. Their conversation furnished the interviewer not only with important knowledge of frustrations many of which were institutionally produced, sometimes only because of failure in the system of communication; it also permitted those interviewed to gain satisfaction from having a listener to whom they could express hopes and aspirations or obtain relief from being able to speak openly about frustrations; and it gave them an opportunity at times to see themselves more clearly in relation to their job. Consequently, the writer found himself almost from the beginning in the role of a participant observer who could provide a useful link in communication, as has already been mentioned, that would at once strengthen confidence and would also permit transmittal of suggestions for improving ward care.[1] After a short time, however, the total hospital situation and Project plans became so much more clearly defined that visits to these various departments and offices could be reduced or restructured to depend upon the need for further information or for help in the solution of some immediate problem. Steering committee discussions, regular ward staff conferences, and special group meetings that grew out of the work of the committee largely supplanted the writer's original role in facilitating communication about ward care.

To give the Project some formal assessment of the attitudes of personnel toward patients a scale was devised by Professor Daniel J. Levinson and Dr. Doris Gilbert. It was designed to measure the degree to which individual staff members "accepted" patients in the social and emotional sense, were optimistic or pessimistic about the outcome of mental illness, and

---

[1] A thorough discussion of the problems of participant observation and excellent guiding principles in assuming this role are given in William F. Whyte's article, "Observational Field-Work Methods," Part II, pp. 493–513, of *Research Methods in Social Relations*, edited by Marie Jahoda, Morton Deutsch, and Stuart W. Cook, Dryden Press, New York, 1951.

believed in the potential social competence of patients and their ability to establish relationships with other persons. This scale was administered in the spring of 1952 and again some eighteen months later, with the help of the nursing supervisors,[1] to aides, nurses, and physicians in the three buildings housing the wards examined by the Project. Through it correspondence could be demonstrated between changes in attitudes of aides and changes in their work roles.

Another instrument for assessing alteration of attitudes was a questionnaire that aides were asked to fill out at two widely spaced intervals. The questions sought to determine what they thought supervisors expected them to do versus what they personally preferred doing. When first tested, their preferences were high for providing recreation on the ward and various activities off the ward, and for working more closely with individual patients, but they felt they were permitted a minimum of such social interaction. In late 1953 what they preferred doing corresponded more closely to what they were expected to do—nursing care, custody, housekeeping functions, as well as engaging patients in activities—reflecting in part the fact that their custodial role had been greatly decreased while their share in social therapy had been enlarged and had received official recognition.

The Project staff spent much time in ward observation, assessment, and indirect intervention. It was the writer's intention for the first few months to visit each ward weekly, after which he would talk with the staff present about developments, and then call on the ward physician for further discussion. In order to sharpen observation of patient behavior and have a measure of changes in ward socialization, Dr. Frederic L. Wells and Dr. Gilbert formulated a ward socialization index that could be checked quickly, thus recording the activity of every patient.[2] This scale allowed for a continuum of interaction ranging from that of patients who were not overtly related to the environ-

[1] We wish to thank William Zink, R.N., and Richard Conway, R.N., for their assistance in this and other phases of the research.

[2] "A Ward Socialization Index" will appear in a forthcoming issue of the *American Journal of Nursing*.

ment but were sleeping, staring, or muttering to themselves, through interaction that represented destructive use of the environment, to types of constructive activity—whether work or recreation—that patients were engaging in alone, to those in which they were participating with other persons. A completed index or a comparison of several such indexes furnished an excellent introduction to the discussion with ward personnel about forward movement of patients, ward changes, difficulties encountered, plans for next steps, and so on. In his visits to the ward physicians, the social scientist viewed himself as a consultant who could contribute to an understanding of the social structure of the ward and the relation of psychiatrist and ward to the total Hospital. These visits also provided opportunity for exploration of the doctor's conception of his role in a program of social action, and of ways for solving a variety of problems. Finally, they supplied moral support needed in the initial phases of rapid change.

The fact that Mr. Hobson spent full time for several months in studying attitudes within the ward setting exerted considerable influence on personnel. Not only in his group interviews with patients but in individual interviews with aides and nurses he was viewed as being so patient-centered in his interests that he transmitted stimulation for a fresh and more sensitive consideration of patient care and how it could be modified beneficially.

While participant observation was going on, study was being made of hospital records, nursing reports, and other documents for the purpose of obtaining information about many matters, such as variety of activities outside the ward available to patients and number participating, or progress in reducing feeding problems and incontinence. Existing records were found to be frequently inadequate both for measuring change and as guides for systematic planning. Suggestions were offered, therefore, concerning the nature and value of more or differently organized data. The response to these suggestions was prompt and the results were often highly useful. How practical data could be was well illustrated both at Bedford and Metropolitan when aides on "untidy" wards began, without any request from the Project staff, to keep records for each patient on soiling and at what time of day and night. The information noted soon permitted those responsible for the programs in toilet training to include decisions about what patients should be waked at night and when, what beds should be assigned incontinent patients to disturb others the least, and so on. It was also discovered that records could be used as a potent factor in increasing staff motivation. Figures and charts began to appear on the bulletin board in the nursing offices showing weekly progress in the reduction of undesirable practices or increase in patient socialization. Ward personnel had at last visible incentive for altering numbers and curves.

THE COMMITTEE FOR PATIENT CARE

The principal instrumentality that the Project created and through which it worked increasingly and with substantial results was the progressively enlarged steering committee. Initially this committee was composed of six persons all of whom, with one exception, represented the nursing service. Since Russell Sage Foundation was concerned with improvement in ward conditions through social techniques and since nurses have traditionally administered wards, the chief of professional services logically concluded that this was an undertaking primarily in their province.[1] Hence, he asked the assistant chief nurse in charge of nursing education to be chairman. Three nursing supervisors and one supervisory aide were selected to be members. As his active representative on the committee, Dr. Hoffman appointed Dr. Rudolph Neustadt, then director of professional education. The contribution of the latter to the collaboration between Bedford and the Project was always important and at times decisive, particularly because one of his

---

[1] This conclusion was later seen to be unrealistic, inasmuch as improvement of patient care even on a single ward can scarcely be achieved, so highly integrated is the social structure of the Hospital, without the assistance of many persons from other services. But it accomplished the important purpose of giving more responsibility and recognition to the service most immediately concerned. The reader will note how often the steering committee was enlarged as realization of the need of assistance from other personnel became apparent.

enduring professional goals was to raise the social status of psychiatric patients whether they were within hospitals or without. In exploratory ventures of this action type, inevitable frictions develop between the sponsoring and institutional groups and between persons within those groups. With his objective knowledge of the social structure of the institution and his desire to facilitate the experimentation, Dr. Neustadt frequently assumed the role of intermediary and brought dissenting individuals together to find some solution to a particular difficulty.

Selection of wards was one of the first tasks that faced the steering committee. A few persons in the Hospital were reluctant to have experimental efforts "wasted" on chronic wards so discouraging did work with them appear. Many more, however, favored inclusion of such wards for the very reason that morale there was extremely low and also because of the preponderance of chronic cases. This problem was resolved outside the formal committee meetings and selection was made, as has been seen, on the basis of factual data and to include both acute and chronic wards. So radical was subsequent improvement on the latter that various members of the staff, some influential enough to further developments elsewhere, testified to a complete change in their point of view about what could be done even for badly regressed patients.

No sooner had the wards been selected, however, than the committee learned that at least two psychiatrists were formulating plans of their own for ward improvement without consulting with it because they were unaware of its purpose. As a consequence, the idea was conceived, to which reference has been made, of monthly task-oriented meetings to include physicians as well as ward staff. Several of the nurses were so dubious, however, about the doctors' willingness to meet with them that they did not even issue an invitation until they were later informed that these particular physicians were now sitting down with their head nurses and aides to formulate ward plans. The ward physicians were also dubious about the value of meeting with the steering committee, but when they were told that its purpose would be to discuss and assist their plans they agreed to participate. Hence, after about six weeks the steering committee was enlarged to include the two physicians from the disturbed ward and Building Six, and at least one nurse and one aide from each unit. It will be referred to hereafter as the committee for patient care. Its function was viewed as that of accomplishing change not initially through administrative techniques but through meetings devoted to group planning, stimulating action, providing mutual support, and evaluating action undertaken. Frequently the action decided upon involved administrative changes.

At the beginning the committee discussions were supposedly for the sole purpose of forwarding developments on the selected wards, and hence there seemed no reason to include personnel not directly connected with these areas or with ward administration in general. Shortly, however, it became evident that not only the ancillary therapists but categories of personnel seemingly far removed from direct patient care were clearly connected with what occurred on the wards. An early problem was that of persuading the rehabilitation department at once to take more patients from the wards and to send workers, such as occupational therapists, with their supplies to the wards to direct activities for patients too sick to leave. As in instances of friction between other groups that did not have a common meeting ground in the wards themselves or in the committee for patient care, ward personnel and the ancillary therapists attributed to each other lack of interest in, and clear understanding of, the needs of patients or reluctance to cooperate wholeheartedly. Considerable rapprochement was achieved through special meetings, sponsored by Miss Mary E. Butler in her role of new chairman of the committee and by Miss Evelyn F. Morton, assistant chief of nursing education, at which nurses and ancillary therapists discussed their respective functions in reference to occupational and recreational activities that might be performed on the wards. Some months later the medical chief of the rehabilitation department and representatives of the sections comprising it were included in the committee to obtain their participation in the group that was striving to further ward progress.

The importance of still other hospital employees seemingly more remote from patient care also became apparent: engineers responsible for the maintenance of the wards, persons delegated to furnish them supplies, members of the record room staff who assembled and controlled use of medical histories and other data. Their importance was initially highlighted in the task-oriented meetings by the then familiar complaints from ward staffs that such employees did not understand the purposes and goals of treatment. To remedy this situation the committee formulated a tentative plan to increase their understanding, and with the support and further planning of the hospital administration a series of meetings was held designed to demonstrate how they could facilitate or hinder patient care.

During the early weeks of the original steering committee the writer had assumed whatever leadership of the meetings was necessary to get the Project under way. With the first enlargement in membership he began gradually by design to relinquish this role to the committee chairman, and assumed the role of a consultant who stimulated cooperative planning and action among the various groups when needed, and who maintained a constant focus on practical problems in ward care and on the functions of each type of staff. By the end of 1952 the committee for patient care was well able to stand on its own feet. Attendance at the meetings ranged from 15 to 33 with an average of some 22 present, several of whom were interested visitors. In addition to the chairman, the administrative nurses exercised overall leadership by providing continuity as a group and by planning flexible, effective use of meetings that resulted in extending improved ward care to increasingly larger areas of the Hospital. This planning function was one that these nurses could perform extremely well, since the fact that their work cut across ward and department boundaries permitted them comparative knowledge about what needed emphasis. As far as individual meetings were concerned, the degree of participation of each group depended upon the topic and area of interest. Physicians were particularly vocal when matters of policy were being considered; aides spoke when specific ward problems were examined.

When the quantitative contribution of various groups of personnel to the discussion was analyzed for seven of the monthly meetings, it was found that that of persons representing the Project decreased from 36 per cent in 1952 to about 10 in 1953. This assumption of leadership by the hospital staff was particularly gratifying for several reasons. The Project desired to initiate only those procedures that seemed to meet the ward-care needs at Bedford and that had some chance of being institutionalized by the end of the experiment. Second, it was the writer's plan continually to anticipate early termination of any excessive dependence of the Hospital on the Project or vice versa. This seemed necessary because of the broad exploratory goals of the collaboration and the fact that the extensive alterations envisaged in ward and hospital structure would inevitably affect the patients. To withdraw provision for more satisfying ward living at the close of the experiment would do them grave injustice. Finally, since learning and practical action moved hand in hand in this exploration, major responsibility for actions taken would inevitably have to reside in the long run with the hospital staff.

Well before the end of the two-year period the question was raised of the desirability of continuing the meetings. The answer was strongly in the affirmative, and several sessions were devoted to considering what kind of constituency would best serve the entire Hospital. The final decision only moved the committee for patient care still farther in the direction of becoming more inclusive. Every major department in the institution was to be represented, thus adding members from several additional groups. When the new plans were completed, the committee was composed of the chief of professional services; director of professional education; chief of clinical psychology; chief of the rehabilitation department; one representative each from the medical staff, research, vocational counseling, special services, and social service; five administrative or ward head nurses each with an alternate, representing the various clinical services; and seven psychiatric aides with their alternates. The manager and chief of nursing service were ex officio members.

Miss Morton was chosen chairman and the writer was asked to serve as a consultant. Announcement was made that all hospital personnel who wished to attend the meetings were not only invited, but would be encouraged to participate in them.

Some uncertainty was expressed when the new committee was formed about the ability of so large and disparate a group to focus attention primarily upon ward patient care. This concern has been proved unjustified. Monthly meetings are now being held at which every ward or building in the Hospital presents its program in turn. Presentations are the joint responsibility of the ward physician, head nurse, charge aide, and those special therapists working on the ward or with patients from it. The meetings have created much interest and appear to be fulfilling the major functions of the committee as now defined: to stimulate and make some assessment of patient care programs, to give support and recognition on a continuing basis to the various groups directly engaged in providing care, and to recommend specific studies or administrative changes.

Achievements of the Committee

Thus far little has been said specifically about what the committee did through its meetings other than make selection of wards.[1] Space does not permit adequate review either of the content of the sessions or the methods used to build confidence and gain consensus. A brief reference must be made to types of subjects discussed, however, if only to provide further background for an evaluation of what it accomplished. Planning for improved patient care was viewed as a joint function of the committee and the ward staffs. Consequently, attention was given to formulation of general steps to be taken, discussion of their probable effects on patient behavior, consideration of the

---

[1] The process of development of this committee, the functions undertaken, and the motivation of its participants are analogous to those in community self-surveys as outlined by Margot H. Wormser and Claire Selltiz in "Community Self-Surveys: Principles and Procedures," Part II, pp. 611–641, of *Research Methods in Social Relations*, edited by Marie Jahoda, Morton Deutsch, and Stuart W. Cook, Dryden Press, New York, 1951.

potential contribution of other departments, and so on. The care of disturbed and of untidy patients received special thought, since both categories had been included in the experimental areas chosen. Because ward staffs were relatively large, however, the committee did not have to engage in direct decision-making for each ward as did its counterpart at Metropolitan State Hospital, where there was frequently neither ward physician nor nurse available to assist even the limited number of attendants. Instead, the Bedford committee was in a position to focus upon broader aspects of patient care, and to contribute more than at Metropolitan to coordination of the work of the wards and other departments and to assessment of progress.

One of these broader aspects around which much discussion revolved was that of new functions and roles for ward personnel, and how such personnel could be given sufficient support to enable them to assume the larger responsibilities implicit in revised alignments of duties and status. The subject of the role of aides on the experimental wards created so much interest that the department of nursing education held special meetings with them and with nurses and aides from other parts of the Hospital in an attempt to define a generic role. Questions that were the basis for much discussion were the following: To what degree were the weekly staff meetings that had been instituted on many wards instrumental in improving interpersonal relations and clarifying goals? To what extent were everyday ward relations between nurses and aides satisfactory; to what extent were those of nurses and aides with patients therapeutic?

At intervals the committee reviewed the original statement of goals of patient care, examined what had been done thus far, and then as a group tried to make some evaluation of the results. Social science concepts were introduced in the sessions whenever they could be directly related to concrete instances. Thus, motivation, interpersonal relationships and group norms, communication, and social structure were discussed over and again. Since the sociological concept of social structure is relatively new to hospitals, continuous illustrative reference was made to the way in which that structure can handicap or facilitate patient care. To demonstrate how much is lost when it is inflexible, certain patients who were transferred frequently from ward to ward were followed through one year of hospitalization. It was found that the planning done prior to transfer and the medical records accompanying them were almost always inadequate to permit them to adjust readily to their new environment or to permit staff to provide a continuous and consistent therapeutic program. The question of how patients who became badly disturbed, for example, were handled on wards that had formerly sent them elsewhere became in itself a topic for discussion. Finally, the implications for the rest of the Hospital of what was being learned on the experimental wards was a subject for repeated consideration.

Obviously, the achievements of the committee for patient care extended far beyond the mere forwarding of the learning process instituted by the Project. Perhaps they can be summarized under five points: (1) Through Dr. Neustadt as the direct representative of the chief of professional services, the committee brought the sanction of management to pronounced changes in the functions and status of ward personnel and in procedures connected with patient care. (2) It provided a collective instrumentality for assessing ward conditions and the results of the changes instituted. Never before had there been a *group* closely associated with patients who had been given opportunity to express such experienced judgments and as a result to build their consensus into continuing ward patterns of action. (3) The committee stimulated interest in improving patient care among departments and services some of which were far removed from the ward. It coordinated the work of other departments and evaluated the appropriateness of their programs not only in reference to the experiment, but increasingly to the overall needs and goals of the Hospital. (4) It brought diverse groups of personnel into closer working relationships. Persons who would not otherwise have discussed with each other the practical significance of their professions, conferred freely. This fostered communication both vertically and horizontally in Bedford's social organization. Common goals were clarified, thus helping to integrate the interests and abilities of the several groups included in the committee. (5) As progress could be reported concerning the experiment, group solidarity and individual incentive were both increased—and with these gains all types of personnel were able to assume more responsibility for patient progress. Finally, responsibility and reward were shared on a broad basis as recognition grew that staff-staff and staff-patient relationships were interconnected in positive as well as negative patterns of hospital communal life.

15. A Disturbed Ward

IT WILL BE RECALLED that two demonstration wards were originally selected in Building Four which housed the entire acute service, and that the disturbed ward, known as 4C, was to be the control ward against which to measure improvements on the somatic treatment ward. When 4C began to plan after the reorganization how to institute extensive alterations, the Project decided to participate actively with it because of the exceptional opportunity provided for documentation of basic social change. Before analyzing developments further attention must be devoted to its history and constituency. This was the ward that had long been thought of around the Hospital as a place where the most undesirable problem patients could be sent. We have noted that one attendant characterized it as a "hell hole." Working on it was known as "tough," and prior to 1945 assignment to it had been occasionally used as an informal method for disciplining staff who failed to conform to hospital regulations. For years it had received alcoholic patients who abused their weekend pass, earned through long periods of good behavior, by returning to the Hospital highly intoxicated. Here were means for dealing with them while they sobered up, and here they stayed for three months as punishment for their offense. Until the winter of 1952, moreover, the practice had continued of sending other kinds of patients who became severe management problems to this unit, since it had the only extensive facilities, consisting of 12 seclusion rooms, for the discipline and control of "overactive" and "assaultive" patients.[1]

[1] Seclusion was also used on Ward 4D and the admission and medical wards for their own disturbed patients, but their combined number of monthly hours of seclusion was generally less than the number for Ward 4C alone.

Exaggerated stories were told throughout the Hospital of how unpredictably dangerous and mean some of these men were. Altogether it was a very sorry ward! Almost everyone had assumed, however, that such an area was necessary in order to assure the maintenance of equilibrium on other wards. The earlier successful abandonment of mechanical restraints implied that the immediate social environment had been a major determinant in patient-patient and staff-patient disturbances. Unfortunately, this implication did not evolve into a positive working hypothesis systematically utilized in ward planning until the ward physician, Dr. Ian D. Funk, gradually perceived the opportunity for restructuring relationships and the Project explicitly stated the hypothesis.[1]

When examination was made in April, 1952, of the 60 patients on Ward 4C, half of them were found to be "regular" residents who became so disturbed as to warrant being put in seclusion. Some 12 of the 30 were the ones who had gained reputations for assaultiveness and meanness and had been kept for considerable periods in seclusion. Another 15 of the 60 patients had been sent from time to time to other parts of the Hospital, but had been returned because of their seeming inability to adjust themselves to a new environment. The remaining 15 consisted of recent admissions to the Hospital who were assigned to this ward and of men from other wards who had become unmanageable. The medical diagnoses indicated that 93 per cent of all the patients had schizophrenia, predominantly of the paranoid or catatonic type. Almost a third had been at the Hospital under two years, 64 per cent had been there from two to ten years, only two men had been there more than ten years. Seventy-five per cent were under forty years of age. Thus, the majority were younger World War II veterans who, although housed on the acute service, were chronic in the sense that their illness had resisted treatment for a considerable period of time.

[1]The writer gratefully acknowledges Dr. Funk's collaboration in preparation of this report.

STEPS PRIOR TO SIGNIFICANT WARD CHANGES

The most obvious difficulty that disturbed patients have in living with others is in frequently asserting themselves with such physical force that they provoke retaliation from other patients and restraint from the staff. On Ward 4C their assaultive behavior was considered by some personnel to be an inherent part of an irrational illness; by others it was viewed as an expression of resentment toward confinement and the restrictions of hospital life and hence was reasonable resistance. Psychiatrists commonly express the hypothesis that disturbed patients have, in their very self-assertion and psychological accessibility, a therapeutic potential that is far greater than that of resigned, apathetic, and withdrawn persons who constitute the much larger numbers in mental hospitals. In actual practice, however, aggressive acting out at Bedford was most frequently treated by further confinement and restriction or by medical sedation. Even those who believed that these disturbed patients had greater potential for recovery were vague about how such hostile behavior could be modified and constructively channeled within the ward and hospital community. The successful elimination of mechanical restraints and the reduction of currently assaultive patients to about 60 on Ward 4C were generally attributed to the "activity" groups of a recreational or athletic nature that had been instituted concomitantly with the reduction of use of restraints. As will be seen from much that follows in this chapter, the value of these groups was only one of many contributing factors.

In 1951 two psychiatrists had become interested in this ward and had attempted to reduce seclusion, improve morale, and raise the status of the unit. When they took several patients out of seclusion, however, windows were broken and minor altercations occurred with other patients and with aides. Conditions were not favorable, it was quickly found, for demonstrating the physicians' theory that such behavior was only part of a testing out process and that it would improve after a time. Management was not yet willing to risk destruction of government property or injury of personnel for what then seemed a dubious therapeutic hope. Accordingly, when these first incidents occurred, the ward physicians were ordered to return the patients to seclusion. It must also be remembered that the aides had learned from training and experience that their task was to prevent these very incidents. Hence, they were skeptical about this initial attempt. The lack of continuity, furthermore, in staff-staff, patient-staff, and patient-patient relationships made it difficult to motivate and integrate the ward staff sufficiently to permit change in attitudes toward seclusion procedures.

Every aspect of the reorganization of February, 1952, directly facilitated the planning and development of an effective program for Ward 4C. Patients and staff, it will be recalled, had been stabilized; a physician had been given primary responsibility for this one ward alone and large autonomy besides; even the change in the nurse's station was an asset. The only order by management to the physician was that seclusion doors should be removed. It was suggested that they be removed gradually, two at a time. Since the physician was one of those who had tried unsuccessfully to reduce seclusion a year earlier, he was understandably doubtful about adequate support from the administration. In a sense, however, the order to *remove* doors conveyed by its very boldness the belief of management that it could be done under the new circumstances created by the reorganization.

The ward physician not only wanted to get patients out of seclusion, but his long-range goal was to remove the stigma attached to 4C through demonstrating that a disturbed ward could be run with the minimum of destructive behavior by giving patients greater freedom and enlarged facilities for activities and social interaction. He did not know what specific methods or procedures could be used to achieve these ends. He was aware, however, that the full participation of the aides, under the immediate supervision of the head nurse,[1] would

---

[1] Glen Schoff, R.N., and Patricia Lynch, R.N., were given and exercised increasing degrees of responsibility for ward leadership as the program developed.

be required if anything of permanence was to be accomplished. That necessitated as a first step helping them accept more initial deviation in patient behavior than they had ever before been expected to accept or face physically. The Project workers and the physician were in complete agreement from the beginning about the necessity for changed attitudes by and toward the aide. They also assumed that nurses possessed capacity for a deeper understanding of patients if only administrative support and therapeutic supervision were supplied. Beyond these generalizations the ward physician believed that detailed procedures could best be worked out in full consultation with his staff through regular ward meetings and continuous individual consultations with the nurses.

REDUCTION OF SECLUSION

So much has already been said in this book about seclusion that we hesitate to add further details. It seems essential for two reasons, however, to examine briefly from the viewpoint of the specific ward as a social unit how seclusion was reduced to negligible proportions. This was *the* problem that had to be faced and solved if any positive conclusions were to be drawn about the benefit of ward socialization. And through its solution there evolved techniques for producing change, the development and significance of which can best be measured by viewing them in relation to the problem that necessitated their creation.

Attitudes of Aides

When the order came for gradual removal of seclusion-room doors, aides were still being utilized primarily to watch patients. At least two would be posted usually in a guardlike stance, ever watchful of the patients congregated in the day room. It had become their habit to try to keep patients sitting down on the plain solid chairs arranged against the walls of the room which had the appearance of a dingy railroad station. The attitude

The writer wishes to acknowledge their assistance in the collection and interpretation of data.

of suspicious watchfulness that they had adopted was easily felt by the visitor who, upon entering the room, immediately found himself with an aide on each side to protect him. He could scarcely fail to conclude that these were really dangerous patients. When incidents occurred, such as fights or breaking of objects, the aides would hurry the patient or patients into seclusion and then get the ward physician's order that was required. But it took an order from the chief of service to remove a man from seclusion! As a consequence of such attitudes and procedures, a quarter of the patients were frequently put in the 12 seclusion rooms to await an indeterminate order for their removal, and some six or seven had been kept there or in mechanical restraint almost from the time of their admission to the Hospital.

We have already seen how chronically fearful aides seemed to be at Bedford of difficulties with administrative and supervisory personnel. When the termination of seclusion was mentioned, one aide reiterated the old worry with the words, "We're afraid of getting into trouble. Things like, 'Why weren't you there to break it up?' or 'So, you go in and break it up.' There's always got to be someone responsible and usually it's the aide who gets caught." When the ward physician assured the aides categorically that *he* would be responsible to the Hospital for any incidents that might occur, their fear was partially allayed. It disappeared when they discovered that there were in fact no repercussions to the first mild misfortunes.

Fear of the administration was replaced for a few weeks, however, by fear of the patients themselves and how they could be controlled. Interviews by the Project staff with the aides shortly after the first two seclusion doors had been removed produced frank admission of great anxiety. "I thought there'd be murder out there! These guys had records! Some of them had been in seclusion for years!" Another attendant actually on duty in the seclusion corridor said, "Me? I don't mind if they take the doors off, just as long as that other door out of this corridor is open so that if anything happens I can get out *quick!*" Of immediate practical significance, on the positive side, was the fact that most of the staff had been trained to accept without protest the authority of the ward physician and the administration. Many aides would "go along" with the plan, and did go along with it in the initial stages, only because it was a medical order. As one of them expressed this kind of acceptance, "It's the doctor who has the ward that counts. When Doctor Z was here he didn't question seclusion, and so we had it. Who am I to take a guy out—much as I'd like to? Many a guy is high only for a brief time, but he's slapped into seclusion and stays there six months. So—who am I to take him out? It takes a doctor's order to put him in and another to get him out. His opinion about how he wants to run things is what counts." Another great asset in helping aides over the early weeks was the fact that mechanical restraints had been eliminated previously, and those persons who had been on the ward at that time had learned much from experience. Even the unsuccessful attempt to reduce seclusion the previous year was of value since some aides thought it should be given a second try.

Ward Staff Meetings

The weekly ward staff meeting was the essential means whereby seclusion could be ended and other large ward changes instituted. Through it aides were given and gave each other substantial amounts of group support, in addition to what they received individually from the physician and head nurse during daily work and from the active interest taken in them by members of the Project. It was the medium through which their conflicting feelings were resolved; where they as well as the nurses were consulted before any significant ward decisions were made by the physician; and where each step in the evolving program was carefully considered. The fact of being systematically consulted in all matters affecting their work raised their self-esteem from its former low level, and assured the involvement and commitment that were requisite to any fair trial of the program. They began gradually to perceive their status as members of a competent, progressive ward team and to find this status more rewarding and rewarded than their former role of performing restricted, routine functions.

The importance and effect of these ward meetings, as well as the meetings of the Hospital steering committee, can scarcely be overemphasized. Among the staff itself there was agreement that the program could not have developed so successfully, if at all, without them. One aide commented about the ward sessions, "The doctor explained the changes he had planned to us. We felt that he believed it was worth a try. Actually, the meetings give you a pretty good feeling. You can get things off your chest and the group will listen to your ideas."

Often meetings designed to improve ward conditions fail to accomplish their purpose because of the difficulty of finding a time when representatives of all three work shifts can be present. The ward physician realized that if the program was to be successful, at least the evening as well as the day shift must be included. Fortunately, at Bedford the second shift reports for duty at half-past two in the afternoon, one hour before the day shift leaves. Hence, by scheduling meetings at that time two of the three shifts could participate in planning and evaluating the undertakings. Both the day and evening head nurse kept in constant touch through these meetings and otherwise with the plans, procedures, and decisions of the other shift. As the immediate supervisors of the program, these nurses provided active leadership of the aides; encouraged close and friendly contact with patients; and interpreted the newly evolving capacities and problems of the patients who were being removed from seclusion, in handling increased freedom. The evening nurse was particularly enthusiastic about developments. Said he, "In my twelve years of psychiatric nursing, I have heard a lot of talk about the 'team concept,' but until I came to work on this ward I had never actually seen it in practice. About the same crew was on this ward before, but they didn't work as a team until now. It makes a world of difference when all the shifts feel like part of a common effort."

Several specific aspects of the leadership provided by the physician explain much of the effectiveness of the ward meetings. Initially, for instance, some aides passively resisted proposed changes by saying that they could not attend the meetings because they had to cover the ward or were not on duty during the day. Instead of interpreting their resistance directly, meetings were arranged to accommodate them. The time was not only set when the two shifts overlapped but the place designated was the nurse's office where the day room could be watched through the large glass window. In the second place, these meetings were not merely discussions out of which came no decisions and no action. Everyone was encouraged to express his opinion about a particular question. Then the ward physician decided what action should be taken. As a result the staff felt, according to their own statement, that they had a fair hearing, were given a chance to contribute to decision-making, and were motivated to carry out the proposed action.

Third, meetings at which difficult patients were discussed, rather than ward change as such, served perhaps equally important ends. The very fact that a particular patient could be talked about openly and freely, with the group making suggestions about his management and furnishing psychological support, was often sufficient to allay the anxiety of the responsible aide. Often a problem that had troubled some member of the staff excessively seemed to disappear later without specific action by anyone. Sharing a problem with others produces change in feeling or clarification of conflicting ideas; probably, too, the dynamics of ward alterations were sufficient to refocus attention upon other issues. Finally, when administrative matters, problems of maintenance, or lack of assistance from other departments which interfered with the smooth running of the ward were brought up at these meetings, the physician made an immediate examination and sought prompt action from the appropriate department or supervisor. The very fact that the Project sponsored wide interest in the detailed aspects of this ward program facilitated his success in obtaining action. This in itself did much to win the support of his staff that had formerly had the experience, characteristic of most large hospitals, of finding legitimate requests delayed interminably by red tape or lack of decisiveness in the ward administrator.

Procedures for Removing Patients from Seclusion

Insofar as possible, all details of removing patients from se-clusion were worked out in the ward staff meetings. Since most of these patients had participated only sporadically and with difficulty in regular ward life for several years, social interaction was encouraged in graded doses involving a variety of tech-niques. It was facilitated primarily by the understanding atti-tude of the aides, and their excellent on-the-spot judgment was usually of crucial importance.

One patient was removed at a time. The door of the seclusion room would be left open, in the expectation that he would come out and explore the corridor and then the day room. When required to take some initiative to obtain this amount of freedom, many patients appeared both cautious and con-fused. If undue difficulties were encountered in the day room, a man would be left there only briefly during the first few days. The dosage and timing of more intense social exposure were varied according to each patient's problem and pattern of social relationship. These questions were regularly discussed in the ward meetings to assure agreement and consistent action by all the staff. In general, initial mild signs of inability to be reason-ably comfortable with the large group of patients in the day room were ostensibly ignored by the aides. Careful ob-servation was maintained, however. If tension seemed to be building up and the patient became more upset, he would be asked if he wished to rest for a while or go back to his room. Often before tension became too great an aide would go and talk with him or invite him to play a game, thus providing not only diversion but friendly security and relaxation.

Certain types of incidents occurred that were ignored by the staff, since they were considered necessary steps in the testing-out period. Thus, the patient who broke windows was not re-strained from doing so and this behavior tapered off in several weeks to an occasional outburst. Some reactions were noted that appeared to be panic responses to unfamiliar or startling aspects of the environment. One patient, for example, went to a moving picture, shown on the ward, for the first time in years and attacked the screen. Instead of being taken from the group he was allowed to remain and he did not repeat the attack. The acceptance of such behavior without retaliation and restraint had the basic effect of conveying to the patients the staff's confidence in their ability to control their own actions. It likewise served to remove their immediate cause of resentment about what had been an unduly restrictive ward.

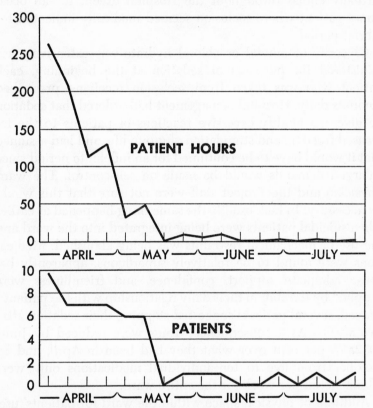

CHART 2. PATIENT HOURS AND PATIENTS IN SECLUSION, DISTURBED WARD 4C OF BEDFORD V.A. HOSPITAL, APRIL 6 TO AUGUST 3, 1952

Within six weeks from the start of the program all seclusion patients had been integrated into regular ward life to the point where separation was required for only a few for brief periods daily. As illustrated by the accompanying chart and Table 6, the 265 patient hours of seclusion on the ward during the week of

April 6, 1952, were reduced to zero in the week of May 18. From the middle of June until December, 1953, when the Project staff ceased keeping the record, there were only two or three hours of seclusion a month at most. What is more, the three other wards that had used seclusion for their own patients followed the example of Ward 4C, so that by midsummer 1952 its use had virtually ended throughout the Hospital except for an occasional patient where seclusion seemed medically indicated for a brief period.

Glycerite of amytal or chloral hydrate was extensively administered for purposes of sedation at the beginning, each patient who was taken from seclusion receiving prescribed amounts daily. Hospital management had ordered that sedation be given to modify excessive reactions of patients to the increased freedom and stimulation of group life, and had assumed that it would have to be continued for an indefinite period since enlarged demands would be made on self-control. The ward physician and the Project staff were not sure that this would be necessary. In fact, exactly the same thing happened as earlier when suicidal patients were being integrated into the ward and the use of mechanical restraints was being abolished. Medications were found to be relatively superfluous, apparently because adequate support, confidence, and friendliness were supplied by the staff in their daily relationship with the patients. Indeed, several patients suggested stopping their sedation after two weeks. As a consequence, drugs were reduced by June, 1952, 75 per cent over what they had been in April, and by October from five to ten individual medications only were administered per week for the entire ward.

Addition of physical space within the ward for patients' use, the sending of more men to activities in the rehabilitation department, and the introduction of recreational facilities on the ward all helped to reduce patient-patient and staff-patient friction, thus aiding the removal of those in seclusion. Since these improvements were primarily designed to benefit the entire ward population, however, they will be described under Enlarged Facilities for Socialization.

TABLE 6. DECREASING USE OF SECLUSION, DISTURBED
WARD 4C OF BEDFORD VETERANS ADMINIS-
TRATION HOSPITAL, APRIL 6 TO AUGUST 3,
1952, BY WEEK

Week beginning	Patients in seclusion	Patient-hours in seclusion	Hours in seclusion per patient
April 6	9	265	29.4
13	7	207	29.6
20	7	114	16.3
27	7	131	18.7
May 4	6	32	5.3
11	6	49	8.2
18	—	—	—
25	1	9	9.0
June 1	1	5	5.0
8	1	9	9.0
15	—	—	—
22	—	—	—
29	1	1	1.0
July 6	—	—	—
13	1	1	1.0
20	—	—	—
27	1	1	1.0

When changes began to be made on Ward 4C, the head
nurse instituted the posting of charts showing daily number of
seclusion hours, number of patients participating in social activities, and other facts in which the Project was interested. As
mentioned in the preceding chapter, this graphic portrayal of
results provided a definite incentive for increased efforts toward
a visible goal. At the end of two months the staff felt they had
survived what had originally appeared to be great risks. Everyone concerned throughout the Hospital was surprised at the
speed with which the problem of seclusion had been solved.
Clearly the administration was supporting the ward program,
high staff solidarity had been established by reaching a specific
goal through group participation, and the capacity of aides
and patients for developing mutual acceptance and friendly
relationships had surpassed original expectations. The ward
physician and nurses, therefore, were confident that further
exploratory steps could be begun. One of the most important
of these steps was noninterference in fights between patients.

MANAGEMENT OF ALTERCATIONS

Careful analysis at ward meetings of patient behavior seemed to indicate that fights were primarily of two types. The first could be described as a "one-blow affair" by the attacking man. Frequently it resulted in no retaliation at the time from the person attacked. Six months or a year later, however, the second man would sometimes return the blow without any obvious, immediate provocation. The second type usually began with a verbal argument and led to an exchange of blows. In the past, aides had been instructed always to prevent fights if possible; if not, to stop them at once. This often placed aides in a difficult position and aggravated ward tensions. Little could be done to prevent the unexpected one-blow occurrences except to restrain every potential striker and thus produce unfortunate repercussive effects. As for those fights that began with an argument and ended with blows, aides generally tried to restrain both men with at least three possibly undesirable results. Whatever the issue, intervention left it unresolved and the patients would try to fight it out again later; to prohibit a fight seemed to indicate lack of confidence in a man's ability to take care of himself and thus created psychological problems; occasionally physical injury to a patient or an aide would be caused.

In June, 1952, it was decided that aides should no longer jump in blindly to stop a fight but should observe the incident and evaluate it. Their attitude was to be more like that of an understanding parent with his young son or even of the average man witnessing a street fight. If two patients were arguing or threatening each other, no obvious attention was to be paid to the difficulty. If they began to fight but were fairly well matched, the aides were to watch very carefully but still not interfere. If the fight should become unequal or unfair, then the aides would be expected to step in and stop it. The results of this plan were immediately remarkable. When patients discovered that they attracted no attention or interest, they often walked away from each other after exchanging a few blows. On one occasion a man dropped down on the floor saying, "I'm tired. Let's stop." He then asked if anyone had a cigarette, whereupon the patient with whom he had been fighting pulled out a pack and gave him one. Men of the "bullying" type soon came to light. Patient T started a fight, as was his habit, soon after the new procedure was instituted. He was so taken aback when no one interfered that in a matter of seconds he stopped short and shouted to the aide across the room, "Hey, doesn't a guy have any protection around here?" It was obvious that he could be a brave fellow only as long as he was supported in that role by a "protective" staff. Contrast such behavior with that which existed formerly when two aides rushed to end a fight, perhaps one of them and one patient received minor injuries, while the second patient was considered assaultive and forcibly marched off to seclusion! Fighting presented little difficulty after the function of the aide was changed. It must be said, however, that the imminent expansion of social activities may also have been a significant factor.

ENLARGED FACILITIES FOR SOCIALIZATION

While the grosser problems of disturbed, assaultive behavior were receiving major attention, more subtle facets of socialization were explored. As a consequence, social therapy proceeded along three avenues almost simultaneously: greater use of pre-scribed individual treatment in such special units as corrective and occupational therapy, expansion of organized off-ward group activities and initiation of group therapy on the ward, further modification of the ward's physical and social environment.

In the year previous to the introduction of the new program on Ward 4C only 12 of the 60 patients were going, accompanied by two aides, to recreational and occupational activities. The number had been increased to 18 by April, 1952. Then the decision was made to form two groups of 12 patients each with one aide apiece. Confidence in the capacity of patients to handle greater freedom and to conform to reasonable expectations had increased sufficiently so that additional assistance was not deemed necessary. The role of the two aides, however, was restructured. Instead of merely accompanying patients to scheduled activities they were to stay with and work and play with the 12 men who were to be "their" patients. In order to maintain continuity in activities and stability of personal associations, orders were given the nursing service not to "raid" these group aides for such purposes as substituting for sick staff members or doing unexpected routine chores.

To keep patients busy and off the ward would have been justification enough for attempting to enlarge the numbers. All members of the ward team reported that these men paced the floor less, were more relaxed, and slept better as the result of going to activities. While they were away, moreover, problems and frictions resulting from overcrowding of the day room were fewer. But the main purpose in sending men to the rehabilitation department and elsewhere was to provide them with opportunity to acquire or relearn social skills, achieve self-mastery through game and task accomplishments, and gain self-esteem through individualized relationships of a supportive nature with personnel. The plan for group socialization was geared to the concept of patient movement in steplike progression. Hence, the activities and goals of the two units were differentiated. The more withdrawn and disturbed patients were assigned to one unit, the purpose of which was to stimulate moderate socialization and direct self-expression through simple physical and recreational activities. Men in this group went to the gymnasium, warm-water swimming pool, and bowling alley. Typically, a new patient would pick up a basketball after several days of noncommittal, passive participation, would be encouraged to toss it back and forth with the aide, and subsequently would be worked gradually into playing with the other patients.

The men in the more advanced unit were stimulated to a higher level of self-expression and development of their capacities, with a wider range of geographical and social movement. They frequently went for a walk, followed by a visit to the Hospital canteen where they were permitted to make their own purchases and associate informally with men from other wards. Then several hours were spent in working on individual or group undertakings of an artistic, educational, or vocational nature under the guidance of specialized rehabilitation therapists and with the assistance of the aide. Interests and capacities developed in the workshops and classrooms continued to be pursued when the individual patient was "graduated" from this group or was transferred to a convalescent, open ward.

As the new program evolved, the number of men participating in prescribed therapeutic activities increased month by month until in July it reached 46 of the patients. It was not possible, however, to form further groups and hence the additional men were merely escorted by ward aides to activities operated by the rehabilitation department or special services. Throughout the next eighteen months during which the Project was interested in Ward 4C, this level of participation was well maintained but the number never exceeded 48. By August it was apparent that a fairly consistent group of some 14 patients remained on the ward day after day. Although encouraged repeatedly to go to activities and at times almost pushed off the ward, they seemed too immobilized, fearful, or intrenched to leave it. The ward physician, who had felt the need of more assistance and consultation than the writer could possibly provide, obtained in September a part-time clinical psychologist from the regular hospital staff to assist in clinical and social evaluation of patients. After the psychologist had had an opportunity to observe this small group of inactive men, he suggested group therapy for them.

They were informed that three meetings a week would be held in a small room close to the day room but that attendance was voluntary. At the beginning the ward psychiatrist acted as group leader and the psychologist as observer. Several months later the psychologist became group leader with the ward nurse as observer. The initial purpose of the meetings was to get better acquainted with these almost nonverbal patients by breaking down the barriers of formality and fear that existed among themselves and between them and the staff. Friendliness and informality were at first encouraged by leaving the door open so that the patients could come and go according to their degree of tension. Coffee was also provided but they were obliged to serve themselves. When the atmosphere gradually became more relaxed, the door was closed and emphasis was placed upon the fact that this was their group. Only then did the psychologist begin to ask patients directly about their feelings and reaction to others in the group. The discussions were kept focused upon observable behavior and practical ways of helping the men to be more socially adequate.

In the course of time it became possible for them to express in words more of their fears and hostilities. Naturally much hostility was directed toward the Hospital. Relatively early in the meetings when the low level of verbal participation in the group was stressed by the leader, one man blurted out that after all the ward atmosphere wasn't very friendly and patients weren't encouraged to become acquainted with one another. He specifically suggested that the nurse and attendants introduce patients, particularly new ones, more frequently to other patients. In this connection we recall the emphasis placed earlier by Dr. Greenblatt upon the fact that many protests from patients are not merely an expression of psychotic hostility, but are often reasonably accurate reflections of realistic situations. Not only to react positively to these protests in the meetings, but to incorporate the implied changes in ward management, when appropriate, gives the patient a feeling of worth and responsibility and may indeed improve living conditions. Because psychotherapeutic and ward administrative functions have so often been separate, either by tradition or design, with little communication between the members of the staff accountable for each, ward management has had small opportunity to benefit from the protests expressed by patients either in individual or group therapy sessions. It is our assumption that linking personal therapeutic relationships with administrative relationships need not jeopardize the discrete function of either, depending on the overall social orientation of the ward and the specific capacities and goals of the individual members of the staff. The very fact that the ward physician or the head nurse was present at all of these therapy sessions gave him direct opportunity to learn about many legitimate dissatisfactions with group living that could be modified.

This leads us directly to the question of the repeated alterations in the physical and social setting of the ward that were made on the basis of suggestions by patients, staff, and Project alike, and of plans evolved in the ward staff meetings. So closely in touch with everything did the ward physician keep that he was most productive of ideas for modifications. The use of space and of physical facilities was recognized as a vital determinant of social climate and individual behavior. Nothing could be done to alter limitations in the design of the building or the ward, but potential resources could be maximized. Besides symbolizing the more liberal trend, the removal of seclusion doors provided unexpected space that could be converted to other purposes. For a time one of these rooms became a dining-room for four patients who had extreme difficulty eating in the large dining-hall off the ward. The door from the day room to the spacious T-shaped corridor was left open during specified periods, thus permitting the men more freedom of movement. In good weather the screened porch was used for ping-pong and quoits. Chairs that for many years had been backed against the walls in straight lines, although not fastened to each other as in many psychiatric hospitals, were rearranged in varying informal ways to produce something of the appearance of a clubroom. Several were grouped around a spot from which patients could readily see the television screen placed on the wall well above a man's reach. These changes, combined with the fact that a large proportion of the patients were spending some part of each day off the ward, did much to alleviate monotony and overcrowding and to provide a setting that fostered more meaningful contact of the men with each other and with objects.

Interestingly enough, several proposed changes were not initiated, either because earlier experiences of individual members of the ward staff contraindicated them or because it was decided that they were premature and could wisely be tried only later. The physician and head nurse showed great flexibility in not insisting that particular suggestions of theirs be accepted when the suggestions failed to obtain consensus in the ward meetings. Almost every new arrangement or procedure was a learning experience, particularly at this time when

emphasis had shifted to attempting more individualized attention to each patient. As new plans revealed the capacities or
limitations of patients, original purposes and concepts were
revised. As an example, the staff were most surprised at the
use made of a former seclusion room that had been arranged as
a "quiet room" with reading materials and cards. It had been
expected that the quieter, more withdrawn patients would like
to go there to escape from the frequently very noisy and active
day room. Its first visitor, however, was one of the most disturbed and loudest patients, who spent almost the entire day
it opened reading and occupying himself. He had removed
himself from the overstimulating day room, and utilized the
space and facilities provided in a way more satisfying to himself and acceptable to others. Enough indications of this kind
appeared to convince the staff that many patients could wisely
handle some of their personal tensions and interpersonal difficulties if there were more latitude in living arrangements.

The role of personnel in fostering socialization and encouraging spontaneous, constructive solution of immediate problems
received increasing attention as crucial to success in the upgrading of the ward. It had been obvious from the beginning
that progressively freer and closer staff-staff and patient-staff
relationships were essential. The physician set the tone for
greater informality and more equality of status not only in the
ward staff meetings but in his morning rounds. Instead of holding the customary formal interviews with specific patients or
being presented by the nurse with their problems, he began
sitting down leisurely at a table in the day room and encouraging the patients to talk with him.

Many informal recreational activities had been introduced
on the ward to help aides become better acquainted with the
men, and to give them a tool for rearranging or manipulating social contacts. From the ward staff meetings at which the
clinical record and behavior patterns of individual patients were
discussed, arose the further idea of having each aide select
one or two men of his own accord with whom to work more
closely. When going on routine errands to other parts of the
Hospital an aide would take "his" patient or patients with

him, would play games with them on the ward, and so on. Mutual interests were frequently found that helped to foster closer relationships. An aide said of one of the men, "This guy used to be very assaultive, always in seclusion. Now he's with our activity group. I've taken quite an interest in him because I'm an amateur boxer. He gets a big kick out of sparring with me. When he gets a little rough, I say, 'Look, there's a limit here, do you want me to get in trouble?' He respects this caution." In talking with the patient the aide would say something such as, "You sure gave me a run for my money today, and I'm supposed to be a pro." And the patient would respond with a broad grin, "You are pretty good yourself." When examined closely such exchanges between patients and personnel indicated intuitive recognition by the aides that patients were trying to prove themselves and show that they were "somebody." Whenever there was greater acceptance and contribution to self-esteem by personnel, so the staff learned, patient behavior would often be modified to conform to reasonable expectations.

Emphasis was placed not only upon expanding patients' privileges, but upon insisting that both patients and personnel had rights as individual persons that required mutual respect. How to deal with those men who failed to understand this and appeared to be deliberately provoking to staff was a difficult problem. It was finally decided that once the ward environment had become thoroughly warm and friendly, partial retaliation would be tried if provoking conduct still persisted. Patient J was the recipient of such retaliation. Early in his hospitalization he had made crude attempts to show affection by patting other patients. Some had responded by assaulting him until he had been put in seclusion for his own protection. While there he had regressed to complete untidiness and the smearing of feces. When the new ward program began and he was removed from seclusion, the staff gave him much personal attention, including gifts of cigars and other things he liked, in an attempt to reverse the behavior pattern. Progress was so marked that in a few weeks his appearance was acceptable and he was able to eat in the dining-room with very good table manners. But his

habit of spitting at people, especially women, persisted, although he was careful not to hit them directly. Talking to him
was without effect. Hence, it was agreed in ward staff meeting
to communicate with him in his own language by judiciously
throwing water in his direction whenever he spit at anyone.
After this had been done several times, the spitting decreased
notably. Thereafter he continued to improve in his ward adjustment, and before the Project staff ended their visits to 4C
he was in one of the groups going to the rehabilitation department.

One observation that was particularly interesting to the
staff and to the Project because of its potential therapeutic importance was that objects in the physical environment having
social significance are often utilized in the testing-out process.
An illustration of this was the demand of Patient F shortly after
his removal from seclusion to use the physician's telephone for
personal calls. The aide who knew him best and also the
physician felt this request was an attempt on his part to determine how much confidence they had in his ability to handle
himself. His request was granted and he talked to his family
for twenty minutes. The next day the doctor was reminded by
the administration of the rule that patients were generally not
to be allowed to make telephone calls. The physician explained
the purpose as therapeutic, and said he wished to continue the
privilege. The patient used the telephone each day for a time
but the duration of the calls decreased, and finally he used it
briefly and only occasionally. His mature handling of this situation impressed not only the ward staff but the management of
the Hospital. From a series of such instances the institution
gained the needed confidence to conclude that much of the
earlier emphasis upon minimizing risks and providing adequate
controls had been a misuse of time and energy and a misdirec-
tion of goals.

TRANSFER OF MEDICAL LEADERSHIP

In November, 1952, seven months after alterations had been
begun on Ward 4C, Dr. Funk accepted a position of greater

responsibility in another V.A. hospital to which he was to move in a few weeks. The prospective change in leadership was viewed both by the ward staff and the Project as a critical test of the stability of the new procedures, roles of personnel, and emerging values of ward care. Particularly vulnerable was the status and function of the aides. Their role of agents for patient socialization, rather than custodial officers, had been so newly established that it had not yet become institutionalized. Their effectiveness still depended upon what was expected of them by the physician and head nurses and upon the guidance and support provided them. What would happen if the physician appointed were to consider their role inappropriate, or if he were unable to give them needed suggestions and encouragement? Could the head nurses support the aides sufficiently to guarantee continuation of their role without the consent and cooperation of the physician?

All facets of the ward reorganization, moreover, were far from being stabilized. Alterations had been so rapid and drastic that even before the staff learned of the impending change in leadership, they were not certain that the new program had come to stay. When they heard that the physician to whose leadership they attributed much of their success was about to leave, they were assailed by doubts, insecurity, and fear of slipping back into old ways. In order to understand the psychological importance of this change in leadership, it is necessary to summarize briefly the sequence of emotional and intellectual responses that had developed with the various ward modifications as they affected attitudes in November, 1952. *Fear and skepticism,* with varying degrees of underlying hope, had been the dominant reactions seven months earlier. *Suspended judgment,* rather than expectation of success, characterized the initiation of every early change. To the extent that anxiety was allayed, it had been largely through the *psychological support and confidence* provided the aides by the physician and the head nurses and all the staff collectively, by the chief of professional services and the Project. Regardless of skepticism, fair trial of a proposed change was assured through the democratic group conferences that elicited *positive involvement* from each member of the staff. When the first changes were made rapidly and successfully, *genuine surprise* was felt and overtly expressed, and this surprise continued as the process of exploratory learning evolved. Success reinforced liberal procedures, positive commitments, and a friendly social climate, and with success came *pride and group solidarity*.

The ward physician knew that the record of actual accomplishment and of emotional development was good. But he was also aware that the newly found sense of security was tenuous indeed, and that with only minor administrative changes the climate of a ward often fluctuates notably. Consequently, he and the Bedford administration took many steps to assure the smoothest possible transfer of leadership. A successor, Dr. Paul Dunstan, who was especially interested in the therapeutic potential of ward management and in the relationship of individual pathology to patterns of group participation, was assigned to the ward several weeks in advance of Dr. Funk's departure in order to become acquainted with goals, procedures, and personnel. A brief summary of each patient's problems and activity program was prepared.

Dr. Funk had an opportunity to see both staff and patients testing their capacity to maintain the new values, and discovering the therapeutic aspects of separation when it is recognized and handled discreetly. One patient, for example, who had relied upon him a great deal began gradually to reduce the number of interviews, and the physician permitted the man to restructure the relationship in his own way. "We just won't slip back" was a phrase commonly heard among the staff that frequently took the initiative in weaning themselves from dependence upon the doctor. He encouraged them in this. When he returned from a day or weekend off duty, the staff made a point of asking his opinion about the way in which they had handled some situation. He would respond by asking them if they would have done differently had he been there. The usual answer was a somewhat self-conscious "I guess not." He assured them of his confidence in their capacity to carry on and reiter-

ated that the new physician would continue the basic program
with additional ideas of his own.

When he left Bedford the head nurses, psychologist, and
supervising nurse for Building Four were important assets in
maintaining continuity and supporting his successor. The transfer of leadership was made smoothly with no disruption or re-
trenchment in the established pattern. After a few months,
however, tension appeared between the new psychiatrist and
some of the ward personnel. They had expected him to be as
active as his predecessor in suggesting still further ideas to be
tried and in intervening immediately when the cooperation of
other divisions of the Hospital was needed. On his part he was
still not entirely familiar with administrative procedures, and
he had as one of his goals encouraging the staff to take more
initiative and responsibility upon themselves. Tension was gradually resolved and further changes were initiated. The staff
learned that time is required for a new person to adjust his ideas
to working dimensions in a practical situation and that part of
the progress being made was their assumption of more responsibility. A very important function for the physician, they discovered, was that of slowly fostering increased awareness of
the many subtleties of interpersonal relations, some of which
have been indicated in the preceding section.

The staff now entered a period of more difficult learning when
knowledge of sociopsychological factors in their own and the
patients' lives began to replace earlier assumptions that had
been used to alter gross aspects of behavior and the physical
setting of the ward. The problem had become that of individualizing patient care further and of reexamining the total
situation for the purpose of more effective utilization of resources. In an attempt to make care more personal a second
unit of group therapy was started; nursing students, who had
been given regular assignments on the disturbed ward, were
requested to devote their attention to selected patients under
the supervision of the psychiatrist; and he himself began long-
term psychotherapy with several men. In the reexamination
undertaken it seemed appropriate to look at the ward in rela-

tion to the rest of the Hospital. By early 1953 it was little different from any other ward in the institution except that it was perhaps more congenial than many. Gone were the extremely restrictive atmosphere and the old stigma of being the worst place in which to work or to live as a patient. Having solved the primary problem of management of disturbed patients and put it in perspective, the staff could now afford to consider what its place was in the total institutional program.

They discovered that the relative isolation produced by the order to refuse transfers of patients and personnel had had several very different results. On the positive side, other wards had learned how to handle many of their own presumably disturbed, assaultive patients. Indeed, there was no longer any good reason to send men with management problems to Ward 4C, since seclusion there had virtually ended. On the negative side, its separateness from the rest of the institution, the close in-group feeling of the staff, and the dramatic nature of the changes accomplished had created some misunderstanding and resentment elsewhere. Some persons purported to believe that the patients on 4C were not "true schizophrenics" but had lesser behavior disorders. At one time a completely unfounded rumor was circulated throughout the Hospital that patients had been given too much freedom, had got out of control, and seclusion would be reinstituted. The conclusion was apparent that there had been inadequate interpretation to the rest of the Hospital of what had happened. Although reports had been made to the committee for patient care, that body had not assumed sufficient responsibility as an institutionwide channel of communication.

In the spring of 1953 a moderate amount of transferral of patients and the occasional exchange of a staff person was begun for the purpose of establishing more reasonable relationships with other wards. Some months later the opening of another neuropsychiatric V.A. hospital nearby resulted in a sudden and large patient turnover in which Ward 4C participated as did all others. Toward the close of 1953 the adjoining Ward 4D, composed of an assortment of younger men many of whom were incontinent, mute, or disturbed, was integrated administratively with the disturbed ward by placing Dr. Dunstan in charge of the two wards as a single unit. Through this managerial change the staff on 4C could share its extensive experience and successful methods in a very direct way, joint staff meetings could be instituted, and requests for more resources of contributory departments and personnel could be justified to meet the needs of some 130 rather than 60 patients. Ward occupational therapy, which had been planned a year earlier for the disturbed ward but had been delayed through failure to obtain the services of an occupational therapist, was instituted on a part-time basis with the aides actively assisting the worker. A request was made, although it has not yet been acted on, that a full-time clinical psychologist be assigned to these two wards, and that a social service worker be provided to permit Ward 4C particularly to establish closer contact with relatives and encourage them to participate in the ward program as a step in preparing patients and their families for more rapid discharge.

16. Two Programs for Chronic Patients

THE PROBLEM OF THE DISTRIBUTION of resources and effort between patients who have shown little improvement during long periods of hospitalization and newer patients with recent onset of illness exists in every mental hospital. The setting up in recent years of active treatment units where the dramatic shock therapies frequently produce rapid improvement has raised the morale of hospital personnel in general. However, morale on the chronic service has understandably suffered by comparison, since there is relatively less chance for job satisfaction in terms of patient progress. On such a service personnel tend to maintain security and self-esteem through solidarity in their professional groups and pride in the performance of routine duties. The well-polished floor and the quiet patient are frequently the criteria of a "good" ward. Often personnel caring for the long-term patient compensate for the feeling that nothing is being done medically to get him better by performing many little tasks of daily living for him, thus decreasing his opportunities to exercise initiative.

The clinical management of psychiatric hospitals has been characterized by this administrative division between chronic and acute services, with proportionately high concentration of personnel and facilities on the acute service. This is probably realistic from the point of view of differences in the patients' immediate clinical condition and response to specific treatments such as shock. A further characteristic, however, has been the segregation of patients in ward groups according to actual or expected behavior. Thus, patients are typed by such categories as disturbed, untidy, or eloper, and wards are known by these names. While these divisions have apparently simplified certain aspects of hospital administration and nursing care in the past, they tend to support limited perspective regarding treatment possibilities, maintain the status quo in ward management, and enhance pathological aspects of the patients' behavior. Extremely homogeneous groupings of patients are likely to reinforce the very behavior that the members share.

A further difficulty that cannot be overlooked in the care of chronic patients is the frequent lack of coordinated effort between the special or ancillary therapists, attached in the V.A. hospitals to the various sections of the rehabilitation department, and members of ward staffs. These therapists not only tend to concentrate attention on the more acute patients, but they are often opposed to working on the wards. They feel that it is preferable to receive patients in their own workshops, gymnasiums, or classrooms, which are generally pleasant and well equipped and where they can more readily help the patients individually. The drab and crowded setting of the ward, they reason, does not provide a favorable atmosphere for their therapy. Transportation of supplies and provision for enough persons to work on a ward basis, moreover, are formidable obstacles that they frequently stress.

But there are problems of a different nature that make these statements, correct though they be, sound somewhat like rationalizations. The fact is that the growth of extensive specialization among the ancillary therapies, which has come in late years simultaneously with the setting of higher educational standards and the requirement of certification, has contributed to the lack of collaboration between these groups and the nursing service. Each group tends to emphasize its own unique characteristics and contribution without considering its relation to the work of others, and to apply techniques that are more highly evolved and individualized than are practical for reaching large numbers of chronic patients.

Since the men who are fortunate enough to go to special therapies are generally off the ward for only a few hours a day and since large numbers are either clinically unable to go, or the hospital is unable to make provision for them, the need for the more extended use of simple occupational and recreational therapies on chronic wards is critical. However, the specialized ancillary therapists have become so highly organized and pro-fession-conscious as virtually to constitute craft unions. They have not only opposed working on the wards, but they have not clearly seen their responsibility for teaching nursing per-sonnel those simple skills that could be immediately applied or for developing latent capacities among aides and nurses. Nurs-ing personnel have also contributed to the problem through sometimes maintaining that they are not expected to change the ward environment to make it more attractive. Because neither they nor the special therapists have considered such change a matter for direct responsibility, the inevitable result has been psychological stagnation for the ward, with physical and social barrenness in addition.

Still other, and even more basic, reasons exist for the failure of both nursing and the special therapists to establish closer and continuing relationships with patients on the chronic serv-ice. Because the belief has been widely held that persons who are chronically psychotic have extremely limited social capaci-ties, there has been a tendency for staff to avoid making any considerable emotional commitment in the way of investigating their needs or their potentials for development. Hospital ad-ministrators, moreover, have been so overwhelmed by the mag-nitude of the problem of reaching large numbers of patients that they have often neglected not only to give their personnel posi-tive support necessary to stimulate change, but have appeared to sanction the status quo.

PROBLEMS ASSOCIATED WITH THE CHRONIC SERVICE AT BEDFORD

With these generalizations as an introduction we turn now to the situation at Bedford and to a sketch of developments on the chronic wards that were selected by the Project for study. As the result of the reorganization of the building for acute pa-tients in early 1952, differences between the chronic and acute services became more marked, increasing the social distance between the two. Approximately 60 patients from Building Four, who were considered least hopeful or amenable to treatment, were transferred to the chronic wards, and in return the "better" patients from those wards were transferred to the acute service for treatment. A supervisory nurse expressed feelings widely held in the Hospital at that time when she said, "It might be interesting to see if patients in the acute building are actually getting the intensive treatment we think they are. Aides and nurses there maintain that their patients are sicker and need more attention. We forget the patients on the 'back wards.' I feel that *this* is the greatest challenge—to determine what can be done for these chronic patients. How do we keep them from being forgotten?" One of the physicians on the chronic service commented on the psychological climate in some such words as the following. The most important problem we encounter is the sense of discouragement. Hospital personnel feel that nothing can be done for these patients. A rumor has circulated to the effect that the staff here *are* inferior to the staff in other parts of the Hospital. Actually, the personnel here *feel* inferior in relation to the others.

To make matters worse, certain facilities like the swimming pool were designated for use by acute patients and were no longer available to the chronic service. Most frustrating of all perhaps was that lack of interest and understanding by the ancillary services in helping to improve ward conditions, which has been discussed in the preceding pages.

Briefly this was the situation that existed when the Project selected the two chronic wards, one supposedly for experimental and one for control purposes, that have been mentioned in Chapter 14. It will be recalled that the entire building in which the experimental ward was located moved forward very rapidly, and a little later the building with the control ward also made marked advances. Before looking at the programs developed in these two buildings, both of which came to involve the extensive utilization of special therapists from the rehabilitation department, a word must be said about the patients. In contrast to the men in Building Four who averaged thirty-four years of age, 32 per cent of whom had been in the Hospital under two years and only 8 per cent over ten years, a mere 2 per cent of the men in Building Six—that supposedly represented an intermediate stage of chronicity—had been in the Hospital less than two years and 37 per cent had been there more than ten. Building Seven housed the patients whose condition is longest chronic, none of whom fell in the category of under two years but 60 per cent of whom were in the over-ten-year group.

THE RESPONSIBILITY PROGRAM INITIATED IN BUILDING SIX

The physician assigned in February, 1952, to this building of four wards with some 185 patients had formerly been in charge of Bedford's admission ward. There definitive therapy was the rule rather than the exception, and the majority of newly admitted patients were discharged from the Hospital within a year. The distinct differences between the acute and chronic services, accordingly, were sharply highlighted by his previous experience. This fact in itself prompted him to consider plans to improve staff morale, attitudes between patients and personnel, and the general condition of the wards.[1]

The character of ward care in Building Six had been determined primarily by the fact that patients considered to be elopement risks were assigned there. Hence, maximum security routine was strictly enforced throughout the building although the "elopers" were largely segregated on one ward. Two wards were allocated to quiet patients who were withdrawn and often mute, and who sometimes presented feeding problems. The fourth ward consisted of noisy and agitated men, some of whom had poor habits of eating and of personal hygiene or tendencies toward self-mutilation, such as tearing out their hair or burning themselves with cigarettes. Most of the patients on these wards had not responded to previous treatment by shock or insulin.

In addition to the psychiatrist, the regular full-time personnel for morning and evening shifts combined consisted of only three nurses, 20 aides, one occupational therapy worker, and

[1] Dr. P. Stefan Kraus, the psychiatrist for Building Six during most of the Project study, has not only collaborated with the writer in the preparation of this portion of the chapter, but has already published an article on certain aspects of what was achieved in this unit of the Hospital. It appeared in *Psychiatry*, vol. 17, August, 1954, pp. 283–292, under the title "Considerations and Problems of Ward Care for Schizophrenic Patients: Formulation of a Total Responsibility Program."

his aide assistant. A librarian, two athletic instructors, and a music director were available for a limited number of hours each week. Morale was high among the nurses and aides as regards many aspects of their work, but it was very low in respect to patient improvement. The staff were highly organized, well trained, and all knew their assigned tasks. Most of them had worked together in this building for a number of years, and the fact that each had a prescribed status and role on the nursing team resulted in a minimum of overt friction. The capacities inherent in this excellent group, however, were not being fully utilized. Of primary concern to them was prevention of escape for which they felt they would be personally accountable. This preoccupation, together with all the other elements of custodial care, sharply limited any therapeutic accomplishments.

Altering the Social Environment

Most of these long-term patients appeared to have withdrawn into a shell, desiring to be left alone. Some 40 of them were never dressed in anything but pajamas, bathrobes, and slippers. Virtually complete dependence accompanied this withdrawal. Everything was done for the patient: he was fed and housed with little expectation or demand that he do things for himself or with other patients. What he should not do was narrowly prescribed. The presence of a dining-room and occupational therapy shop in the building made it unnecessary for him to go outside. Almost no one had ground privileges, or money in his possession. On the surface the men seemed to prefer this isolation and dependency, conforming automatically to the established routine. They made few requests and apparently did not miss the features of a conventional social and physical environment that were lacking. The prevailing professional opinion had been that these regressive states were a final resolution of patients' conflicts, the end result of their illness. As elsewhere, relatives had delegated to the Hospital, and frequently insisted that it take, responsibility for an increasing number of details of the men's lives.

In the context of these considerations the general problem

posed by the psychiatrist and the Project was to explore and define what aspects of a patient's illness were the result of his social environment, and whether, when the situation was defined differently, more mature modes of adjustment would be possible. Several goals were set: to overcome therapeutic pessimism among personnel and elicit their closer, more constructive participation with the patients; modify fixed routines and restrictiveness, thus providing a sufficiently flexible social environment in which more spontaneous, creative social relationships might develop; reduce the barriers between various special categories of personnel; and emphasize the common tasks of patient care and treatment to which each person could contribute in accordance with his interests and capacities.

The psychiatrist initiated the program designed to reach these goals by using his status and position of leadership to offset the prevailing climate of regimentation and restriction. He personally encouraged an atmosphere of relaxation and informality through conversing with the staff while they were performing their various tasks and by such simple but meaningful social acts as drinking coffee with them. As was true in Building Four, much difficulty had been encountered in getting repairs, supplies, and facilities at the time they were needed. He began, therefore, to make a follow-up of items or arrangements that had been delayed, and was effective in speeding procedural steps through establishing personal relationships with members of other departments to whom he interpreted the needs of his patients and staff. By reducing the social distance between the staff and himself and by assuming obligation for numerous administrative matters that had been neglected, he set an example of responsible effort. The first steps in raising morale were thus taken.

Therapeutic pessimism was counteracted by a series of measures. Electric shock in maintenance doses was instituted for selected patients who had responded briefly to that treatment in the past. This was done not in the expectation of achieving any dramatic results, but in the hope that their ward adjustment might be sufficiently improved to keep alive the therapeutic aspirations of the personnel and of the patients and their families. Two units of group therapy were begun with nine patients in each. Since their primary orientation is toward the outside community, social workers were asked to act as leaders, thus symbolizing broader perspective in patient care. Each of the units was attended by a nurse and an aide; the only occupational therapy worker attended one of the units. Staff members occasionally met with the ward psychiatrist to discuss observations made at the sessions, and they attempted to inform other personnel about what had been learned. The sessions were particularly useful in helping those present to view the patients as unique individuals rather than merely as walking automatons. Although only two aides could attend, so limited was ward staffing, the sessions did much, especially at the beginning, to break down the skepticism of other aides. When questioned by a Project worker one of the two aides made the significant remark, "I didn't think some of these patients would ever open up and express themselves. I'll be darned if we aren't seeing it happen. Joe spoke up today for the first time, and Ed is talking so we can understand more what he means." Then he added, "A lot of the guys [other aides] don't believe these patients are even aware of what is going on around them. I told them I've seen different—in just a little while. They are still very doubtful, but I'm sure they will see it some day."

As the program expanded, a variety of ways were found to compensate for the paucity of ward personnel and the impoverishment of the social environment. A news discussion group and a reading group were conducted by persons from the education department and the library. The time made available to Building Six of the librarian, the two athletic instructors, and the music director was increased by 25 per cent. Particularly interesting were undertakings by patients from other buildings and women volunteers. Several patients whom the psychiatrist knew to have special aptitudes were invited to help in occupational therapy, music, and entertainment. One, a capable artist, was able to get mute patients to express themselves in drawings, many of which were hung around the building. Women from the community organized a writing group, dramatics group, and dance class. It was felt that volunteers are particularly valuable in such assignments because of their lack of preoccupation with psychopathology and their tendency to approach the patient with the firm idea that he can be cured. As a matter of policy, the most withdrawn patients were selected for all these special activities. Each leader, however, was free to choose from among such patients the individuals with whom he wished to work. This freedom of choice was initiated because it had been observed that different leaders attracted and were attracted by different patients, and it is rarely possible for physician or nurse to predict which patients will relate most readily to a particular leader.

Group activities and participation by persons not on the regular staff, together with the interest shown by the Project, stimulated the personnel to discover more effective means for helping patients. Continued exploration of ways for making the ward environment more like the outside community and successive changes in ward routine and physical setting all contributed to relaxed association with, and better understanding of, patients. Games, sports, dances, and music programs were introduced by the aides, furniture was painted in bright colors, and the Hospital added new lounge chairs and couches and gay curtains. A small room on each ward opening off the day room was furnished as a library with books, newspapers, and magazines, and it was found that these rooms were almost always fully utilized. Doors between the two wards on the second floor were left open at frequent intervals, thus permitting increased range of movement and visiting with other persons, and an alcove accessible to both wards was provided with piano, radio, and candy machine.

The social aspects of eating received particular attention. The decision was made that no more patients were to have their meals on the ward, that all were to go to the cafeteria in the building. Gradually its appearance was improved until the tables had white cloths and plastic dishes in attractive pastel shades. In the meantime, to offset some of the disheartening routine of men storming into the cafeteria, rapidly and silently eating their meals and quickly filing out again, picnic-style luncheons with music were served out-of-doors once a week during the summer season. A large tent with tables and folding chairs, made available upon request by special services, was the setting for these picnics and occasional ice cream treats, and for card games, music programs, and so on. The tent with its suggestion of a carnival encouraged patients who had rarely left this maximum security building to want to be outside, and it probably gave some of them a sense of pride after all their deprivation to have something that no other building of the Hospital possessed. However that may have been, the great majority maintained themselves in this first step into the outer world on a surprisingly high level of behavior.

Since this experiment has been designated a responsibility program for men who had long since given up assuming responsibility, it is essential to see what was expected of them. Initially they were encouraged to shave, dress, make their own beds, and keep track of time. As part of the process of introducing them to as many of the normal activities of living as possible, they were provided—in addition to their coupon books—with small change. Although many were at first reluctant to accept cash and some of them lost it, they quickly came to welcome their weekly allotment and to spend it in a responsible fashion. The installation of soft-drink and candy dispensing machines in the building gave patients a chance to make choices for themselves. Some who had not been known to speak for years requested change for a quarter so they could use the machines. Some who had taken little interest in their families, and vice versa, wrote home for money. Previously small groups of patients had been escorted to the hospital canteen by an aide who had a coupon book. When the men hesitated about what they wanted to purchase, he would buy candy for them. After it was suggested to the aides that patients were to make their own decisions and spend their own money, a wider variety of purchases were found to be made, including reading material and knickknacks.

In the past, as has been noted, almost no patients in this building ever had ground privileges. According to the policy of the Hospital such privileges were given only at a man's own request. His initiative in asking for them was supposed to serve as some measure of his ability to be self-reliant. Often they were considered to be a reward for good behavior, performance in occupational therapy, or for services rendered by working on the ward. Patients were also rewarded by being transferred to open wards in other buildings. Since most of these men were seriously lacking both in initiative and in accomplishment, it was obvious that they would have to be encouraged to accept ground privileges, irrespective of their performance in occupational therapy or in ward work. Permission was obtained from the hospital administration to allow selected patients in Building Six to have privileges on a broader base. The obtaining of official sanction to encourage privileges accomplished several ends simultaneously. It did much to remove the stigma of the "elopers' building" and thereby raised the morale of the staff. With considerable pride the personnel received interested inquiries from persons in other parts of the institution about so drastic a change in procedure. All this improved the morale of the patients perceptibly, reaching even those who were not immediately eligible for privileges.

The assumption should not be made that privileges were indiscriminately encouraged. No one was offered them until there had been a thorough staff discussion of whether he could get along without fairly close supervision and whether they would serve to foster additional self-responsibility. Occasionally it was found necessary to restrict temporarily a patient who had received ground privileges. In these instances the nurse or aide who had originally extended them would discuss with him the reasons for restriction, and the same person would reinstate them later. This procedure spread more responsibility among the staff and maintained continuity of relations between patient and personnel.

Before summarizing the results of this program in its totality, two illustrations will indicate how individualized efforts served to advance the patient in his social adjustment. In the first instance the patient, John, was notorious throughout the building for demanding to leave the Hospital immediately. Frequently the staff would "go along" with his idea without giving it serious consideration, by jokingly responding, "Sure, any day now." After discussion by the physician, nurse, and aide together, it was decided to look for signs that John would accept something less than complete release, but which, nevertheless would be a token of giving him increased responsibility. The opportunity came one day when he was again asking to leave and demanded his wallet. The latter part of the request was granted, and having obtained it, John was satisfied. Requests to leave the Hospital decreased, and he was offered ground privileges subsequently, which he very much enjoyed.

Fred had been restricted to the closed ward for ten years. He had been labeled an eloper on the basis of a single incident when he had tried to get out of the car that originally brought him to Bedford. He was convinced that the food in the Hospital was poisoned and that the aides were his enemies. Within the ward, however, it was noted that he took personal responsibility for the operation of the radio and later of the television set. Staff discussion brought agreement that Fred had the capacity to assume greater responsibility. It was planned to transfer him to another ward in the same building where more activities had been started. He objected very strongly, however, although the reason could not be determined. He finally agreed to accept the transfer if he could return occasionally to his original ward. After several months he returned less and less frequently, and appeared satisfied with the food and capable of working for brief periods in the kitchen. Shortly afterward he was offered privileges. These he used only infrequently at first, but finally for the full time allowed. In the course of a year Fred's ideas of being poisoned and having enemies had receded to the point where he would mention them only when specifically asked and then with embarrassed reluctance.

When asked what was different about the building, he said that there must have been a change in cooks because the food was better, and that the aides were much more friendly than they had been before. He added, "The air seems better around here. It is a better atmosphere." In reply to a question about why he had not wanted to leave his original ward, Fred answered that his only friends were there. What is notable in this instance are the carefully guided steps of increased responsibility, which were possible only through the keen sensitivity of the physician and the aides to the significance of Fred's behavior at each step. Personal relationships were close enough to permit the expectations and confidence of the staff to be transmitted to him and he in turn was able to respond with an increasingly wider range of mobility and responsibility.

Results of the Program

Let us now review briefly what had been accomplished by this program eighteen months after its inception. At that time all of the approximately 185 patients were allowed to go outdoors in favorable weather under supervision, whereas fewer than one-third had gone outside previously. Approximately 100 were participating in regular off-the-ward therapeutic activities compared with 38 at the beginning. Twenty-seven had ground privileges and more than half were carrying money responsibly. Noisy and hostile patients had become more relaxed, and the socially withdrawn more active. All the men were not only dressed, but they appeared to take more interest in their clothes and surroundings. After a picnic or other outing during the early months a special ground detail had had to clean up the debris, but such detail was no longer needed. The furniture, books, and games provided were being used continuously and with a minimum of damage.

The attitude of families had changed appreciably. They were showing greater interest in taking patients for rides or home visits. Many seemed to have adopted more responsive, realistic, and less fearful or guilt-ridden attitudes in their contacts with the men. They were spending less time in criticizing the Hospital and giving more attention to the patient visited.

Gains in satisfaction among the personnel were conspicuous.

Their increased prestige within the Hospital could be measured by the ready willingness with which other departments provided services; by the healthy competition that developed between them and the staff of other buildings; and by the frequency with which they were asked in the meetings of the committee for patient care how they handled a particular problem or instituted a new procedure. The entire Hospital expressed interest in developments in Building Six. Not only did it cease to think of the building as containing the elopers' ward but its extreme concern about elopement as a problem virtually disappeared. Facets of the program initiated there were copied elsewhere, particularly the extension of ground privileges to many more patients on closed wards. Recognition of a kind that is eagerly sought and highly valued was accorded the nursing staff when it was asked by the education department to assist in the clinical teaching of affiliate students.

As these significant gains were made, it was realized that a more scientific basis for the evaluation of ward care of chronic patients was needed, whereby results both in group and individual patient movement could be definitively measured, and a body of principles established that could be used for teaching new personnel and advancing knowledge in this long neglected area of patient care. The psychiatrist, therefore, was busily engaged in examining social science as well as medical literature for hypotheses the value of which might be tested. With the aid of a psychologist he had also devised a practical scale for measuring individual patient progress at whatever intervals seemed desirable. Just at this juncture, and partly in recognition of the remarkable job done, he was transferred to the position of chief of the acute service, and hence was unable to continue with one of the most promising aspects of this undertaking.

IMPROVING PATIENT CARE IN BUILDING SEVEN

Building Seven housed some 190 men who, it will be recalled, had been longest in the Hospital. They were the sickest of the older patient group on the so-called "back wards," and averaged between fifty and sixty years of age. Many of them had not been known to speak in years, frequently soiled themselves or were otherwise untidy, and were clothed the entire day in pajamas, robes, and slippers. A considerable number were often observed sitting or lying on the floor hunched up in unusual positions, or standing rigidly until moved by an aide.

Staffing of this building was minimal according to the standards of the Veterans Administration. One psychiatrist and one head nurse were present during the day shift, and there were two aides on each ward. During the evening and night shifts one supervisory aide had responsibility for the entire building, assisted by a single aide to a ward. When the Project began in the spring of 1952, the head nurse had only recently been assigned to Building Seven. Formerly she had been in a hospital where patients of this type were dressed in pants and jacket resembling army "fatigues." She was convinced that these men could well be dressed if enough effort were centered on them. Starting in May, therefore, she and the aides worked consistently until, six months later, all 190 were dressing themselves every day. Because of extreme limitation in number of personnel, she obtained assistance from the rehabilitation department in taking the patients on walks around the grounds. Thus, they were provided with some additional incentive for wanting to be dressed.

In the meantime, the noticeable changes already under way in the adjoining Building Six spurred on this nurse and her aides to want to compete with it. Otherwise no incentive was provided through support or recognition by the Hospital of the work quietly being accomplished. The committee for patient care learned about the dressing program with surprised interest from its administrative nurse members, and promised the staff of Building Seven requested assistance in discussing their problems, making suggestions for change, and evaluating what was accomplished. Since personnel from the other Project wards had already been brought into the committee, their valuable experience could be drawn on. A program of muscle retraining was then being planned by the rehabilitation department for the benefit of chronic patients, and hence representatives of that department were invited to join in the discussions.

The committee made its services available to Building Seven through a series of meetings in 1952 and 1953. Discussions began with a presentation of the problems that had been encountered in getting such badly regressed patients to dress themselves. Emphasis was placed on the fact that a considerable block of time had to be set aside every morning in order not to hurry the men too much, and for staff not to feel obliged to interfere with those who performed elaborate rituals while dressing. For their previously unpublicized accomplishments, perseverance, and ingenuity the nursing personnel of Building Seven received high praise from the committee. Then the question was asked of how these patients could be encouraged to bathe and how incontinence could be reduced. On the most regressed ward, for example, 25 of the 45 patients would not take baths. Aides and nurses from other buildings suggested various procedures they had found useful: get patients who bathe to help those who do not, maintain a comfortable water temperature, use familiar brands of soap, have an aide go under the shower with the patients. Most of these suggestions, however, had already been tried without success.

From the subsequent discussion the principle emerged, which was to have broad usefulness in a variety of situations, that positive or negative potentialities reside in the expectations held, whether explicitly or implicitly, both by staff and patients regarding patients' behavior. An aide illustrated this principle when he said, "The bathing is like your dressing problem. It was pointed out that many patients get dressed if you encourage them but don't do it for them. If you shower them all the time, they will expect it." The subtle tendency for staff to become accustomed to assume that patients cannot do such things for themselves is reinforced when a majority of those on a ward share the same behavior pattern. Besides the fact that more than half the men did not take showers or keep themselves clean, further inquiry revealed that these patients were showered in a group after the others had bathed individually. A psychiatrist suggested mixing those who did not bathe themselves with those who did, "because when you have the whole 25 in one group they practically think that is the way to act. If that is the accepted ward behavior [accepted implicitly by the aides in their grouping of these patients and by each man who is aware that the others are like him], why should they change?"

The occupational therapist present at this discussion referred to her experience with incontinent patients as illustrative of the hypothesis that when in Rome even long-chronic patients can behave as the Romans do. Because of pressure of work in her clinic, two very different groups, ordinarily treated separately, had had to be scheduled at the same hour each day. The group that was sicker was characterized by incontinence and general untidy appearance, the other was much more mature in behavior. As the two groups remained mixed for several months, incontinence gradually decreased until it no longer constituted a problem during the daily hour in the clinic. It recurred, however, when the patients returned to their ward. In her opinion the example set by the less ill men was a significant factor, although there were also factors of interest in occupational therapy activities and of the continuing relationship with the therapist.

A second valuable principle came to light incidentally when one of the supervisory nurses asked the psychiatrist on whose ward seclusion had been successfully eliminated, "Didn't you have rewards for your patients on 4C?" Replied the physician, "Failure in washing, dressing, or anything else cannot be solved if we consider that behavior as an isolated problem. Then it will continue. We try to emphasize positive aspects of the patients' behavior. As long as you treat the symptoms only you get involved in them. In a sense we reward the patient by approving areas in which he functions well." He then said that, in the experience of the disturbed ward, the more ward activities there were in which patients might become interested, the more opportunities would appear to approve and reward constructive aspects of behavior.

From discussions such as these the nursing staff in Building Seven received help of two kinds: help in analyzing the social situation that existed and in formulating broad directions for action, and help in planning and operating specific undertakings. Although the dressing problem had been solved, no play activities were available on the wards in late 1952 when the psychiatrist quoted above emphasized the importance of an indirect attack upon problems. The period from December until May, 1953, was spent, therefore, largely in concentrating on plans for ward improvement, and constituted the second phase in the development of this program. Introduction of games, books, and other recreational facilities, and of bright, pleasant furnishings was begun and will be mentioned in further detail later. In order that the group of 25 almost completely dependent patients, who represented the hard core, could be taken out of their group setting and receive individualized attention from the aides, nursing supervisors gave direct assistance to the staff in rearranging the day's routine.

The rehabilitation department that had planned a project to train patients to button and unbutton clothes abandoned it as inappropriate when the discussants at one of the meetings pointed out that muscle retraining did not sufficiently emphasize *motivation* of the patient for self-care. Following a change in the administration of this department, several projects were instituted based on an understanding of the psychological needs of patients, goals of nursing care, and a consideration of what activities occupational and corrective therapy had to offer. The third phase of the program in Building Seven commenced in May, 1953, when these projects were initiated. A room formerly used for hydrotherapy, in which the tubs were still attached to the floor, was taken over for corrective therapy purposes. The following excerpts from a meeting in July of the committee for patient care indicate how activities had been begun.

Corrective Therapist: We have 110 patients [58 per cent of the total building population] a day in groups of about 20 for one hour each. We started out some weeks ago with only a volleyball, basketball, two bats, and a baseball. There is another therapist with me and an aide. Well, in the first two or three days we didn't attempt to do anything. We let the patients get acquainted with the surroundings and they took their time doing it. We especially noticed their reaction coming into the room for these activities as compared with coming to hydrotherapy, and it showed how they disliked the sight of the tubs. When we had a few of them still uncovered, some of the patients were reluctant about coming in the door. We had to push them a little to get them in. The only objection seemed to be that the tubs were still standing there and brought back memories. After a few days they realized they weren't going to get anything like tubs, needles, or packs. Then they relaxed more. All of a sudden a patient who wouldn't have picked up a basketball the day before did so.

Rehabilitation Administrator: We are going from the simple to the complex in our activities. We set up boards on top of the tubs, with colored squares painted on them. There are also matched movable blocks of color. The first game was an individual one of having the patients match the colored block with the square on the board. Then a game of toss was started with first a patient throwing the rings by himself and then two patients playing together. Equipment for these games is being made by patients in the ward OT program.

Corrective Therapist: We're concentrating on one group of patients who are "soilers." Our lavatory door is always open, and if we see one or two starting to hop around on one foot or otherwise indicating the need to go to the toilet, we ease them toward the door. [Group laughter] Some are catching on in time now.

In this corrective therapy unit a little room was set aside for special work with catatonic patients, who were not only mute but so tense that they did not respond to the regular program of activities in the unit. Even this very regressed group were becoming more relaxed and communicative before the end of the Project. An example of this aspect of the program was observed one day by the writer.

A therapist was working with James who had been mute and rigid for many years and had been regularly dressed by the aides on his ward. James was standing in a corner apart from the rest of the group, eyes fixed, and staring straight ahead. When the therapist introduced the observer to him, there was no sign of recognition. The therapist took him by the arm and said, "Well,

we'll have a little work-out today, and I want you to show the
doctor how much we can do." The patient shuffled stiffly into the
side room as the therapist took his arm. He was helped on to the
comfortable table there. The therapist continued, "Now, James,
do you remember three weeks ago you couldn't even move your
head? Now, we'll move it slowly from side to side." He gently
massaged the patient's neck and shoulder muscles, moving the
head from side to side. Then he did the same with arms and legs,
saying, "Just relax. Make them like rubber." A little later he remarked, "We've got pretty well acquainted. We trust each other.
James is accepting food more readily on the ward, and he'll talk
to me a little bit. What's my name, James?" The patient blinked
his eyes only. "Where do you live?" James moved his lips; the
therapist leaned over. "That's right."

After continuing for some time in this fashion the therapist said,
"Now, James, you've done fine for today. I'll get you some candy."
As he put several jelly beans in the man's mouth, the observer
noticed the patient make the slightest motion to reach out his hand
to take them. The therapist had missed seeing this motion because
he was looking at the patient's mouth. The observer suggested
offering James different colored beans to see if he would choose
the one he wanted. The therapist selected several colors, offered
them in his upturned palm, saying, "Which color would you like,
James?" The patient reached out, turned the therapist's hand over,
and emptied all of the jelly beans into his own. With a quick,
jerky motion he stuffed them into his mouth. With that the therapist and the observer laughed heartily, James joining in with more
than a trace of a rather taut smile.

As has been pointed out, gains made with patients in special
therapy units such as these are frequently lost when the ward
environment is dull, patients are without activities on the ward,
and special therapist and ward staff do not discuss their work
together. In order that gains achieved both on and off the
ward could be consolidated and enhanced, the occupational
therapists started in the spring of 1953 a modest program on
one ward that grew to involve all four in Building Seven. Some
months later this program was reported to the committee for
patient care in part as follows:

First Occupational Therapist: We commenced with the patients
who had no activity, catching the man who doesn't get the other
things the Hospital offers. That's the aim—to catch the poor man

who has never been approached. Because he has never been approached, he has never responded. We held group meetings with the nurse and aides to talk over the program. We included special services that provide many games, parties, and outside activities in the Hospital. We discussed what activities were needed the most.

Administrative Nurse: I thought specific patients were selected at the start of the program.

First Occupational Therapist: The aide cultivated a group of patients he knew on the wards. We went individually to one or two of them and encouraged them into the group. On the first ward we started just painting the old porch chairs that were rather dilapidated and peeling.

Second Occupational Therapist: We began by individual selection, but once one or two began sanding and painting the chairs, others would peer at the activity. One man would come over and say, "What are you doing?" The aide would answer, "Would you like to join?" and he would. It was really dramatic because one patient in particular had never raised a finger in all those years on the ward. You sensed that those who were not active were aware of the activity, and it was a matter of getting them drawn in.

First Occupational Therapist: On the first ward where we began we had as many as 22 patients out of the total of 45 in the program at one time, and I would say on the average 15 or 16 participated. We went from painting the chairs to painting colored checker tables. Having made the things themselves, the men were much more interested in playing with them later. It's very interesting. There isn't just one patient sanding. Sometimes there are two to four. They are all grouped together. One is working on the arm and one on the leg.

Second Occupational Therapist: Then we started on a more disturbed ward, 7C. We didn't introduce chairs there but we did bring in a second table. The patients sanded it and now they're painting it. We have an average of about 8 to 10 patients in the program. I think a lot of credit should be given to the aides on the ward. They have been perfectly wonderful and cooperative. Even though I don't get there sometimes, they have things out and are helping the patients.

Administrative Nurse: I was in the building yesterday. One of the aides said that with all the activity it has been harder to get the patients to do the ward work, but the ward actually looked spotless. I met a group on the way to the corrective therapy clinic. They seemed to be more alert. I asked them where they were going, and they gave me the feeling that they were looking forward to going there.

Chief Nurse: I'm interested to know if anyone has observed changes in the patients' socialization or communication with each other since the program on the wards has begun.

First Occupational Therapist: Before it started I went on the ward to talk to the aides and patients. The men were sitting beside the wall, not seeming to observe what was going on or inclined to recognize me. They're mixing in groups much more now.

Aide: Yes, they're mixing together much more than before, and they enjoy doing things together.

Second Occupational Therapist: The way they used to be lined up against the wall was awful to see. That has changed and they seem to be proud of what they're doing and tell you about it. The other day one of the patients said to me, "I'm a supervisor." And he pointed to the aide. "He's the straw boss." [Laughter] I think, too, they have a sense of doing things for others; not for themselves only but things for the ward.

As these programs were developing, the ward staff was continuing to modify the physical environment much as had been done in the other buildings. The leather furniture and colorful draperies that were supplied made possible the arranging of loungelike day rooms; the small rooms close by became pleasant reading-rooms; doors were often left open between the two wards on each floor, as in Building Six, to give greater freedom of movement and opportunity for spontaneous association between the patients. A variety of games, many of which had been made by the men themselves, were available on all four wards before the end of the Project.

Between April, 1952, and November, 1953, the average per cent of patients engaged in constructive social activity on the wards had risen from 7 to 37 during the daytime. In addition to the 110 patients who went regularly to the corrective therapy unit in the building, 40 other patients were going by November, 1953, to special therapies in other parts of the Hospital. Thus, 150 men, or nearly 80 per cent of the total population, were spending at least an hour a day outside the ward environment.

As part of Bedford's twenty-fifth anniversary celebration,

the New England Society of Psychiatry was invited to meet there in November, 1953. Its members toured the various wards in Buildings Four, Six, and Seven which had been connected with the Russell Sage Project, with three separate groups going to each of the three buildings. After their tour one psychiatrist from each group summarized before a general meeting his impressions of what had been seen and learned. All mentioned the relatively great amount of responsibility the patients were given for their own daily affairs, the attractive and conventional appearance of the wards, the interest and friendly attitude of the staff toward their patients, and the absence of certain symptoms and conditions that are frequently associated with large mental hospitals. The psychiatrist who reported for a group visiting Building Seven introduced his comments with a query as to whether these were really the "back wards" of the Hospital. Assured that they were, he commented:

> The first thing I noticed that was strange was the lack of any odor which you would expect on wards like those. The next thing was the lack of fetal positions and posturing in the patients. That seemed strange. Then we saw the patients eating in the dining-room. They had white table cloths, knives and forks; they were all dressed very neatly and were enjoying their meal quietly. That, too, I have never seen in my experience. Then there were the games on the wards, the aides playing with the patients. The patients appeared quite alert and interested in their surroundings. That I've never experienced. In fact, the patients all seemed in good contact!

CONCLUSIONS

The psychiatrist's report was not exaggerated. Progress had been beyond the expectation of the Hospital itself in both these buildings on the chronic service. Raising ward care to so high a level and preparing to take still further steps in the resocialization of patients, however, is no easy task when the following factors, as a minimum, must be operative: continuous planning by hospital and department leaders; decentralized authority in order that ward personnel may have freedom to explore possibilities for improvement; staunch support of ward staff particularly aides who are in closest contact with patients; group participation in much of the ward life; inter-group collaboration in evaluating existing practices and stand-ards of care.

Sensitive observation of patients and freer choice in select-ing those with whom individual members of the staff wished to work enabled personnel to realize that the men patients had been only superficially satisfied with their extreme de-pendency and withdrawal, and with the maintenance of the status quo. Expressions of active conflicts, as well as a reaching out for more social responsibility and satisfying relationships with others, were perceived. They had unquestionably existed before, but previous standards of ward care had reinforced regressive aspects of behavior and thrown negative features into relief. As personnel began to cease to consider patients in terms of their predominant symptoms and to associate with them as potentially responsive to their total social situation and to the standards set for them, the ward as a social unit could move toward constructive integration.

An important function of the committee for patient care was the breaking down of barriers that had previously existed between the many categories of hospital and even ward per-sonnel. Persons who had never before discussed together the practical significance of their work to patients and to each other were provided with a forum that encouraged them to do so. It became obvious that when persons who see patients under different conditions and from varying points of view begin to exchange opinions, they gain an appreciation of the work of others. Each can identify his own as well as the other's contribution to the improvement of the patient. This improve-ment will more surely occur as individuals and groups perceive that their collaboration is more effective than their sep-arate efforts, and as the patient's day reflects more continu-ously a wholesome and active hospital life. It happened that the initiative for improving conditions in these two buildings at Bedford came initially from the ward personnel. As the wards grew less forbidding and discouraging and as good will toward the staff increased among the patients, the special therapists were eager to contribute their services. With the knowledge we now have that more patients can be resocialized if such therapists work closely with ward personnel, if not actually on the ward, no justification exists for lack in the future of initial and continuing cooperation between them and ward staffs.

This report on the Bedford V.A. Hospital has indicated that *the very regressive behavior of extended duration in these long-hospitalized schizophrenic patients was in no small part the result of the institutional environment.* Such behavior included incontinence and general untidiness, mutism, primitive dependency, and social withdrawal. These chronic wards, together with the disturbed ward previously discussed and another ward that could not be included in this account because of insufficient space, housed approximately one-third of all patients in the Hospital. In some eighteen months these men had been provided with a more stimulating environment, and had achieved definitely higher levels of socialization with concomitant decrease in symptoms of "deterioration." The change had occurred without any appreciable increase in personnel or expenditure of money.

Accomplishment had rested primarily on the strong desire of the staff to win change, and on the initial utilization of a few known principles drawn from psychiatry, the social sciences, industrial management, and experiments in other hospitals. Subsequently, further principles were introduced as they could be found and brought to bear at the point of action. Fortunately, experiments are going on in many places, as will be noted from the references in the Bibliography to those undertakings about which articles or books have already been written. Long and concentrated work is still needed to sharpen and amplify conceptual patterns sufficiently to permit maximum use of the social environment of the hospital as a therapeutic instrumentality. But even the limited principles utilized in the Bedford Project appear so generic in nature and so immediately helpful as to be applicable wherever personnel undertake to investigate patient needs and capacities in relation to the total social situation, of which staff attitudes themselves are the most important.

PART THREE

MOTIVATING PATIENTS ON CHRONIC WARDS AT METROPOLITAN STATE HOSPITAL

RICHARD H. YORK, Ph.D.

17. Characteristics and Historical Development of the Hospital

METROPOLITAN STATE HOSPITAL, situated some 10 miles from downtown Boston, is one of 12 hospitals operated by the Commonwealth of Massachusetts for the care of psychiatric patients. Since all of its buildings were constructed as recently as 1930 of red brick in a modified colonial style of architecture and are well set in rolling country surrounded by beautiful trees and grounds, the Hospital presents a splendid external appearance. A massive building constructed around a large central court, with eight T-shaped wings three stories high and containing 24 wards in all, houses approximately 1,600 patients. Another building close by with capacity for 200 persons is used for medical and surgical cases and for senile patients who are largely confined to bed. There are individual buildings for administrative offices, male personnel, nursing education and nursing students, the auditorium and canteen, laundry, power plant, garage, maintenance and engineering. Recently a fine self-contained children's unit has been completed at some distance from the central unit with provision for 160 children from six to sixteen years of age. Elsewhere is the farm with its necessary buildings.

CHARACTERISTICS OF THE HOSPITAL

Before discussing the experimental work undertaken by the Russell Sage Project at Metropolitan, a brief report must be made of the characteristics of the Hospital as they appeared in early 1952, when it became a participant in the Project, and of the reasons for the minimal level of patient care that existed at that time in an institution that looked from the outside to be both new and prosperous.

Like all state hospitals, it had as head a superintendent

charged with medical and general administrative responsibility. He was aided by an assistant superintendent, a clinical director who occupied the position that was created as late as 1942, a steward who was business manager, and a director of nursing who had immediate responsibility for the daily care of patients. Like most other public psychiatric hospitals it was wretchedly understaffed and somewhat overcrowded. For 1,800 patients there were 10 physicians including the three engaged in administration, 38 graduate nurses, and 275 attendants. The department of social service had only three workers, and the department of occupational therapy had two registered therapists with two or three assistant attendants.

The wards were originally designed for 65 patients but most of them had come to accommodate about 75. Twenty-two of the wards in the large central unit constituted the "continued treatment" services, one for women and one for men. Although technically under the direction of the department of nursing, the 11 wards on the men's service were administered by male supervisory attendants as was the practice in many state hospitals. Except for the two relatively small admissions and active treatment wards that were also located in this building, the Hospital provided only traditional custodial attention. Thus, housekeeping, routine medical oversight, and physical care of patients were the primary functions of the attendants, while the few nurses were occupied with supervision of the women's wards, nursing of medical and surgical patients and those receiving somatic treatments, giving of medications, and training of affiliate nursing students.

The "Fringe" of Hospital Activities

Like all mental hospitals operating with a critical minimum of personnel and facilities, activities were developed largely in areas other than the wards. In the basement of the large central building were the occupational therapy rooms, mending and sewing-rooms, library, lounge where volunteers served coffee and entertained patients, and a space devoted to square dancing. All these units were bright and attractive, and staff members were available to give relatively individualized supervision and to form stimulating task relationships with patients. Here opportunity for self-expression was provided and the more normal conditions of life that promote self-esteem. The personnel took pride in these parts of the Hospital and patients preferred going to them rather than to many of the work assignments.

From the opening of the institution the department of occupational therapy had had central importance. Patients were busy; they were encouraged in expressive artistic and manual activities, and were helped to form social groups. Through individualized craft and occupational training they were prepared for work outside the Hospital. The fact that the department was a clinical teaching center for students of occupational therapy enlarged the number of persons available for supervision of, and interaction with, patients. Unfortunately, the war resulted in such reduction of staff that activities and services had to be curtailed, and the training program was given up. In 1951, however, the department was instrumental in helping physicians and nurses establish and run two small activity groups, one with women and one with men patients, to which further reference will be made later. At the time the Project was initiated the department was serving through its various undertakings about 12 per cent of the patient population.

In addition to the restricted number that it had the resources to reach, some 20 per cent of the patients were engaged in hospital industries. This represented probably slightly less than one-half of those physically able to work. Like many other mental institutions, Metropolitan could not long operate without the help of patients in the preparation and serving of food; making and repairing of clothing and hospital linens; sorting, marking, and laundering of clothes, sheets, and towels; repairing of furniture and mattresses; production of vegetables and dairy products, and maintenance of buildings and grounds. To what extent was such work therapeutic? It has been referred to as providing "automatic socialization." When one saw patients lined up waiting to march to the farm or the laundry, or milling around on the ground detail, one was convinced that they were only going through a routine to which they had become accustomed. Ironing, peeling of potatoes, or hoeing of a row of corn could be isolated activities for the individual patient. Coffee or small parties given those who worked were small inducement or reward for their contribution to the Hospital's existence.

Closer observation and discussion, however, revealed that the skill of industrial employees in working with these patients and in understanding their needs and capacities was therapeutic within limits of custodial expectation. Typically, when a patient was assigned to a work detail he was given ample opportunity to look around and become familiar with the persons and materials. Considerable choice of jobs, moreover, was available. Employees learned to watch for the first signs of interest in activities or individuals, and to encourage patients in such interest. But there was no consistent expectation that these patients would move from their work to the outside community, and planned steps for increasing their responsibility for participation in the hospital community had scarcely been formulated. The tendency was evident for employees to accept only the very best patients, and not to want to relinquish them once they had been trained and become accustomed to their jobs. When they were needed to run the departments, the employees could scarcely be blamed for lack of interest in having them moved progressively from one type of experience to another. Unfortunately, the employees showed no greater interest in recruiting and training other patients left on the wards with nothing whatever to do. So far as the patients who worked were concerned, the significance of the particular job to them was evident by their protests when the suggestion was made that they leave it to do something else. They had found some degree of security. It had provided them with the semblance of a normal life, and opportunity to express themselves in an orderly fashion and achieve some sense of contribution and self-esteem.

The Center of Patient Life

Even for the 32 per cent of the patients who worked or went regularly to the special activities, the major part of their time was spent on the wards. For the other 68 per cent almost all of it was spent there. As in hospitals generally, the ward was the focus of the patients' daily existence, their hospital home. However, except on the two admission and acute treatment wards that accommodated 45 persons each, and in the medical and surgical building where provision was made for bed care, the Hospital was unable in 1952 to furnish individualized attention to patients, anything resembling a homelike setting, or simple recreational facilities.

On the admission and acute treatment wards the day rooms had attractive curtains at the windows, tables with games and magazines, lounge chairs, and a television set. In the dormitories there were bedside tables with drawers for personal belongings. The female ward was staffed by graduate nurses assisted by students; the male ward had a head nurse aided by attendants. There was an air of purposeful activity in the morning during which shock treatment was given to a limited number of patients. Since nursing students gained almost all their clinical training on these wards, they were busy throughout the day caring for, talking to, and carrying on individualized activities with patients. An air of optimism permeated these units because patients were being admitted, treated, and returned to the community, personnel and equipment were more nearly adequate, and relatives and visitors were frequently seen.

But on the 22 continued treatment wards conditions were very different. The day room for each ward, which was approximately 60 by 15 feet, resembled a long corridor. Against the walls were ranged stiff wooden chairs, often attached to each other by slats, on which most of the patients sat during the greater part of the day and evening, idly staring into space. A few slouched on the floor. Their dress was shabby and often incomplete. These rooms were virtually bare of anything attractive and comfortable, or of objects that might create interest or activity. The dormitories were devoid of everything except beds, although individual lockers were to be found in a room outside each dormitory.

Perhaps the most startling experience in walking through

this part of the Hospital was *not* to encounter a single attendant or other staff person on some of the wards. Because the Hospital had been forced by circumstances that will be described subsequently into a staffing pattern that would ordinarily be considered *below even a safe minimum,* one attendant frequently covered two or three wards of some 75 patients each. By leaving the door open between two adjoining wards as was often done, he could keep his eye on a large number of patients. When he had responsibility for wards on different floors, he could not do so much as that. One supervisor for the 11 men's wards and one for the 11 women's could be called for help in critical moments, but everyone acquainted with large hospitals knows how many fortuitous occurrences can intervene to keep such assistance from being immediately available when needed.

Because of the paucity of staff, patients took considerable responsibility in looking after each other and doing the necessary ward housekeeping. Leaders were to be found on every ward, but alert, responsible patients were in a minority and the predominant atmosphere was one of indifference and resignation. Most visitors commented on the fact that these patients seemed much quieter than those in other institutions. This was probably the result of the historical development of the Hospital and the laissez-faire attitude that permitted them considerable freedom and self-responsibility within the physical confines of the wards. They had settled down to a minimum level of activity and social interaction; lacking either constructive or restrictive stimulation by staff members, they had slipped into an isolated, anonymous, apathetic condition.

Women's and Men's Wards

The segregation of women and men brought about distinct differences in patient care between the two sexes on the continued treatment wards. The staff on the women's side of the great central building were, except for physicians, exclusively female; on the men's side in 1952 they were entirely male except for one nurse who gave medications. Few general hospitals would think it conceivable that supervision of patients could be reposed in persons who had had no formal training in nursing. But in state mental hospitals it had been the traditional belief that management of psychotic men was too rough a job for women, and that dire consequences would result should men and women patients mix socially. Although experience had shown how erroneous were both these beliefs, a variety of reasons had kept Metropolitan State Hospital like many other institutions from introducing changes.

As a consequence of this dissimilarity in staffing patterns, the women's wards were more actively and systematically organized. There was less random rotation of attendants on different wards and shifts. Most attendants had one ward for which they were continuously responsible although they frequently had to cover other wards, so few were the persons on duty. Both physical and medical care was probably more adequate on the women's side because the attendants knew their charges better. Male attendants left patients more to themselves, and open doors between wards gave them an opportunity to move about with greater freedom. Since more men went daily to work in industry, there was less crowding on some of their wards and rules could be a little more relaxed. For instance, the men patients were permitted to use the dormitories during the day, while the women generally were not. Concerning this greater freedom one man supervisor commented, "We learned long ago, especially during the war when we were even shorter of help than now, that the patients could handle most things themselves."[1] When the attendants heard later that noninterference in patients' fights was being tried at Bedford V.A. Hospital as something relatively new in psychiatric care, they exclaimed, "Heck, we've been doing that for years simply because there aren't enough of us around to get to a fight in time to stop it. Most always nothing serious happens." One male ward, the parole unit, was run without any oversight by an attendant. Several patient leaders organized the housekeeping and one "trusty," a capable older man, had keys to the doors of the ward and the building.

[1] See Chapter 19.

In part, because life was more restrictive on the women's continued treatment wards, but also because a special therapeutic program had been developed for very disturbed men,[1] the women patients had a seclusion rate eight times higher than did the men. In their very resistance to restriction and greater interaction with personnel, however, there was a livelier atmosphere on the female wards. This fact, together with their flair for more cheerful housekeeping, made the women's area less depressing. The men seemed to have a greater proportion who were unusually quiet and lethargic. However, this may have been only an illusion, since the more active patients worked during the day when the wards were most frequently visited by Project personnel.

ORGANIZATIONAL DEVELOPMENT AND SOCIAL STRUCTURE

After this brief description of the characteristics of the Hospital as they appeared in 1952, enough of the institution's history must be reviewed to give the reader some understanding of why the continued treatment wards, on which experiments were to be undertaken, were in so run-down a condition.

Metropolitan was constructed for the purpose of caring for the "better" patients throughout Massachusetts, and initially patients were transferred to it from all the other state mental hospitals. The ostensible criterion for transfer was a fairly high capacity for self-care. Patients were considered "good" insofar as they were able to work in the institutional industries, could be given considerable freedom of buildings and grounds, and took much responsibility for their own custodial care. Because of its unique purpose and the attractiveness of the setting, the Hospital was often referred to in its early days as the "Country Club," although others who approached it from the rear entrance spoke of the "Bastille." As can well be imagined, other hospitals were reluctant to send it their best patients, particularly when they, too, had to maintain work forces. Consequently, only a few in each transfer met the criterion of considerable capacity for self-care, at least as reported by one psychiatrist who joined the staff eight years after Metropolitan was opened.

[1] See pp. 335–336.

In spite of this fact the Hospital showed great life and vitality until World War II, in large part because of the dynamic quality of the leadership. The superintendent between 1933 and 1943 was Dr. Roy L. Halloran, who later became nationally known as wartime chief of the Army psychiatric section. Dr. Paul Yakovlev was brought to the institution and his postgraduate course in psychiatry for physicians and his interest in neurological investigation attracted much attention. Dr. Emerick Friedman and Dr. Elvin V. Semrad carried on active research in somatic therapy. Encouragement was also given to psychotherapy to the extent of providing opportunity for staff members to pursue their analytic training.

Many of the administrative practices were of a high order, as custodial hospital psychiatry was then conceived. Procedures were well organized and predictable. Every staff group knew its place and functions, and an air of activity permeated the institution. A regular quota of personnel was assigned to each ward. Patients were clean and in excellent physical condition. A "total push" program was instituted, designed to investigate capacity of patients for improved socialization. Occupational therapy was headed by a woman of vision and dynamic understanding, and her student assistants were enthusiastic workers. On the negative side administration was of a military nature. The superintendent maintained rigid control that extended even to the point of his signing all correspondence, and personnel on every level in turn exercised firm control over their subordinates. As frequently happens under such a system, each category of staff was largely closed to communication with other categories, either above or below it. Consequently, the male supervisor of the men's service, for example, determined in great measure what the physician assigned to the service should know and not know about occurrences there. Within this hierarchical structure, moreover, little was done to help attendants understand other than the physical needs of patients. No systematic provision was made to assist them in modifying their attitudes, or to give them aid and psychological support in difficult moments.

Beginning in 1941 Metropolitan received a series of crippling blows. Events and decisions largely outside itself resulted in gradual depletion of personnel and supplies at the very time that it was being burdened with additional responsibilities. The outbreak of war caused the loss, without replacement, of many members of the staff. Shortly, however, the Hospital found itself obliged by statewide policy to begin admitting acutely ill patients for active treatment directly from the community. This required concentration of personnel and equipment on the two treatment wards referred to earlier, largely at the expense of the rest of the Hospital. The war was scarcely over when Metropolitan received another blow. The forty-hour week was introduced without any increase in number of staff. Thus, the time available to patients was further reduced. When critical shortages of personnel appeared elsewhere besides on the wards, moreover, the insidious tendency developed of putting attendants in such positions. As a result patient care could sometimes not even compete successfully with other hospital needs. The most difficult situation with which Metropolitan had to cope and one that caused deep cleavages among personnel was the establishment in 1946 by the Department of Mental Health of a special unit for the care and treatment of psychotic children. With the exception of one graduate nurse no provision was made for additional nursing personnel. The unit was set up in the medical and surgical building, and staff were "borrowed" from the continued treatment wards.

Dr. William C. Gaebler became superintendent of the Hospital when Dr. Halloran entered military service in 1943. He was requested to take the post by the Department of Mental Health, where he occupied an administrative position. Dr. Gaebler reluctantly accepted the superintendency because of the war emergency, but indicated that he wished an assignment less directly associated with patient care as soon as possible. It was not until 1953 that he was reassigned to the Department. During his tenure as superintendent he delegated most of the responsibilities for policy formulation in matters of patient care to other officers and department heads of the Hospital. Under more favorable circumstances this delegation of responsibility might have stimulated greater initiative in these staff members. Without strong leadership, however, at a time when services had been increased and personnel decreased, the problems encountered appeared insoluble. A sense of defeat pervaded the institution and the highly organized social structure dissolved into fragmented groups of personnel. These groups became relatively isolated from each other, developing their own special goals and procedures as best they could. Competition and conflict arose among and within them over the few resources that were available. The effect of depleted resources on patient care and staff performance was indeed serious. Because of the lack of attendants alone, personnel could rarely be assigned to the same ward each day. Frequently one supervisor and only eight attendants were available to cover 11 wards. With arbitrary assignments and continual shifting, there was little incentive for attendants to be interested in assuming responsibility for any unit. Their relationships with patients were so superficial that they failed to note or transmit word about fairly obvious individual needs, and they disregarded reporting requests for necessary repairs and supplies.

The physicians rotated frequently on the different services of the Hospital, so that attendants and nurses did not have consistent relations with them. Often conflicting orders for specific patients would be given within a matter of days, or different points of view expressed about overall patient management. A further complicating factor on the men's service was the relative absence of nurses, to which reference has been made. Thus, when problems arose there concerning ward management, the administrative nurses frequently did not have sufficient knowledge of the situation to reach an understanding with the persons involved, whether attendants, supervisors, or doctors. Such difficulties contributed to the development of a "live and let live" attitude between the groups concerned as far as everyday routine was concerned. This attitude reinforced their isolation and social distance from each other which was bridged essentially only on those occasions when unusual incidents occurred. Then sharp differences in points of view were apparent but little progress was made in resolving them.

Attitudes Toward Patient Care

Paradoxical and conflicting attitudes existed concerning patient care under these circumstances. The feelings of the superintendent expressed those held by the staff generally when he commented on the advantages and disadvantages of the hospital system.

> The patients are in stalls like a bunch of cattle, and we are all very much upset about this. Many patients have made an adjustment here because there is little expectation of their going elsewhere. . . . However it *is* different from years ago. Then, we saw patients sitting around and if they got up, someone would promptly set them down again. We don't see this now. I cannot bear to have patients sitting around with someone else doing their thinking and carrying on their activities for them.

While deep concern over the treatment of patients en masse was allayed to some degree by the satisfaction of believing that they had considerable freedom within the wards, widely varying points of view were expressed when attitudes of all categories of personnel were studied by persons connected with the Russell Sage Project. Many of the staff were so limited in the amount of individualized care they could give that they adopted various stereotypes and rationalizations. For example, one supervisor said, "How can we *afford* to think so much about how little can be done for these people. It seems as if *nothing can be done*. We feel this is the patients' home and it seems like ours, too." To make the protective and security tasks easier, it had become the custom to categorize patients as "good" or "bad." Although such categorization is a tradition in every large hospital, the tendency to do so at Metropolitan was perhaps stronger because there were so few personnel to keep track of the patients. Every patient had a "record" that was considered unchangeable. His most dramatic symptom or greatest deviance in behavior "lived" with him, even though it had been witnessed on only a single occasion or noted on his admission sheet years before. In many cases the very expectation or fear that he would act in a given way and the guarding against it, when repeatedly perceived by the patient, tended to evoke adverse behavior. Three-quarters of the 29 attendants questioned in the spring of 1952 agreed with the statement that "patients need the same kind of protection and control as an untrained child." Two-fifths thought that by and large ward conditions were about as good as they could be, given the substandard conditions existing at the Hospital. If more recreational materials were made available to the wards, it was generally believed they would be destroyed by the patients. Obviously, such opinions reflect relatively low morale and lack of optimism about improving ward life.

Perhaps because the attendants were accustomed to delegate much of the responsibility to patients, they had considerable confidence in the patients' judgment. Although three-quarters of those questioned had said that patients need to be treated like untrained children, an almost equal number felt that patients were "capable of telling right from wrong." Their relatively high degree of acceptance of patients was reflected in the agreement of only a third with the hypothesis that "most patients are not capable of real friendliness." Further indication of potential lack of social distance between attendants and patients was implied in the fact that only one-third concurred in the supposition, "Close association with mentally ill people is likely to make even a normal person break down." The majority of attendants felt secure in assuming a friendly role, and were proud to tell how well they knew patients. Fewer than one-third of those sampled approved the statement, "Only persons with considerable psychiatric training should be allowed to make close relationships with patients." Obviously, since there were so few nurses and physicians at the Hospital, the attendants were virtually the only ones in a position to form such relationships.

A particularly interesting variation in attitudes appeared among the nursing students. They came for only a twelve-week period, were unfamiliar with the complicated factors that had led to the deterioration of patient care, and possessed youthful energy and enthusiasm. Consequently, they were more optimistic and eager to make improvements than were regular ward personnel. The stresses that they indirectly induced in the social system, as well as their accomplishments in the Project experiment to which they were assigned, will be described in the next chapter.

Special Therapy for Disturbed Patients[1]

The picture we have portrayed of deterioration of ward patient care after 1941 is in general a gloomy one. As in many other state hospitals that have fallen into periods of serious decline, however, individual members of the staff could be found who were unusually successful with patients even in the face of extraordinary obstacles. Among such persons at Metropolitan was Granville Hopkins who, with his associate Clifton Mindingall, was achieving remarkable results in caring for severely regressed and disturbed patients at the time the Russell Sage Project was begun. Although his undertaking was largely unrelated to the Foundation experiments in patient care, it is being presented here for two reasons. It was, and continues to be, so highly encouraging in its results and implications that it furnishes a hopeful note on which to end this chapter. More significantly, it is reported because of the importance, particularly for hospital administrators, of studying the methods of persons who can elicit response even from very ill patients, and of identifying and encouraging such creative foci of social treatment within the institution.

As hydrotherapist for the Hospital, Mr. Hopkins had treated seriously disturbed patients with cold wet packs for several years. After the use of packs was given up, he was assigned to placing patients in hospital industries. When Dr. del Bosque became junior staff physician on the men's service in 1951, he was so concerned about conditions on the disturbed ward and the extensive use of seclusion that he inquired about the

[1] This portion of the chapter has been written with the assistance of Dr. Hugo del Bosque.

possibility of utilizing packs. He was referred to Mr. Hopkins, and the hydrotherapy room was reopened. The patients selected by the physician were not only given wet packs but they were kept with Mr. Hopkins during the day, since it was apparent that he was skillful in making them quiet and comfortable. Gradually the packs were abandoned as unessential, Mr. Mindingall was obtained as assistant, and additional men were sent to join the group that spent its day in the hydrotherapy quarters.

The object of the program was to reduce or prevent seclusion, and to help patients who had long been in seclusion to achieve more satisfactory levels of social adjustment. It must be noted that Mr. Hopkins and Mr. Mindingall had had no previous experience with management of severely regressed patients other than through hydrotherapeutic techniques, nor did they have any theoretical knowledge of group dynamics. Dr. del Bosque did not undertake to teach them any specified theories or procedures. He observed that a dominant characteristic of the two leaders was their sincere interest in their work, their attention to the details of the patients' welfare, and their understanding permissiveness. Mr. Hopkins seemed to sense when a patient needed firm supervision or was ready for more autonomy. He could work with several patients simultaneously and maintain expectations and activities suited to the special needs of each. Beneath all this was a deep affection—his patients came before anything else. Affection, flexibility, confidence, and close working relationships with each one were key factors in his eventual success. The physician's role was one of observing the social interaction, and fostering discussion and clarification of ideas. His support of the program and its interpretation to the Hospital were crucial for its continuance.

After a few months Mr. Hopkins and Mr. Mindingall were able to handle 16 patients at a time for some seven hours a day. Initially, there was no defined program. It was simply a matter of talking to the patients, asking questions, and getting to know them. After a testing period, they began to open up and tell their troubles. Since they had been rejected by industry and occupational therapy as being too disturbed, Hopkins began to think of appropriate activities for the group. He took them for walks, drove them to Concord, and told them about the historic battlefields. He took them to the seashore, to the zoo, and out for dinner. "I acted as though they were normal. I made no issue of their sickness." Soon, in an effort to occupy them more productively, he sought instruction and supervision from an occupational therapist, who taught him and his assistant how to make key cords, belts, cigarette cases, and to weave. Together, they taught these techniques to the patients. Then, they undertook to paint, decorate, and improve the physical appearance of the hydrotherapy room. When two additional rooms and the hallway were allocated for their use, the whole area was made comfortable and colorful. Many of the furnishings which the Hospital was unable to provide came from Mr. Hopkins' own home or were contributed by his neighbors.

The amount of individual care and attention given to the patients was staggering. Some had to be bathed, dressed, fed, and taught to brush their teeth like small children for months before they responded with interest in their own appearance. Those who were incontinent had to be toileted at intervals, but gradually as they emerged from their psychological retreat, they began to take reponsibility for physiological functions. At first, they would not soil or wet themselves when they were receiving direct attention, but they would become incontinent as soon as Hopkins' back was turned. Later, after weeks or months of further attention, they would maintain themselves in a tidy state throughout the day. At the end of the day, however, they would be put into seclusion, since their behavior had not as yet improved sufficiently for them to be with other patients on the crowded ward. Too often, these seclusion rooms were not clean and the tendency to incontinence was aggravated. With the cooperation of ward personnel a definitive effort was made to keep the seclusion rooms clean, and after this was accomplished it became possible for these patients to remain tidy during the entire twenty-four hours.

In spite of the outstanding success of this program, its goals and methods were poorly understood by others in the Hospital.

Since personnel were so scarce, it appeared as somewhat of a luxury unit. Fortunately, it received so much favorable comment from the hospitals and staff cooperating in the Russell Sage Project that it was not only continued but a comparable unit for disturbed women patients was opened.

In April, 1953, after the program had been in operation for a year and a half, the following accomplishments were reported. Because it served seriously disturbed patients exclusively, the use of seclusion during the day on the male wards had been completely eliminated. Twenty-nine patients in all had participated in the treatment program, 16 of whom were then sharing in it and 13 of whom had been discharged from the unit. Five of the 13 had gone home. The other 8 were working on the wards, in the residences for men or women employees, or in the various shops or the laundry. Of the 16 who were currently in the group program, the majority had already begun to show better psychological integration and improved social relations. The most dramatic improvement among the 29 was made by a young, active, and strong schizophrenic patient who had been in and out of seclusion rooms for several years. Patients and staff feared him because he had once seized a knife and threatened murder. After some months in the group program, he had been sent to work in a hospital industry and then had been discharged to his home. He enrolled in college, and when reported on was attending classes during the day and working in a restaurant at night.

18. Social Activities for Chronic Women Patients

In 1945 METROPOLITAN became one of Massachusetts' clinical teaching centers for nursing students from general hospitals that thus made provision for three months of classroom work and clinical experience in psychiatric nursing. This provision brought to the Hospital the optimism, vitality, and enthusiasm characteristic of students. During their rotation through the admission and acute treatment wards, the children's unit, and the department of occupational therapy, they not only learned about mental disease and the care of psychotic patients but made a significant contribution to nursing service. So depleted were ward staffs, for example, that had it not been for them many patients could not even have gone to various hospital activities.

The initial impact on the institution of this affiliation was very threatening, however. Some attendants attempted to resign, and much tension appeared between students and graduate nurses that has never been completely allayed. There were two principal reasons for the difficulty. The arrival of students stimulated a feeling of inferiority among attendants and some of the nurses because of their lack of formal preparation. What the attendants had learned came primarily from the school of hard experience, with little systematic training and supervision of an educational nature provided them by the Hospital. Some of the nurses had not had even the advantage of an affiliation in psychiatric nursing. Both groups could learn the meaning of their own and the patients' behavior only under the frequently trying circumstances of daily patient management. To them, recognition, good salaries, and authority seemed to be accorded exclusively to nurses with higher education. Although the students came predominantly from schools attached to hospitals and not to degree-conferring institutions, the very fact that they were receiving some training in psychiatric nursing, for which the Hospital made a degree of provision that had not been made for its own personnel, caused the staff to identify them with privilege and opportunity.

The second cause of misunderstanding lay in the students' reaction upon arrival at the Hospital. When they saw the impoverished condition they asked the natural question, "Why don't you do something about it?" Frequently they made concrete suggestions about improving some aspect of patient care without sufficient knowledge of why the situation had come to be what it was. To the staff who lived with hospital problems month in and month out and felt that they were doing their best, the students' suggestions appeared like personal criticisms and aroused resentment.

Early in 1949 Mrs. Esther D. Dufford, director of nursing and nursing education, began to consider what could be done to alleviate two problems. How could more effective service be extended to long-hospitalized patients who had been allowed to sink to lower and lower levels of socialization? And how could constructive use be made of the sensitivity and concern of the students who felt that almost nothing was being provided these patients? Until that time students had been assigned for experience with adult psychotic patients only on the admission and acute treatment wards. They had never been sent to the continued treatment services because these services were inadequate in staff and facilities for training purposes. However, with the arrival of a nurse interested in developing a teaching program for chronic patients, students were assigned to her for one of their regular rotations in the Hospital. Under her supervision they were to provide group activities for three hours each afternoon to a small number of inactive, incontinent, or depressed patients who were selected from various chronic wards by the physician in charge of the women's continued treatment service. These patients had not responded to other forms of treatment but were still considered to have some potential for improvement.

An attempt was to be made to improve the interest of these

patients in themselves, their environment, and other persons; to help them obtain social acceptance by patients and staff throughout the Hospital; and to encourage them to express their individuality through such activities as music, dancing, and painting. During the first year a total of 58 patients took part in the group program. Of this number, 38 showed no improvement, 16 improved in varying degrees, and 4 improved after being given electric shock treatment. Seven gained sufficiently to be placed and remain in a hospital industry, two were transferred to occupational therapy, and three were discharged from the Hospital.

The students were enthusiastic about this portion of their training and felt that they were doing something to help the "forgotten" patients. They were gaining nursing skills in a difficult but challenging area and were rewarded by seeing some success for their effort. The value for them and the patients was sufficient to encourage the department of nursing to continue the activity group even though the nurse supervisor resigned. A successor, Mrs. Patricia Pierce, was found and was given the title "special therapist."[1] Besides carrying the responsibility for the afternoon activity group, however, Mrs. Pierce was expected to supervise the training of students on one of the admission and acute treatment wards, give nursing care to patients having electric shock, and supervise the care of postoperative lobotomy patients. Her schedule of duties is a good example of how far the services of one nurse had to be stretched at Metropolitan in order to maintain preparation of students and nursing for acutely ill patients.

AFFILIATES' SPECIAL THERAPY PROGRAM

When the Hospital joined the Russell Sage Project, the service and training goals of the nursing department and the exploratory objectives of the Project were readily fused. A specific area of investigation and action became the Affiliates' Special Therapy Program, which was somewhat modified and intensi-

---

[1] The writer wishes to acknowledge the aid given him by Mrs. Pierce in preparing this chapter.

fied. The former plan of working with a small activity group outside the ward setting was altered, in order to explore and develop whatever potential for socialization there might be within a ward as a functional unit and between the selected ward and the larger hospital community. Within the framework of existing resources it was believed that more patients could be mobilized in the physical environment where they lived and spent most of their time. Any effective methods and procedures learned could then be easily transferred and extended to other wards.

The purposes of this social experiment were for students to participate, with a new set of expectations, in the ward living of the patients; to investigate their personal and social needs and capacities; and through the utilization of social skills to stimulate and guide their activity in a constructive manner. The affiliates were to use recreational games, arts and crafts, group activities, and casual conversation in stimulating the patients, and an attempt was to be made to "normalize" the environment. Answers were to be sought to the following questions: To what extent can socialization be developed through the student-patient relationship? How much resistance and hostility will patients show when affiliates infiltrate their stabilized social structure and attempt to produce changes in long-standing ward routines? What contribution will this experience make to the student in terms of her own personal adjustment, nursing skills, insight, and attitudes toward mental patients?

Selection of Ward F3

Ward F3 was selected for the experiment because both its appearance of neglect and its patients were representative of chronic wards in most state hospitals. The corridor-like day room where the 74 patients spent almost all their time was devoid of nearly everything except chairs; since the room had windows on both sides the lighting was good, but the walls were bare. Eighty per cent of the patients had been diagnosed as schizophrenic; half of them were more than fifty years of age; and 71 per cent had been hospitalized for five years or longer. Among them were disturbed or incontinent patients, the ward "reliables," and the seemingly fixed chair-sitters. When a visitor entered the day room he would find the large majority sitting on chairs, some in hunched-up positions, either staring idly or muttering. A small number would be moving about aimlessly, talking incoherently. Perhaps a half-dozen would hastily pull their dresses over their heads as if to exclude all stimulation, or would quickly move away when anyone approached them. An average of three patients would be in seclusion, and a few others would be in strong dresses designed to restrict the range and speed of their movements. Many were without shoes or stockings and their hair was disheveled. Most showed little concern for their appearance.

Actually this ward was more fortunate than some others in the Hospital because Miss Emma Flynn, the attendant in charge, had been there more or less continuously for fifteen years and knew her patients well. She could give them and the ward housekeeping about half of her time on duty. The other half had to be spent on wards where there was no assigned attendant, or in getting supplies and looking after administrative matters. Under the circumstances, she relied upon several of the "better" patients who took pride in helping her run the ward and in assisting other patients in eating, dressing, going to bed, and getting up in the morning.

Initiation of the Experiment

When students were completing their third week of classroom work and were about to begin their clinical experience on the wards, they were informed of the experiment and of the fact that two girls from each affiliating school of nursing might volunteer to participate in it, as an additional rotation, during their remaining nine weeks at Metropolitan. Thus, 10 or 12 students were enrolled in the special therapy program, although no more than two or four were generally available at one time for the activities in Ward F3, to which three hours five afternoons a week were devoted. The writer oriented each group to the program as follows:

We are working with chronic patients some of whom appear very much upset. They have had no organized program designed for social stimulation for years. To a large extent they are socially disturbing to others, or they have withdrawn themselves from all but minimum participation in their environment. We want to understand what their capacities are, what their life is like on the wards, and whether or not we can help them regain the social skills necessary for a moderately happy social life either in an institution or in the community.

You have social skills, interests, and understanding of people, and we should like to have you get acquainted with the ward and the patients there. First, using a survey scale, we should like you to look for indications that a patient is aware of the environment, is inclined toward an activity going on, and is inclined toward or away from other persons. Then, under the supervision of the nurse, we should like you to try your own ideas in your own way in interesting these patients. You are free to make suggestions about changes and the initiation of new procedures. This is primarily an exploration; it is a process of learning together what the possibilities and limitations are for these patients in the hospital environment.

The survey scale the students were asked to use was the ward socialization index described in Chapter 14, which permitted a simple and quick tally of the number of patients in each category of socialization at any particular time. Its use provided data whereby changes in constructive activity and interaction could be followed. Students were also requested to keep a log in which, after each period of ward activity, they would describe what they had done, the reactions of the patients, and whether there had been changes in behavior, unusual incidents, or new activities.

Weekly meetings were held at which the students, nurse supervisor, writer, and frequently visitors were present. They afforded opportunity for continuous evaluation of the program, patients' behavior, students' ideas, relationships between patients and between students and patients. Administrative matters were also facilitated. The role of the social scientist was that of defining and redefining the area of interest, stimulating observation, and evaluating reports. The role in the ward situation of the graduate nurse who supervised the students was in general consistent with that of the social scientist. She encouraged them to exert initiative, and she helped them guard against the common error of concentrating too much on the "better" patients at the expense of the quiet or hostile ones. She also had the difficult task of providing what continuity existed in ward activities, since the same students could not come regularly to the afternoon sessions.

The obtaining of necessary supplies presented a constant problem. Because there was no budget for the program and scarcely so much as one table with which to begin, the nurse canvassed all departments of the Hospital for possibly useful materials. Occupational therapy was particularly generous in sharing its limited supplies, and the students themselves donated many needed items.

As plans for the program developed, some concern was expressed about the possible reaction of Miss Flynn to having students on the ward that she had so long thought of as hers. At the beginning she believed, as did many others, that supplies would be destroyed, activities would dirty her very clean ward, and patients would become disturbed since there had been almost no visitors in years. Fortunately, it was discovered on the very first day that the students could help her and she them. She appreciated their interest in her large group of patients. Her thorough knowledge of the patients and her ability to utilize factors in the ward routine to dovetail with the goals of socialization made her of real assistance to them. The management of Patient A is illustrative. For some months Mrs. A had been neglected because of her withdrawn condition or her occasional overt resistance to students' efforts to work with her. The attendant knew, however, from long experience that although the patient was untidy and noisy, she would respond positively to continued attention. Miss Flynn encouraged the students to persist in attempting to draw her out of herself, and gradually they were able to bring Mrs. A into their activity group.

The physician in charge of the women's service played a significant and necessary role in the evolution of the program, particularly since the nurse felt free to bring to her for help whatever problems arose. As time elapsed and patients improved, the doctor permitted some to go off the ward under proper supervision, others were given permission to use tools and sharp instruments, and still others were transferred to different wards.

DEVELOPMENT OF SOCIAL INTERACTION BETWEEN MAY, 1952, AND JUNE, 1953

The amount of social interaction on Ward F3 was minimal during the first three weeks, when the students simply observed the patients without intervening. Only a few were seen in interaction of even the most basic types. To gather a group was difficult, since many patients disliked being in close proximity with the students or with the other women. Many questions were raised in our minds as to how to approach the individual patient and what could be accomplished. There were so many persons on this ward that it was decided to concentrate on those who showed the first signs of interest, while still trying to encourage the others by making equipment available to them.

Portions of a student's log during the first week after intervention began tells of her initial approach:

Miss M and I went into F3 at three o'clock with several magazines and picture puzzles which we *placed* on a table and *then watched* to see what would happen. Immediately several patients came up and each took a magazine. They appeared very much pleased. One woman took a puzzle and after walking around with the box under her arm for a while was joined by a friend. The two patients then started working the puzzle. They worked well and seemed quite excited. Periodically some other patients would stop by for a moment to look, but they appeared to be timid and would not participate in the fun. In going around the ward, I would *sit down and talk* to the patients. Many patients like to have someone just sit and talk with them. Several who spoke a foreign language were eager to have a listening ear.

Miss M and I went to F3 at 9:15 a.m., and after getting a few women started on a puzzle we began playing whist with two patients. *As others became interested Miss M or I would drop out and let them play.*

In the afternoon we again went over to the ward and *were taught a game* by one of the patients. It was the only game she knew and she took great pride in showing it to us. It resembled rather closely the game we had started with the women before.

Two of the women *helped us in encouraging more timid patients* to take the magazines to read. The patients gradually picked them up, read them, and passed them on to the next person to read. Several requested other kinds of magazines. No magazines were destroyed and the patients handled them carefully.

At the beginning the students did not attempt to push the patients into activity, but offered them opportunities to make their own choice. Most of the affiliates seemed to understand naturally that the program was primarily for the patients, were sensitive to their needs, and did a good job of informal social stimulation. Women who showed a potential interest in something were encouraged to become active participants. As the first indications emerged that some patients were not only interested but had initiative or could express themselves to the students, the enthusiasm of the latter increased and they found new ways of relating to the patients. A log written in the second week reported:

At this time I took a large rubber ball and started playing catch with several quiet women who sat all day and never seemed to move from one spot. Before our game was over, thirteen patients had participated and seemed to be enjoying themselves. *Many patients watched* and said they would like to play next time. I asked some patients if they'd like to start a garden. I got five positive and three negative answers; some, however, gave no response whatever.

Another student brought paper, pencils, and nail polish to the ward with the following results:

Several women took up paper and pencil eagerly as if indeed it had been a long time since they had written anything. This group consisted mostly of those who previously could not be persuaded to join in any of the group activities. I was surprised at the response.

I brought a bottle of bright red nail polish and started painting as many as twenty sets of nails. Patients who had not responded to any other activity asked to have their nails done.

By the end of the third week a new dimension in the social relationships of this group of long-term patients began to be demonstrated to the students. We quote excerpts again from the log:

As Miss M had the day off, I went by myself to F3. A patient had the misfortune to become sick to her stomach. One of the women immediately got a rag to clean up, while another one and I got her to the bathroom and eventually into bed. The attendant was off the floor at the time, but the *patients had perfect control of the situation.*

In the morning I took a small radio to the ward. Several patients *offered suggestions* about placing the radio on the table and when I was unable to find the right switch several others made suggestions.

Only one woman objected to patients who were putting a puzzle together, and she attempted to brush some of the pieces on the floor. She was quickly *put in her place by the other patients.*

One of the women was extremely hostile and told me that I was not to talk to her. She really got quite mad and attempted to brush me off with her hand. One of the other patients jumped up, ran across the room, and told the woman to leave me alone. The two women exchanged words.

The manifestation by patients of responsibility for each other, their attempts to set limits to the manner and extent of expressing hostility among themselves as well as to the affiliates, and the positive aid given the students were crucial elements within the ward's social framework in making these prospective nurses feel accepted and confident. They recognized more clearly than before that this patient group, left largely on its own over a period of years, had developed a pattern of group controls and individual responsibility.

Off-the-Ward Activities

It soon appeared that seven patients were regularly and easily participating in the ward program. The graduate nurse recognized that most of them were patients who had been in her original special therapy group. They so monopolized the time and attention of the students that the latter could not concentrate on patients that were more withdrawn. With the assistance of the department of occupational therapy, therefore, the nurse devised the plan of taking them to activities elsewhere, thus leaving the affiliates on the ward to work with the more isolated and resistant patients.

When asked what bothers them most about ward life, patients frequently mention the lack of privacy and freedom of move-ment. Nevertheless, in many instances it is not easy to persuade them to leave the ward, because they are afraid to make a new adjustment to places and persons. Additional responsibility goes with increased space, range of movement, and contacts. Once outside, however, patients dislike returning to the ward. In early attempts to get these seven patients to go to activities in another part of the building, the interest of only five was aroused. This unit was gradually increased until it reached 25 by the end of one year. Most of them came to be construc-tively engaged in group activities and all expressed personal pleasure. They participated in the square dancing sponsored by the department of occupational therapy, and in bowling. They went on picnics, to hospital radio programs, and the li-brary, and they did gardening. Excerpts from the log of one student reflect physical and psychological movement:

Group in the courtyard today. Fifteen patients participated; two or three knitted; six or seven bowled; two read; four played ball. Everyone walked around the courtyard for exercise. Refresh-ments of cake and milk were served which were enjoyed by all. General atmosphere seemed happy.

In the afternoon Mrs. P [a volunteer] and the students took 15 patients to Brookside [a recreational area]. Most of them were eager to go and could not remember when they last went. We took the victrola and played several folk dances to which one patient did her native dance. Included in the group was an escape artist [eloper]. We had no difficulty in keeping the group together and they seemed to enjoy the walk thoroughly.

The group liked bowling very much and competed to see who would get the highest score. After bowling we returned to the courtyard and played horseshoes. The competitive spirit remained friendly. When two of the patients got a ringer the others were enthusiastic in their praise.

As patients with whom the affiliates were working on the

ward improved in their social adjustment, they were encouraged to join the off-the-ward group. They also began to participate in hospital activities other than those associated with the F3 program. For instance, 10 or 12 joined other patients in bicycle riding and baseball in the courtyard one evening a week under the supervision of a volunteer. They mentioned how enjoyable these evenings were as they had never been allowed outside at night before. As the experiment developed, the level of expectation for all patients on the ward was progressively raised, and further steps in group behavior were taken. One was the successful mixing of men and women patients, who had been kept entirely separated. This was initiated by the holding of ward parties to which men were invited. Another came about after the manager of the laundry expressed the need for some help. A "tour of the laundry" by five patients was arranged, and two of them remained to work there and enjoyed it. Some patients commenced to go to occupational therapy regularly, where they obtained more individualized attention and opportunity for developing occupational skills. Thus, as this "off-the-ward" group increased in size by additions from the ward itself, it began to become a part of, and contribute in turn to, the larger hospital community.

Course of Ward Social Changes

By far the most difficult problem in working with these long-term patients was the large group who at first appeared completely unresponsive, or actively avoided any stimulation or interest shown in them. They seemed unaware of what was going on around them, had no basic needs that the students could meet, and preferred to remain uninvolved. It was only through close study and continued interest in them that they began to move on the most elementary levels. As described already, some made their first contacts by scribbling, some through nail polish, others through simple physical games and exercise. A log notes additional effective media:

We have made a point of speaking to some of the older patients a few minutes each time we appear; they look forward to it and say more each time. They have little to offer spontaneously, but it is increasing.

We had been using a victrola on the ward. One day when the regular record cabinet was closed in OT we found some old records elsewhere which we brought to the ward. To our astonishment, we noticed that the most regressed and elderly patients recognized these old songs and joined in, both actively and passively. We have made almost constant use of this technique to stimulate the older women.

Gradually many very resistant and isolated patients began to respond, almost despite themselves. As soon as an initial positive response was obtained, a strenuous effort was made to maintain the contact primarily on the patient's own terms, and later to encourage consistent, self-determined involvement either in individual activity or preferably in relationships with other persons. By the middle of the year we had learned to appreciate the slowness of the resocialization process, but more importantly we had also learned not to underestimate the fact that these patients were continually and actively testing out the new situations and calculating their chances of gaining satisfaction from participation. Our repeated observations of women who attempted to watch proceedings or take some small part without being seen by the students, and who later achieved fuller participation, suggests that an initial period was needed for passive sharing in activities. This passive sharing seemed to reassure these patients by allowing opportunity to discover the intentions of others, and the nature and degree of the affiliates' acceptance of ward behavior. It also permitted them to determine the circumstances under which they might participate more actively and, so to speak, commit themselves.

Further evidence of the testing-out process is the fact that when one patient committed herself to something—such as a specific activity on the ward, the numerous steps involved in going elsewhere for the first time, or other difficult advances in socialization—several others often followed. No active patient leadership emerged, however. Gradually the women established groups of three to five, and established enough rapport with one another to play a game together without help. Toward the end of the year it was noted that if the materials were available they rather consistently initiated an activity themselves, although no staff person was present. By the close of the experimental period even the majority of the "chair-sitters" and the "avoiders" had moved from passive to active interest, and then to at least limited group participation or individual constructive tasks.

The appearance of the patients had notably improved as a result of the combined efforts of students, supervisory nurse, and attendant. All wore shoes and stockings, dresses were more attractive, and many were obviously taking some pride in how they looked. A new group of affiliating students commented, on seeing the ward for the first time, that it appeared similar to the women's admission and acute treatment ward which was the best in the Hospital.

Just as the social scientist and other observers learned to respect the improvement potential of the patients, so they also respected the ability of students, under minimum but competent supervision and encouraging leadership, to understand these patients, exert initiative and ingenuity, and utilize social skills with mature judgment. Some seemed to be particularly astute and sensitive in observation; some related effectively with the more disturbed patients; others were most effective in group leadership.

Statistical Results of the Experiment

The accompanying table traces the development of both constructive isolated activity and constructive social interaction on the ward from May 1, 1952, to June 30, 1953, as defined by the Wells-Gilbert Ward Socialization Index.[1] Observations made during periods of student participation on the ward are separated from those when there was no student participation. In early May, 1952, only 4 per cent of the patients could then be classified as interacting with each other and 12.5 per cent as engaged in isolated activity. Thirteen months later 22 per

[1] See p. 284.

TABLE 7. AVERAGE PROPORTION OF PATIENTS IN WARD F3, MET-
ROPOLITAN STATE HOSPITAL, ENGAGING IN CONSTRUC-
TIVE ACTIVITY ON THE WARD, AS MEASURED BY THE
WELLS-GILBERT SOCIALIZATION INDEX, DURING SUC-
CESSIVE PERIODS IN 1952 AND 1953[a]

| Period | Percentage of patients engaging in constructive activity on the ward | | | |
| | Without student participation | | With student participation | |
	Social interaction	Isolated activity	Social interaction	Isolated activity
May 1 to 8, 1952	4.1	12.5	–	–
June 13 to July 9, 1952	6.4	19.7	12.3	28.6
July 21 to August 15, 1952	9.9	23.2	9.9	36.9
January 9 to February 2, 1953	24.4	7.6	28.2	30.5
May 28 to June 30, 1953	22.3	8.7	39.4	19.6

[a] The percentages shown for each of the specified periods are based on aver-
ages of ratings made in successive observations of the patients on the ward.
Except in the first period observations were made both when students were
present and participating and when they were not. In any one observation of
the ward, the same patient could not be rated as engaging in both isolated
activity and social interaction. But the rating of a patient might change in successive observations in the same period.

cent were participating in constructive social interaction when
the students were not on the ward and 39 per cent when they
were present.

This is quantitative documentation of the informal observation that much of the improvement in socialization made
through relationships with the affiliates was maintained by the
patient group itself when alone. Particularly significant is the
fact that social interaction showed proportionately greater gains
than did constructive isolated activity, such as reading or sewing. Thus, the more difficult adjustment of relating to others, as
distinguished from merely pursuing one's own interests, had
proceeded encouragingly. It must be borne in mind, moreover,
that during this same period patients able to assume larger responsibility for themselves were progressively sent to activities
off-the-ward. Had they been present during the later months
when the observations were recorded, the percentages for constructive social interaction would probably have been considerably higher.

Social Interaction: Constructive and Regressive

We have referred to the fact that attempts to stimulate social movement met with some resistance from patients, but indicated that both active and passive resistance to socialization were being gradually overcome during the experiment. Many persons had predicted that with increased stimulation to social interaction and responsibility and with disruption of routine security, patients would be resentful and aggressively "act out." When individual interactions of patients were broken down into those that were constructive and those that were hostile and regressive, the results revealed that there was no proportionate increase in hostility or regressive behavior. A further analysis of interaction when students were present and when they were absent showed that the percentage of activity that was antisocial remained approximately the same.

One probable explanation was offered earlier when we remarked that this group itself had methods of controlling the intensity and nature of its members' reactions. As a rule patients came to the assistance and were protective of students when someone seriously threatened them. Interesting comments appear in the affiliates' log books about manifestations of hostility, and how they or the other patients handled these manifestations:

Throughout the morning there was only one fight between two women in which a few blows were struck and a great deal was said. One finally turned her back on the other, and the fight ended.

There is a patient who stays on the porch and is very resistant to us. She feels we are psychiatrists disguised as nurses. It is not possible to interest her as she becomes almost assaultive when approached. We show an interest in her but do not get close enough to upset her.

Again, we were cordially received by the patients on the ward. This morning it seemed that the two women who had been most hostile toward us at first were getting over the feeling. Miss D conversed with one and I with the other. One woman who, before, would have nothing to do with me or would tell me in no uncertain terms to get out of the ward, today asked me in a very pleasant manner to go home and stay there.

One patient made several attempts for recognition and approval by the students. When they failed, she tried to take all her turns [at bowling] at once. She made derogatory remarks about various patients, but she was ignored by them and finally stopped.

One patient hallucinated and answered loudly and profanely. She was ignored by the other patients and her behavior soon changed.

Since fear of hostility is one of the great barriers to forming relationships with patients, it should be stated that during the experimental program more than a hundred students, psychiatrically untrained previous to their three-week classroom course at Metropolitan, were in close contact with patients on this large ward. In that time one received a kick in the leg and another a punch in the stomach, with no after-effects. As to destruction of property and the fear of patients escaping, the following excerpts describe typical incidents:

In the afternoon I accompanied a group of eight patients by myself to the small courtyard for tossing ball, smokes, and sitting in the sunshine. One of them discovered the gate was unlocked and started to pull it open. Having been rather dubious about taking eight patients by myself in the first place, it sort of gave me a fright. However, I helped close the gate and asked her not to open it again for I could not lock it. No one made any attempt to escape; I needn't have worried in the least.

One of the patients who went to Brookside with us was an "escape artist," but nobody made any attempt to wander away from the group.

Given paper and pencil, some wrote letters; one woman did complicated long division which was accurate; and some just drew aimlessly. One of the patients tore her paper into little bits, the first such action I have observed.

I went over with a makeup kit. Several patients guarded it to protect it from misuse.

To provide patients whatever activities they wanted or were interested in was again a matter of concern, as we were somewhat apprehensive about using objects that had to be supervised closely. Scissors and needles required our attention, but we had little difficulty with injuries.

One of the patients jumped on the students for playing ball on the nice clean floor. This was verbally, however. She wanted to know what kind of homes we came from, and didn't we have any sense. She said that we weren't to come there any more. She didn't work hard all that morning just to have us mess up the floor. She finally quieted down and seemed to be quite pleasant.

It thus appears that although patients did have hostile, resentful, regressive attitudes and opportunity frequently presented itself for their expression, they were adequately handled either by the patients themselves, by ignoring the behavior, or by turning it into constructive channels. *Under the conditions* that existed, fears about uncontrolled hostility and destructiveness were largely unfounded. We italicize "under the conditions" because it should be remembered that the significant increase in socialization and improvement of the environment was achieved by a group who did not push the patients psychologically too fast or hard, were considerate of their wishes, and gave them a chance to test out new situations. The students also were sensitive enough to perceive, and skillful enough to utilize, the constructive aspects of group experience and individual relationships in handling any potentially difficult situations.

19. Motivation of a Chronic Men's Ward

WARD C1 HOUSED 65 MEN PATIENTS who had been hospitalized for many years. It was selected in June, 1952, for study by the Russell Sage Project because it was representative of the eight men's continued treatment wards that made provision for generally quiet and uncommunicative patients. Aside from about one-third who worked in hospital industries, the patients rarely left the colorless, materially empty day rooms, halls, and dormitories except to go to meals or to wander through connecting wards remarkably similar to their own. These men shifted for themselves. There was no regularly assigned attendant, nurse, or employee of any kind. They never knew who was going to wake them in the morning, or to whom to bring requests with any assurance of serious consideration. In large measure they had given up expressing personal needs or caring about what they did because there was no one who cared.

The day's routine was very simple. Perhaps so little was required of them, they followed it automatically. Someone would call them between six-thirty and seven. They might possibly wash, usually without shaving, put on their dilapidated clothes, and file downstairs and through a tunnel to the dining-room. The working patients arose earlier and were taken to their assigned unit by an industrial employee or the supervising attendant in charge of industrial placement. For most of those who did not work, the time from breakfast to dinner, dinner to supper, and supper until bed at ten o'clock was a succession of periods of "just sitting" or dozing. Occasionally someone polished the floor, cleaned the toilet, or helped the attendants who performed routine chores on the ward. One or two of the working patients had a pack of cards with which they might play after supper. The hospital radio that had an outlet in the day room was generally turned on, but it was difficult to tell whether the patients were listening. Beyond these items there was virtually nothing that could be used for play or to create interest. The patients did not approach the infrequent visitor to the ward with questions or requests, or otherwise reveal any of the usual minor indications of interest. There were few odd postures, and little of the incomprehensible muttering characteristic of most chronic wards. The patients did not look frightened, distrustful, or sullen. One could not appropriately speak of them as withdrawn, because there was nothing in their environment with which to be involved or from which to withdraw. Frequently the visitor found himself becoming silent as if he too reflected the vacuum.

PLANNING FOR WARD CHANGES

Both hospital and nursing service administrators welcomed collaboration with the Project for the purpose of determining whether these long quiescent, unstimulated patients would respond to interest shown in their ward, investigation of their needs, and systematic attempts to meet these needs. Obviously, there could be no thorough, consistent learning of what patients did need and to what they would respond if no staff member were on Ward C1 long enough to make an investigation, to be responsible for and responsive to these men, and to utilize any resources that might be furnished through the Project. Hence, as a first step the director of nursing and the male supervisory attendants devised a plan whereby one ward attendant was to be assigned regularly to C1 during the day shift at least three times a week beginning in August. Even this modest provision was made with difficulty for the reason that an average of only 10 attendants was available each morning to staff the entire acute and continued treatment male services, six of whom had to be assigned to the admission, disturbed, and incontinent wards.[1] As the plan worked out, the attendant was often unable

[1] Enough positions had been provided for in the budget to staff all the men's wards with one attendant during morning hours. Because of unfilled vacancies,

to devote his entire time to the ward on the designated days. Not infrequently he was obliged simultaneously to cover a second ward or go on frequent errands.

It should be noted, moreover, that this plan and the greater interest manifested in Ward C1 for study purposes created resentment among some of the attendants and other hospital personnel. The resentment could be attributed in part to the attitude of defeat that permeated the institution concerning the possibility of improving ward conditions. In the past the interest and hope of personnel, as well as patients, had been built up as new programs were started and progress was made in altering conditions. These programs had ended, because of the war or otherwise, with a return to the status quo and accompanying disillusionment. One supervisory attendant expressed this attitude of defeat very succinctly. "Oh, another special push. Why should I get involved? They build you up and then let you down." Jealousy was also associated with the resentment. Most of the staff would have liked the opportunity to work on the same ward each day and begin to do more for and with a smaller group of patients. In many instances an overt attitude of indifference or hostility toward this Project ward was perhaps protection against deeper feelings of interest and concern.

Regardless of resentment, advances obviously could not be made on the experimental ward without personnel, and so in October, 1952, when several vacancies were filled, an attendant for each of the three shifts was assigned to it.[1] Interestingly, a woman was given the shift from three-thirty until eleven o'clock at night. Thus, the initial break was made in the policy of employing only men to care for the male patients in continued treatment. Her experience, to be described later, was so suc-

---

sick leave, and vacations, however, the maximum possible number of attendants was rarely present on any one day except when inspection by the state department was scheduled. Then, as was probably true in many other hospitals, every employee was asked to be present since the institution wanted to make the best appearance it could. On those occasions staffing looked to be so much more adequate than it was in actuality that this practice may well have contributed to the Hospital's failure to obtain budgetary provision for numerical increase of staff.

[1] During the Project the following attendants served at some time: Alberta Allen, Robert Cormier, William Holway, Patrick McCarthy, and Jerry Di Pietro.

cessful that within a few months a second woman was assigned to an adjoining ward. In November, 1952, moreover, a graduate nurse was made supervisor for the first time of the entire male service, in line with the long-range plan of the Hospital to bring the men's wards more directly under the jurisdiction of the department of nursing.

Meetings for the Improvement of Ward Care

In order to develop a coordinated plan for gradually introducing and integrating changes on Ward C1, to determine what existing institutional resources could be offered the patients, and to provide for continuing evaluation of the ward situation, a monthly meeting of hospital personnel was immediately instituted. In many aspects of its composition and function, the meeting resembled the committee for patient care, described at length in Chapter 14. It differed, however, in two important respects, the first of which was in its assumption of far more responsibility for policy-making. Because there was, even after October, only one attendant for each shift and the physician who took special interest and responsibility was the junior staff doctor for the entire service, strong reliance had to be placed upon persons not working directly on the ward if any program were to be developed. At Bedford, it will be remembered, each ward or group of four wards was staffed by a physician, nurse, and relatively large attendant group who were responsible for the ward program. The meetings at Metropolitan also differed from those at Bedford by including from the very beginning representatives from all departments, services, and levels of administrative authority.

Attendance consistently averaged about 22 persons, including the assistant superintendent, the director of nursing who together with the writer served as informal chairman, several physicians and nursing service supervisors, and attendants both from men's and women's wards. Also present was an occupational therapist and representatives from such hospital industries as the farm, laundry, kitchen, and marking-room. Some of the affiliate students participating in the activity program on

Ward F3 regularly attended. The first two meetings were taken up with general discussion of the goals of the Russell Sage Project, and with the needs and problems of the Hospital approximately as described in the early pages of this section. Thereafter attention was centered primarily upon Ward C1, although the activity program received periodic consideration as did many general hospital difficulties that arose in connection with the two wards.

Provision for Simple Physical Needs

In the opinion of the physician, Dr. del Bosque, and the attendant who was initially assigned to Ward C1 for three days a week, the first step in improvement consisted in making a survey of ward conditions and simple physical needs of patients. When the survey was completed and presented to the meeting, these were the results. There were only 30 chairs for 65 patients. Fourteen mattresses were torn or in poor condition, and 46 pillows were needed. Most of the lockers, provided for the private use of each patient, were broken or unused. Only six razor blades were available for the entire ward. There were not enough clothes so that patients could change to clean ones upon return from their work. Many men had no underwear at all. Only 10 of the 65 had toothbrushes. Some of the others did not need them inasmuch as they had neither their own nor artificial teeth.

Many of the deficits were not the result of inability of the Hospital to obtain from the state department reasonably adequate supplies, or materials for making and repairing clothes and furnishings. They *were* the result of there being no regular, systematic audit of ward needs, no well-established procedures for getting these audits to the appropriate persons, and no equally well-devised system for prompt delivery of necessary items or provision for repairs and maintenance. This lack of planned procedures was clearly illustrated during the meeting at which the survey was discussed when the industrial employee responsible for repairing furniture said, "One day while walking through a corridor in another part of the Hospital, I happened to see 52 chairs that needed repairing. We had just had two weeks when we weren't very busy in the shop. Had I known about them before, they could have been repaired by this time. Now the canning season has started, and the men will be busy for several months."

The attempt to obtain the needed mattresses was not only wasteful of time for many persons but must have induced such frustration that the ward might well have been in a dilapidated state, even if it had formerly had a responsible attendant. To procure the mattresses the physician went to the supervisor, who sent him to the chief supervisor. That supervisor sent him to the assistant director of nursing, who in turn sent him to the assistant superintendent. The assistant superintendent referred him to the supervisor to whom he had gone first. Everyone to whom he spoke knew that some new mattresses had been delivered to the Hospital, but no one was certain where they were. The next week they arrived on Ward C1. When this fact was stated at the monthly meeting, no one could tell how they reached there.

When similar difficulties were disclosed about other necessary items, the steward was invited to a meeting in order that the entire matter of supplies could be reviewed. As a result more effective communication was established, and the attendant was later able to report that soap, razor blades, new mops and brooms, and other necessities were coming through to the ward more regularly. Within three months after the presentation of the survey, most of the simple deficits had been made up. Patients' needs for expensive personal items such as spectacles, dentures, and artificial limbs, however, could not begin to be met during the period of the experiment. The question of the obtaining of supplies and particularly repairs, moreover, on a regular, reliable basis continued to plague the ward. Volunteers, for instance, furnished new locks for the lockers, but when they became broken and the Hospital had to be depended upon, repairs were almost impossible to obtain. Especially frustrating was the difficulty in getting clothes for the patients. Supplies were received by the Hospital; in fact the Department of Mental Health ordered them distributed to the wards and the patients and not kept in storerooms. They were held back, however, because of fear that not enough would be received in the future. This hoarding and psychology of deprivation illustrate how self-defeating attitudes in the administrative sphere can directly affect patient care and treatment.

Particularly revealing of the effects of deprivation were the reactions of the patients to developments on their ward, as reported at the monthly meeting. Many of the men had so long been accustomed to doing without the simplest amenities that they could not understand what was happening or readily utilize the new supplies. Twenty patients refused towels when first distributed. They had ordinarily washed only on bath days, and it was several weeks before they began to give themselves more personal attention. Other patients seemed to comprehend events, but did not believe the changes would continue and hence were reluctant to take part in them. Said one patient who had been in the Hospital for twenty years, "There is actually nothing you should count on, and you have to make up your mind that nothing will really happen." It was two months before he allowed himself to accept the fact that the attendant's interest in the patients was genuine and could be depended on to continue.

Meeting the basic physical needs of patients proved to be a medium for reestablishing their confidence in personnel and the Hospital. In view of the length of their hospitalization and degree of regression, various persons had thought little could be expected of them, and that the sponsors of the experiment would be disillusioned. Events showed, however, that such pessimism was unjustified. Not long after daily living conditions had been improved, attendants and patients appeared ready for social activities. It had been originally planned that the introduction of such activities would be a second distinct phase in the experiment. But as the attendants became better acquainted with the men they no longer emphasized the difference between physical and social needs; instead, they initiated the second phase informally and well ahead of schedule.

Social Activation

Thanks to the volunteers who had responded to requests made through the monthly meetings for magazines, 20 a day were put on Ward C1 for one month. Two things happened immediately. First, the men began hoarding the magazines. They kept them in their hands, pockets, under their mattresses, or in their lockers. Almost all disappeared each day. They were afraid of not getting any more, and so they wanted to make sure of keeping what they had. Second, word got to other wards about the magazines and patients came from them to make forays. When the men learned, however, that 20 would be put out regularly each day, the hoarding ceased. Gradually some of the patients who had not been interested in the magazines at first began to enjoy them. In spite of the fact that several members of the hospital staff had predicted that the magazines would be destroyed, the attendant discovered that only two of the 65 men were actively destructive of them.

A piano and radio were added to the ward. Baseball games, news, and The Lone Ranger program had a consistent radio following. With the assistance of the attendants, some patients put pictures on the walls. Over a period of many months the beds were painted, and in the early spring a garden was started outside the ward. These latter projects proceeded sporadically and the attendants began to express frustration because, with only one to a shift, they felt that they could not spend enough time to help the patients follow through with their gradually expanding interests.

Each attendant was, however, becoming better acquainted with a group of patients with whom he or she seemed to work well. Illustrative of how relations developed are the following notes regarding Mr. B, taken from one of the log books. In October, 1952, the attendant wrote: "I passed Mr. B. He is generally uncommunicative. Tonight, however, he clenched his fist and swore at me as I went by." In November the following note appears: "Mr. B came to the office door and in a pleasant voice asked me for a cigarette. I gave it to him, and when I asked him if he wanted me to light it he said, 'No, thank you.'"

Finally, in January, Mr. B took a large forward step. "In my estimation he has improved considerably. Yesterday he came and sat down beside me in the day room. Since he has acknowledged my existence before only when asking for cigarettes, this was unusual. He *laughed*—that was something I had never heard him do before."

Attendants used the old colloquialism, "coming out of his shell," to refer to such progressive changes. As basic supplies and little amenities became available, more and more men came out of their shells, generally at first by making specific requests for cigarettes, a pair of shoes, or paper for writing a letter. Gradually the patients gained more confidence and with further acquaintance, some began to tell the attendants about their problems. The following paragraphs are taken from the log of one of the attendants:

> Mr. G seemed rather depressed so I asked him if he would like a cigarette. He said he had some thinking to do and wanted to be alone. He told me he used to have all kinds of thoughts running through his mind, and needed to "send someone ahead" of him to talk, so he could stay in his own world. He said that "someone" is absent most of the time now, and he's beginning to feel that he does things for himself. But he wants to be alone in order to think over the thoughts that were running wild before.
>
> I asked him if it would help by talking with me. He said all his life someone had done his thinking for him, but they were not going to from now on. He reported that he didn't want to go home because although his family is a close one, he doesn't get along with his father.

As the patients became more at ease with the attendants, the latter observed that they were increasingly able to work and play in small groups among themselves. This was a stage of development similar to that on the women's ward reported in the preceding chapter. As previously stated, the attendants at first had found it difficult to get the patients interested in playing a game or working in groups. After some months, however, it was possible to achieve this. The attendant could get the game or other activity started and then leave with some confidence that the men would continue it.

Value of Women Personnel

When a woman attendant was assigned to Ward C1, interest was aroused throughout the Hospital and some dire predictions were heard. Because the department of nursing itself was concerned for her safety among sick men, she was not expected to assume many of the regular duties of an attendant. It shortly became apparent, however, that none of the patients was going to assault her. Instead, shy, awkward, and very cautious indications of friendliness were often observed. Consequently, within a month she was carrying full responsibility for the ward exactly as a man attendant would have done.

Approaches to her by the patients were roughly of three kinds, all of which she handled easily. One was the direct expression of affection; this she interpreted as a friendly gesture. As she became acquainted with Mr. L, for example, she liked him and felt that he liked her. One day he brought her two apples, put his arm around her shoulder, and kissed her on the cheek. She did not respond to the kiss but thanked him for the gift, and they then fell to conversing in a normal fashion. Other men used the technique of testing her courage. One of the incidents she noted in her log was as follows: "Mr. M asked me tonight if I realized where I was working. I told him I did. Then he asked, 'You realize this is an asylum full of crazy men, but you still go along and mind your business? What would you do if you were attacked?' I answered, 'Fight.' The conversation changed to other things."

The third was the most common type of reaching out to her and the easiest to use constructively. The men approached her much more frequently than the male attendants with requests, comments, and indications of interest in her as a person. She accepted this interest naturally and objectively, and reciprocated by attending to matters of immediate personal and social importance in ward living. The patients assumed more responsibility for their appearance because they liked her and wanted her approval. Even those who were inappropriately dressed would button their clothes upon her request, and later begin to do it spontaneously. Several patients who appeared afraid of men attendants gradually established a relation with her. One of them was Mr. T who "runs away from people when they approach him. He has always run away from me, too, whenever I have spoken to him until today," she wrote. "When I asked him if he would like to exchange his towel, he came to me and *talked*." She could more easily interest the men in social and recreational activities than could the other attendants. They would bring their art work for her approval, or start a game of cards so that she could be invited to join them.

At one of the monthly meetings an attendant raised for discussion the problem of a small group of patients whom none of the ward staff had been able to reach. Some of the students present were then concentrating on the very withdrawn women patients on Ward F3, and they offered to help the attendants. Thus, two or three students began going to the men's ward for short periods that they could work into their schedule. They succeeded in encouraging three or four of the designated group of approximately a dozen to join in various activities, including walks and games in the courtyard. The first reaction of the patients to these girls was similar to their initial reaction to the woman attendant. They were very shy but also curious. When the students were in the courtyard playing ball with some of the patients, other patients who had remained on the ward would cautiously peek through the corner of a window but would immediately draw back if they saw a student look up in their direction.

After several weeks of working for brief periods on Ward C1, the students suggested the interward party, already mentioned in the preceding chapter, to which the women on Ward F3 invited the men from C1. Aside from the weekly hospital dance attended only by selected patients, this was the first time that men and women had had an opportunity to meet socially. Again some of the personnel of the institution predicted sexual aggressiveness that would be difficult to manage. Instead, the party was slow in getting started because of the extreme shyness of the men. With persistence, however, the students succeeded in getting a few couples to dance and a somewhat larger number to talk together in small groups. It was obvious that a long period of cultivation would be necessary to counteract the effects of the traditional, ingrained separation in the hospital community.

Needs of the Attendants

The physician who had assumed much of the responsibility for management of Ward C1 and for developing the experimental program, initiated a weekly meeting with the three attendants. It was the nearest possible approach to what would be known in psychiatric hospitals with larger and more diversified staffs as a ward conference. He saw the pressing need to provide an opportunity for the attendants to discuss freely the personal, emotional, and administrative problems involved in their work with the patients. He viewed the experiment as primarily concerned with an investigation of the needs both of patients and staff in their mutual relationships, and this perspective was accepted by the writer as basic to the learning process in which the Project was interested.

As the attendants became acquainted with the patients individually and the ward, they began to identify themselves with the men and to show frustration when basic supplies and facilities were not available. As a consequence their needs, as expressed in the ward meeting, ran nearly parallel with those of the patients, but were communicated more clearly and at a more mature level. One of the most consistent difficulties that the attendants faced was in maintaining simultaneously adequate physical care, smooth-running ward routine, and at least minimum social activities. Even though Ward C1 had an advantage in staffing over the other men's wards, each attendant felt there was insufficient time to carry out all the objectives. If an attendant spent the greater part of his day on social activation such as gardening or painting beds, he found that the problem of supplies or ward cleaning got out of hand. By the time he was able to return to activation, the patients showed flagging interest that resulted from lack of consistent stimulation. Frustration was particularly high in the spring of 1953 when the planning meetings emphasized the importance of movement on all three fronts. However, the attendants unanimously agreed that even this arrangement was vastly better than their previous tours of duty when they had been rotated at random through various wards without specific plans or goals for patient improvement. They enjoyed becoming acquainted with the patients, and staying on the same ward long enough to watch the men progress step by step to greater interest in the environment and confidence in the staff.

There were other frustrations besides those encountered from having too many things to do on the ward. Reference has already been made to the continuing difficulty in obtaining supplies and repairs, and to the resentment felt by some of the other personnel because of the larger staffing. In its early stages the experiment was almost stopped by this resentment, and by a pervasive climate of pessimism on the continued treatment services about whether anything could be done for such patients. Supervisory attendants showed resentment by giving these ward attendants far more duties than under ordinary circumstances. They were sent on errands, required to help with special treatments, given cafeteria duty, and so on, thus keeping them off the ward for considerable periods. After they brought up this problem at the weekly meeting with the physician, he began periodically to discuss the ward program with the supervisors. He explained that an attempt was being made to determine what advantages or disadvantages might appear with a slightly more consistent staffing pattern that would give attendants some opportunity to develop continued interest in patients individually. The result was a gradual but definite decline in the extra duties assigned, and much less talk among other attendants about how the "C1 boys" were loafing, sitting down talking with patients, and "goofing off" by playing games with the men.

One of the greatest sources of strength in the experiment was the interest Dr. del Bosque took in the ward and in the problems of the attendants. He not only supported it and them by presenting the case for the ward to persons in authority, but he gave them psychological support particularly through the

weekly meetings, where they felt free to talk about their difficulties. The two excerpts with which we close this chapter are
attempts by these attendants to express what this help meant
to them, and to answer the doctor's question as to what *in their
opinion* would do the most to improve patient care. Beyond
these attempts the excerpts present, with all the realism but
awkward phraseology of the man on the job, what the attendants considered wrong with the hospital system—a system in no
way unlike that of many other institutions.

When you associate regularly with these same patients, you just
can't ignore all the things that you know they have to have. For
two years before this, it would go along so that if the patients
didn't have a shower today, or if the sheets didn't come up to the
ward you were on, you might call the office and make some attempt to find out why. But often there wasn't too much interest
or follow-up there, so after a while you just got so you ignored
the whole thing. When you get to know the patients and feel that
it is your own ward, you damn well follow up yourself and find out
what's holding things up. When you know the patients and like
them, you feel morally responsible for them—more so than before.
The old way, nobody could pin responsibility on you so you took
the easy way out. Now, I've come to realize that the whole problem about the way the wards are usually run is *plain apathy*. I
don't think all the way up and down the line, they [the staff]
cared whether or not shop kept. If the doctors didn't care, nobody
else cared. It's the same way with an attendant: the patients are
going to see what you will put up with and what you won't put
up with, and when they find out what you really want, then it will
be done that way. The biggest thing I've learned working with you
[Dr. del Bosque] is that you can run a ward with authority and
still develop the respect and friendship of the patients. It means
a little harder work for us but it is so much more worthwhile and
rewarding.
    Very few times in the two and a half years I have been at this
Hospital until I came to work on the C1 Project has a doctor actually come up to me and said, "What do you think of this fellow?"
The attendants know a lot about the patients, about how they're
actually behaving. The doctor might see some patients once a
week, and only for a minute then. I'm positive that if the doctor
asked the attendant, then the attendant himself would be more
interested in the patients. I don't think that the attendants know

what's going on in the doctor's mind, and I don't think the doctor knows what's going on in the attendants' minds. For example, I once heard a doctor ask if Joe acted like that very often. It so happened that he had been acting like that for more than two years, and the doctor was just finding it out. No doubt the doctors are interested in the patients in their own way but the attendants don't realize it. If the attendants could know that the doctors are interested in the patients, then they would put much more into their work, I am sure.

20. Assessment of the Hospital's Collaboration

THE SIGNIFICANCE TO Metropolitan State Hospital of its eighteen-month collaboration in the Russell Sage Project or the degree to which the institution's program of patient care was modified during that time is difficult to assess. This difficulty results in part from the fact that the interests and efforts of the Project were merged in large degree with the ongoing program of patient care. We shall therefore summarize changes that occurred during that period, and then attempt to relate them to the problems of the social community of the Hospital described in Chapter 17.

From the exploration on Ward F3 substantial evidence was obtained that the chronic psychotic patient is capable of a large measure of resocialization within the hospital if provided with only moderate material resources and a little spontaneous, democratic leadership. Through the efforts of the nursing students, the regular ward attendant, and such supplies and equipment as were made available, much constructive social activity was developed.

During this period the students became a more integral part of the nursing service. Nursing conferences were instituted on the admission and active treatment wards where they received most of their clinical training. The fact of their being included in these conferences gave them an opportunity to gain larger comprehension of some of the problems facing the Hospital, and by implication facing many other psychiatric institutions.

A clearer understanding was gained from the study of Ward C1 of the extreme difficulty encountered by a single attendant in effectively maintaining basic custodial services—housekeeping, physical care of patients, and adequate clothing—for 65 men. Support and contributions from many other departments were obviously necessary to help him with his task. The monthly meetings at which problems were discussed and clarified and systematic planning undertaken were an essential instrumentality in providing assistance to the ward. Resocialization of a limited kind was first stimulated as patients began to express their personal needs again and to participate in a few simple games. Subsequently when nursing students gave some time to ward motivation, a more active social community emerged. Constructive activity as measured by the spot-check method had increased from an initial 6 per cent to 25 per cent at the end of the Project. Since that time Patient Government has been instituted on the ward, a special recreation room has been opened and equipped with games and hobbies, and the entire area has been freshly painted. A nurse, attendant, and occupational therapist from outside the Hospital have furnished weekly volunteer service to the ward, while volunteer women from neighboring towns have given frequent parties and supplied many of the patients' personal needs. As a consequence of these various undertakings, activity now rises to as high as 70 per cent on a day when two or three volunteers are present.

Programs on these two wards stimulated some interest elsewhere as personnel and patients borrowed ideas and began to compete with each other. One of the most conspicuous improvements was made on the untidy men's ward during 1953, when incontinence was reduced to a group of eight patients through selective and consistent staffing, initiation of systematic habit training, and introduction of diligent attention to individual patients and of social activities.

In both ward programs sponsored by the Project the necessity for at least two types of group communication was obvious. The first was for discussions among persons working regularly on the ward, in which they could clarify their own personal and professional relations with patients, express their problems, and obtain suggestions and support. The second was for discussion of patient care by ward personnel at meetings with other groups of hospital staff. In these monthly meetings interrelationships between the wards and the total hospital system became some-what clearer through consideration of a variety of practical in-stances. A beginning was made in breaking down barriers to free expression and in decreasing the isolation of special groups. Those present gained better understanding of other persons' problems and goals, and this understanding permitted closer working and planning together in behalf of improved attention to patients. A particularly encouraging by-product resulted from discussion at one of these meetings of the problems of patients working in hospital industries. As the result of informa-tion gained, two employees who had responsibility for industrial placement increased the percentage of patients leaving the ward to go to work units from 20 to 35 in one year.

LIMITATIONS IN THE DEVELOPMENT OF PATIENT CARE

The most obvious and often-discussed limitation was lack of sufficient personnel. This deficiency was the cause of much strain. In many cases two activities or hospital functions could be carried on only by borrowing from Peter to pay Paul. For instance, rehabilitation work with disturbed patients suffered from lack of continuity because the physical therapist was fre-quently needed to assist with shock treatment, which itself suffered because of inconsistent staffing. When one attendant was assigned to each shift on Ward C1, it meant more work for the supervisors and slightly less coverage on other wards. The fact that nursing students could be available only in limited numbers and for brief periods on Ward F3 constituted a serious handicap to the experiment there, and was reflected in regres-sion in the patients' behavior when they were not present. Be-cause the two experimental wards were permitted more workers than were other comparable units, envy, resentment, and criti-cism were not only expressed but could be viewed as entirely justifiable. In any situation where total resources are so meager, those receiving more than their proportionate share are likely to be looked on with disfavor. The rapidly achieved change in appearance of the experimental wards increased the feeling of resentment. Here were more supplies, more activities, better-dressed patients, and the rewards of recognition from persons outside the Hospital. It is not surprising that no matter how effective the changes may have been, some of the staff discredited them as having occurred under special circumstances or having involved only a small, atypical group of personnel.

But a beginning must be made somewhere when a hospital with generally inadequate staffing and equipment reexamines its values and practices in order to speed the recovery process or make the institutional environment healthier. Only on the basis of concentration of resources can a demonstration of improvement be achieved sufficient to attract the interest and support necessary to extend improvement to other areas. Many persons at Metropolitan regarded as wasteful providing two attendants for 16 seriously disturbed patients, inasmuch as there was not even one ward attendant daily for several groups of 75 patients each. Yet it was the very demonstration that such patients could be kept out of seclusion and simultaneously moved toward conspicuously increased social adjustment which brought Metropolitan many interested visitors and gave it a program of patient care it could report to other institutions.

When viewed in retrospect, persons connected with the Project see many things that should have been tried for purposes of minimizing the strains expressed and maximizing the use of such resources as existed. The administrative affiliation of the social scientist was primarily with the nursing service office. Because of the staffing problem, that office itself was in an ambivalent position. It was engaged in encouraging intensive social activities on some wards, while requiring that housekeeping and custodial functions be carried out so effectively on other units as to exclude time for such activities. The monthly meetings provided one important means for bringing other parts of the institution in touch with ward problems. But clearly the Project staff should have undertaken thorough consultation with the entire hospital administration and with several groups that, by virtue of their functional relationship to the wards, had interests in patient care and leadership to contribute to it.

Inclusive planning in every phase of this Project was indicated, just as it is in all undertakings that attempt to modify any part of the social environment of an institution. In spite of the fact that social scientists recognize that the total organization, both formal and informal, is important in determining what may or may not be achieved in a specific unit, the *degree* of importance of the social structure of the Hospital was nevertheless underestimated. It was gradually discovered that a limitation quite as severe as lack of numbers was lack of solidarity among personnel. Many small groups or cliques existed with strong hostilities and diverse allegiances, and there were confusing divisions of attitudes and authority. Channels of communication were so inadequate that even routine requests for supplies and repairs did not move promptly or in straight lines.

These were problems that would have required solution if negative blocks had been removed sufficiently to free enough energy and enthusiasm to produce broadly effective action in improvement of patient care. In the solution of these problems the Project accomplished relatively little. If the planning had included more comprehensive segments of the Hospital, it is not improbable that achievements on the selected wards would have been greater and the impact on other wards more substantial. It must be recognized, however, that in any hospital where the problems are of such magnitude, no undertaking of eighteen months' duration, no matter how large, could work them through to solution. This is the task on which Metropolitan is now embarked in collaboration with Boston Psychopathic Hospital, as described in the introductory chapter. That it was instrumental in creating initial interest in this collaboration, the Russell Sage Project takes pride.

CONCLUSION

ESTHER LUCILE BROWN, Ph.D.

MILTON GREENBLATT, M.D.

21. Social Treatment

MORE THAN ONE HUNDRED YEARS ago an enlightened and effective management of mental diseases flourished in the United States that was spoken of as "moral treatment."[1] Mental hospitals were governed by liberal principles which held that the insane were essentially normal people who had undergone excessive stresses that had robbed them of their reason. These stresses of a social and psychological nature were called moral causes, and the therapy that emphasized close and friendly association with the patient, intimate discussion of his difficulties, and the daily pursuit of purposeful activity was called moral treatment. Its significance in the history of American psychiatry arises from the fact that it was the first practical, systematic, and responsible method of care for the mentally ill, and that it achieved results in terms of patient improvement that challenge the best achieved today.

MORAL TREATMENT

The conceptual foundations and cultural setting of moral treatment were rooted in the liberal philosophical and political movements of the nineteenth century, and in the teachings of the great French physician, Philippe Pinel. American life between 1830 and 1840, when moral treatment was at its height, was based upon a small, well-knit society whose members were mutually interdependent and united by religious ties. The village with its democratic government was essentially an experiment in communal living in which the individual was held in high esteem. Organizations were formed for the abolition of

[1] The sections dealing with moral treatment are based upon the research of Dr. J. Sanbourne Bockoven and have been written by Dr. Milton Greenblatt with his collaboration.

slavery, and Emerson proclaimed, "The world is nothing; the man is all."

The early leaders with whom moral treatment is specially identified include Isaac Ray, associated with Augusta State Hospital in Maine and Butler Hospital in Rhode Island; Eli Todd (Hartford Retreat in Connecticut); Amariah Brigham (Utica State Hospital in New York, and Hartford Retreat); Samuel B. Woodward (Worcester State Hospital in Massachusetts); Luther Bell (McLean Hospital outside Boston); and Charles Page (Danvers State Hospital in Massachusetts). Their writings reveal the concepts underlying the care of the mentally ill in this period. They believed with Pinel that insanity was not the result of an irreversible lesion of the brain, but that it was in very many instances curable if adequate attention were paid to psychological, experiential, or emotional factors. "Attention to these principles [of moral treatment] alone will, frequently, not only lay the foundation of, but complete a cure; while neglect of them may . . . [exacerbate] each succeeding paroxysm, till, at length, the disease becomes established, continued in its form, and incurable."[1]

How the superintendent should function was cogently stated in Isaac Ray's prescription.

> He constantly striveth to learn what is passing in the mind of his patient, by conversation and inquiry of those who see him in his unguarded moments. He also maketh diligent inquiry respecting the bodily and mental traits of his kindred, knowing full well that the sufferer is generally more beholden to them than himself, for the evil that has fallen upon him. He endeavoreth so to limit the number committed to his care, as to obtain a personal knowledge of every wandering spirit in his keeping. He boasteth not of the multitude borne on his registers, but rather, if he boasteth at all, of the many whose experience he has discovered, whose needs he has striven to supply, whose moods, fancies, and impulses he has steadily watched. To fix his hold on the confidence and good will of his patients, he spareth no effort, though it may consume his time and tax his patience, or encroach, seemingly, on the dignity of his office. A formal walk through the wards, and the order-

[1] Pinel, Philippe, *A Treatise on Insanity*, translated by D. D. Davis. Printed by W. Todd, Sheffield, England, for Cadell and Davies, London, 1806, p. 5.

ing of a few drugs, compriseth but a small part of his means of restoring the troubled mind.[1]

The attitude toward useful work was expressed by Amariah Brigham as follows:

Bodily labor as a measure for benefiting and curing the insane is generally recommended. . . . We think every such institution should have a good farm attached to it. . . . We think several work shops should be connected with every large establishment. . . . One or more rooms in connection with each hall for patients, is needed in order to afford employment to all that would be benefited by it. In such rooms, dressmaking and tailoring, cabinet work, the manufacture of toys, basket-making, shoe-making, painting, printing, book-binding, and various other employments may be carried on to the advantage of many patients. . . .[2]

In his *American Notes,* Charles Dickens described the home-like atmosphere of the Institution at South Boston, now the Boston State Hospital, its emphasis on kindness, sociability, and satisfying group experiences for the patients. Even a form of patient government apparently existed in that day.

. . . The State Hospital for the insane [is] admirably conducted on those enlightened principles of conciliation and kindness, which twenty years ago would have been worse than heretical. . . .

Each ward in this institution is shaped like a long gallery or hall, with the dormitories of the patients opening from it on either hand. Here they work, read, play at skittles, and other games; and when the weather does not admit of their taking exercises out of doors, pass the day together. . . .

Every patient in this asylum sits down to dinner every day with a knife and fork; and in the midst of them sits the gentleman, [the superintendent]. . . . At every meal, moral influence alone restrains the more violent among them from cutting the throats of the rest; but the effect of that influence is reduced to an absolute certainty, and is found, even as a means of restraint, to say nothing of it as a means of cure, a hundred times more efficacious than all the strait-waistcoats, fetters, and hand-cuffs, that ignorance, prejudice, and cruelty have manufactured since the creation of the world.

In the labour department, every patient is as freely trusted with

[1] Ray, Isaac, "Ideal Characters of the Officers of a Hospital for the Insane," *American Journal of Insanity,* vol. 30, July, 1873, p. 67.
[2] "The Moral Treatment of Insanity," *American Journal of Insanity,* vol. 4, July, 1847, pp. 10–11.

the tools of his trade as if he were a sane man. In the garden, and on the farm, they work with spades, rakes, and hoes. For amusement, they walk, run, fish, paint, read, and ride out to take the air in carriages provided for the purpose. They have among themselves a sewing society to make clothes for the poor, which holds meetings, passes resolutions, never comes to fisty cuffs or bowieknives as sane assemblies have been known to do elsewhere; and conducts all its proceedings with the greatest decorum. The irritability, which would otherwise be expended on their own flesh, clothes, and furniture, is dissipated in these pursuits. They are cheerful, tranquil, and healthy.

Once a week they have a ball, in which the Doctor and his family, with all the nurses and attendants, take an active part. Dances and marches are performed alternately, to the enlivening strains of a piano; and now and then some gentleman or lady (whose proficiency has been previously ascertained) obliges the company with a song: nor does it ever degenerate, at a tender crisis, into a screech or a howl; wherein, I must confess, I should have thought the danger lay. At an early hour they all meet together for these festive purposes; at eight o'clock refreshments are served; and at nine they separate.

Immense politeness and good-breeding are observed throughout. They all take their tone from the Doctor; and he moves a very Chesterfield among the company. Like other assemblies, these entertainments afford a fruitful topic of conversation among the ladies for some days; and the gentlemen are so anxious to shine on these occasions, that they have been sometimes found "practising their steps" in private, to cut a more distinguished figure in the dance.

It is obvious that one great feature of this system, is the inculcation and encouragement, even among such unhappy persons, of a decent self-respect.[1]

The success of moral treatment can be partly evaluated from the follow-up report of Dr. John Park,[2] a successor to Dr. Woodward at Worcester State Hospital. The report concerned 1,173 patients discharged as recovered from that Hospital during 1833–1846, the period of Woodward's superintendency. The discharged patients comprised approximately 70 per cent of

[1] Dickens, Charles, *American Notes for General Circulation*. 3d ed. Chapman and Hall, London, 1842, vol. 1, pp. 105–111.
[2] *Sixteenth Annual Report of the Worcester Insane Asylum, 1893*. Wright and Potter Printing Co., Boston, 1894, Table 28.

those admitted who had been ill less than one year prior to admission. Dr. Park's last progress report was in 1881, but the inquiry continued until 1893, with the remarkable showing of 1,157 replies. Some 984 of these patients were considered to have given relevant information. Of these, 568, *substantially one-half of the original number,* had experienced no recurrences. Of 416 persons who relapsed, one-half had required permanent custody, the other half had remained at home. An additional small number, 67, had been rehospitalized, but again discharged. Considering the fact that a proportion of the patients were afflicted by the then fatal neurosyphilis and that modern somatic treatments were not available, these results are truly remarkable.

Moral treatment was no specific procedure aimed at a disorder specifically conceived. It was a way of life offered to the sick, under the direction of physicians whose philosophy of mental illness was based on a high valuation of the individual and belief in his recuperative powers. It was an effort to create a favorable environment in which recovery could take place. Recovery or discharge represented to a large extent the natural course of the illness when it was not artificially obstructed. Moral treatment was the art of eliminating obstacles and providing aids to the recovery; these aids being whatever action seemed indicated to supply a psychological need. Forbearance on the part of the hospital staff allowed expression of antagonisms, while opportunity to work furnished release to creative urges and satisfaction as recognition. Games of chance and skill provided a setting for competitive drives, writing and acting of the drama gave rein to exhibitionistic tendencies, and plastic arts offered sublimation of childish impulses. Liberty to handle sharp instruments served to allay fears of impotence and mutilation and to reassure patients of their normality in these respects.

When physicians and attendants shared hospital living with patients twenty-four hours a day, seven days a week, as was the case in the "moral" era, it is not difficult to see how this group experience could be fashioned into a highly therapeutic tool. Indeed, we may ask if psychiatrists have ever known their patients so well or labored so earnestly in their behalf. Aside from the period of moral treatment, few psychiatrists have had opportunity to observe their patients intimately in so many varieties of actual situations. They strove to develop organized group living, with integration of work, play, and social activities, where every aspect of daily life was utilized for its therapeutic effect.

DECLINE AND FALL OF MORAL TREATMENT

Perhaps as much can be learned from the decline and fall of moral treatment as from its success. Although its founders argued for small hospitals as the basis for close human contact, mental institutions were doubled and redoubled in size after 1850, in response to the rapid increase in population and the growing demand for beds. Emphasis on economy and imitation of industrial methods led legislators to accept the large institution and close their eyes to human needs. While the cost of patient care in the general hospital rose with the per capita income, the cost in the mental hospital went down sharply. A proportional decrease in the number of physicians, with increase in that of attendants, removed the physician from his charges and left them largely in the hands of untrained staff. The doctor became administrator rather than personal therapist. In the meantime, the relative fall in the wages paid attendants increased the economic distance between physicians and them, and lowered the value of their job. Increasingly, the physician became an extremely busy man, too busy to indulge in simple human intercourse with either attendants or patients. In 1894 it was calculated that if each state hospital physician in Massachusetts worked ten hours a day and could move from patient to patient with the speed of light, he could perhaps give ten minutes daily to each patient.

Contributing significantly to the increase in population with its pressures for ever enlarging the size of hospitals was the tremendous influx of immigrants. A less tangible, but none-the-less important factor in the decline of moral treatment proved to be the attitude of some segments of the population to these newcomers. Physicians of colonial ancestry who were filled with compassion for the mentally ill who had a similar heritage, were often revolted by the "ignorant uncouth insane foreign pauper." The annual report of the Worcester State Hospital for 1858 commented as follows:

This large class of people stand in false relations to nearly every thing about them . . . to which they cannot adapt themselves, influenced by motives often extravagant and wild. . . . They receive in prosperous times high wages, and are able at the cheapest rates to gratify vicious indulgences. They seek for labor in the most menial capacity, huddle together in the most objectionable places, neglect all rules of health, and prefer the excitement or solace of rum or tobacco to the quiet, intelligent influences of well-ordered homes.[1]

". . . The Hospital at Worcester," declared the annual report four years earlier, "is fast becoming a Hospital for foreigners, and its doors are becoming practically closed against that class of persons who for many years enjoyed its advantages . . . the intelligent yeomanry of Massachusetts, who can afford to pay the cost of their board, and will not ask for charity . . . would have shrunk most sensitively from living next door even to a wretched hovel, and from intimate association with those who are accustomed to, and satisfied with filthy habitations and filthier habits."[2]

". . . It would be no wonder," again quoting the 1858 report, "if the insanity of a highly educated, intelligent and refined person should be increased rather than cured, if the person is brought into close contact with those who were always coarse in their habits and tastes, rough in disposition, and filthy in their dress."[3]

Such an antagonistic attitude toward the immigrant group among the mentally ill stacked the cards heavily against moral treatment, and as the patients were physically and spiritually abandoned to barren dormitories adjoining even more barren day rooms, the recovery rates began to fall. In the highly reputed Worcester State Hospital, for example, they declined from about 50 per cent in the 1830's to 5 per cent in 1880. The

---

[1] *Twenty-Sixth Annual Report of the Trustees of the State Lunatic Hospital at Worcester, 1858.* William White, Boston, 1858, p. 20.
[2] *Twenty-Second Annual Report of the Trustees of the State Lunatic Hospital at Worcester, 1854,* pp. 10–11.
[3] *Op. cit.,* pp. 9–10.

change was so striking that psychiatrists of reputation, like Pliny Earle, began to argue that mental illness was becoming essentially an incurable malady, for cold statistics showed decade by decade a fall in improvement rates. It was an inexorable march, they believed, toward malignancy. To prove their contention further, these clinicians began to point to the early reports emanating from the pathological laboratories where new techniques purported to show microscopic lesions in the central nervous systems of patients who had been mentally ill. These observations profoundly impressed many physicians, particularly those who leaned toward the biological interpretation of the etiology of disease. Psychotic behavior could no longer be looked on as representing an accumulation of bad conditioning that had resulted from unhappy stresses, social and emotional deprivations, and the like, but could be viewed entirely as the consequence of mechanical defects in parts of the brain. Psychiatry shifted from an attitude of accepting the challenge of mental illness as a problem to be attacked with every means at hand, to one which dared not try anything without clearance from the pathologic laboratory. If mental disorder was "organic" in etiology, the simplest and cheapest custody of the largest number of persons was the only answer to the social burden imposed by it.

The success of the pathological method in uncovering the etiology of general paresis (brain syphilis), describing its course, and relating the patient's symptoms to advance of the disease, contributed further to the dependence of the physician upon laboratory investigations. This inclination increased through advances in other physical sciences—physiology, pathology, and bacteriology. The more the laboratories grew in size and importance, the weaker the philosophical premises of the "moral" psychiatrists. Being men of faith who worked largely by intuition, they possessed no systematic theory of mental illness, such as was elaborated later by Freud; they carried on no organized research and instituted no training program for younger men who might follow in their footsteps. Thus, without any strong group of believers to stand against the force of "scientific" medicine from within or socioeconomic pressures from without, the spirit and content of moral treatment faded away, though residues of its externals survived here and there; residues that in some quarters passed as moral treatment itself, but in reality did much to discredit it. The peculiar custom of taking patients for walks, like exercising a dog, was such a residue; another was *persuasion* of patients to work (more to maintain hospital industries than to provide wholesome and instructive occupational activity); and another was the formalized dance, performed by emotionally starved persons at the insistence of administrative authorities.

THE ROAD BACK

There are encouraging signs that America is on the road back to more enlightened and responsible care of the mentally ill. For the mass of psychotic patients in hospitals the accomplishments as yet have been meager, but favorable signs are many. When Dr. Von Mering's report is available of encouraging developments in state hospitals throughout the United States, readers will undoubtedly be impressed with the strenuous efforts now being made, generally under very difficult circumstances, to provide patients with a new deal. It must be added, however, that even in those large hospitals that have done the most, achievements are still very inadequate when measured by the need for giving improved care to all their patients. But out of these many undertakings examined collectively, together with the results of more structured, experimental work such as that described in this book or noted in the Bibliography, certain general principles of social treatment are emerging. In many respects they are not unlike those of the moral treatment of the 1830's; in fact, they might be viewed as a reinterpretation of such treatment in the language of contemporary concepts that are being evolved by psychiatry and the behavior sciences. To the expansion and refinement of these general principles, as well as to their application, much work will have to be devoted for the next several decades. They are nevertheless already sufficient in number and substance to provide a base for more systematic examination of the quality of patient care provided and direction for its improvement.

Emerging Guideposts to Social Treatment

1. Once more it is becoming accepted that psychotic patients need a setting that is cheerful, comfortable, friendly, and resembles closely the normal aspects of family and community life. To remove from ill persons suffering from "desocialization" those appurtenances of daily living to which they have been accustomed is like consigning an anthropologist, who supposedly leaves his own culture briefly to study that of a "primitive society," to an indefinitely prolonged existence of physical and emotional deprivation with little contact through books, letters, or visitors with his former environment. The results of many experiments demonstrate that destructiveness of patients or security regulations can no longer be used as valid reasons for the continued impoverishment of hospital wards or for keeping so many patients closely confined to them. Needed are not only bright and pleasant living units with abundant supplies of pictures, games, music, and reading and writing materials, but other symbols of the home such as plants, pet animals, provision for making and serving snacks, and so on. Needed equally are meals attractively served in dining-rooms, and a wide variety of social activities both on the ward and to the largest possible degree in other places where men and women may participate together.

Important to successful use of an enriched physical and social environment is the introduction of the patient to, and his integration into, it. The patient who enters the hospital for the first time, is transferred from one ward to another, or is taken out of a prolonged stay in seclusion, requires individualized help in making an adjustment to an unfamiliar and frequently threatening situation.

Concern for the details of the patient's life from admission to discharge and from morning to night will, we believe, achieve several ends simultaneously. Selected games and social activities, for example, can be utilized to allay some of his anxieties, increase progressively his interpersonal competence and skills in recreational and occupational situations, and as a means for helping the staff and other patients to establish relationships with him, and him with them.

2. To create and maintain a warm supporting environment and to help patients gain positive benefit from it is the immediate responsibility of all members of the staff who work directly with patients in the ward or group situation. In order to achieve this goal the roles particularly of nurses and attendants will have to be changed from those of persons burdened with administrative, custodial, and routine ward procedures to those of persons expected to view homemaking and the use of the social environment creatively and to spend much of their time in social interaction with patients. Because of extreme limitations in their number and preparation for such tasks, ward staffs will need the help of members of other hospital services, such as occupational and recreational therapists who have been trained in encouraging social interaction but have not yet made improvement of the ward social situation their major concern, and of all the volunteers and relatives that can be encouraged to assist.

3. Even though their roles be changed, ward staffs cannot be expected to establish close, friendly relations with psychotic patients, which are often psychologically disturbing, unless they themselves receive large administrative support, are given ample opportunity to express their anxieties and frustrations, and are stimulated to increased motivation through recognition of their accomplishments and provision for personal growth and development.

One device being used to achieve these ends is the organization of the closely knit team, composed of the entire staff of the ward or other unit of the hospital, in which each person is expected to assume a defined role of direct relationship with patients. In such a team it is the function of the nurse as captain to give help and strong support to the attendants, and it is the function of the ward physician to give similar help and support to the nurse. Where such teams exist, regular ward staff meetings have proved effective means for the planning of environmental changes, discussion of problems of individual patients, release of anxieties and frustrations, creation of mutual confidence and reliance of the staff upon one another, and giving of much needed recognition to attendants as full partners in patient care.

In addition to changes in role and status at the ward level, it is important that the hospital make provision for continuous in-service training, under whatever forms or names offered, for *all* categories of personnel, including volunteers. Psychodrama, seminars and discussion groups, the ward staff meetings mentioned above, supervision of a counseling nature, and group therapy sessions are among the useful techniques for helping members of the staff gain deeper insight into their own motivation and that of patients, and to learn how to use the social environment of the hospital more effectively for treatment purposes. Also recommended is the establishment of a service-wide or hospital-wide committee on improvement of patient care, composed of representatives of the staff most immediately in contact with patients and others in strategic positions. Such a committee will seek through discussion of problems and plans, mutual encouragement and support, and evaluation of undertakings—rather than through administrative processes—to raise standards of care and furnish an additional channel of communication. Recommended further is provision of opportunity for the staff frequently to play together as a psychologically validated medium for lowering status barriers, reducing myopic misconceptions and misunderstandings, and developing a spirit of camaraderie.

4. Organization of the ward staff, as noted above, has presupposed the existence of a physician who would serve in several capacities quite aside from giving medical or psychotherapeutic care to patients. He and the supervisory nurses would be intermediaries between the administration of the hospital and the ward and would thus facilitate the transmittal of messages

and suggestions in both directions; he would represent the interests of the ward in getting needed supplies and repairs, if the head nurse should request his assistance, and in helping to remove unjustifiable hindrances that almost everywhere create such frustration on wards as seriously to interfere with staff motivation. He would provide substantial leadership in the initiation of new programs for improvement of patient care, and would give the head nurse steady support in her role as captain of the ward team.

At the present time it is impossible to obtain physicians who can generally fulfill this role for two reasons. Their number in large psychiatric hospitals is so small and their length of stay so brief that no substantial part of ward administration can be reposed in them. Quite as important is the fact that through their medical and residency training they are still conditioned to see themselves almost exclusively as individual and direct therapists, even though that self-image has already become considerably outmoded by the exigencies of contemporary diagnosis and medical treatment. To prepare them to assume the role of coordinator and administrator of a team effort, and to convince them that much of their best work with any considerable number of psychotic patients will perhaps be done by working through other categories of staff is the challenge to which psychiatric education has yet to direct its attention.

Because of the reality of this present situation, other devices must be found for those many hospitals with a mere handful of physicians. Although the situation concerning number and adequacy of preparation of psychiatric nurses is scarcely better, the future appears more immediately hopeful. The Veterans Administration neuropsychiatric hospitals have demonstrated what can be done, and the national nursing associations and nursing education generally have committed themselves to active assistance in recruitment and preparation of nursing personnel. It seems essential, therefore, for hospitals to work toward enlarging, strengthening, and giving increased recognition to their nursing service, and toward providing nurses and attendants particularly with greatly improved in-service training and opportunity for fuller integration into the therapeutic goals and social life of the hospital.[1] Enough experience has been gained, moreover, to indicate that social workers and clinical psychologists, as well as occupational and recreational therapists, could be valuable assets in working with groups of patients on the wards. Particularly helpful in the absence of ward psychiatrists, we believe, would be those service- or hospital-wide committees on improvement of patient care to which reference has been made.

5. The function of "top administration" in the patient-centered therapeutic hospital begins to appear very different from that characteristic of most custodial institutions. In the latter, administrators tend to be governed by the dictates of the organizational chart. Its parallel horizontal lines represent levels of authority and status, with the patient by implication on the lowest level, except in those few institutions where some instrumentality such as patient government has been introduced. Parallel vertical lines represent the several services—medical, nursing, occupational therapy, social work, and so on—composed of profession-centered, semiautonomous groups. Needless to say, there is no line for patients, although they might conceivably be represented as workers in those institutions dependent upon their labor. Within this power structure plans, formulated largely in the form of orders, generally move in one direction—from persons with higher status to those with lower. Few plans, or even suggestions and pertinent information, flow in the other direction, while reasonable requests for supplies or repairs often move so slowly and with such distortion along extended lines of communication that patients and ward staffs conclude that "the hospital" is not interested.

[1] Recently Dr. Leo H. Bartemeier had this to say: "Nurses and attendants as well as occupational and recreational therapists often render a quality of care which is more responsible for the recovery of patients than the professional services of other more thoroughly trained members of the hospital staff. This is particularly so in those hospitals in which the value of their services to patients and their families is recognized and adequately appraised and in which they are assisted in their general understanding of mental illness and the specific problems of individual patients. In such hospitals the relative absence of any distinction between this group of workers and other professional personnel has the same wholesome influence on their individual morale as it has upon the morale of the patients under their care." See "Mental Hospital Care," *Bulletin of the Isaac Ray Medical Library* (Butler Hospital, Providence), vol. 2, April, 1954, pp. 41–49.

We believe, therefore, that it can be stated as a general proposition that in hospitals concerned with therapeutic goals the function of those persons in overall administrative positions (superintendent, clinical director, director of nursing, business manager, and their assistants) is primarily one of attempting to establish a psychological climate that fosters initiative, rewards well-considered suggestions and emotional commitment to the job, and emphasizes patient treatment and care in all their forms as the central and unifying purpose of the staff. In this connection a statement by the Expert Committee on Mental Health of the World Health Organization is pertinent:

> The most important single factor in the efficacy of the treatment given in a mental hospital appears to the committee to be an intangible element which can only be described as its atmosphere. . . . As in the community at large, one of the characteristic aspects of the psychiatric hospital is the type of relationship between people that are to be found within it. The nature of the relationships between the medical director and his staff will be reflected in the relationship between the psychiatric staff and the nurses, and finally in the relationship not only between the nurses and the patients, but between the patients themselves.[1]

It has frequently been assumed that if interpersonal relations, in and of themselves, could be improved sufficiently, the atmosphere of which the Committee speaks would result. Consequently, psychiatry and the social sciences have concerned themselves increasingly and productively in recent years with dynamic studies of such relations. We are of the opinion, however, that interpersonal relations are determined in no small degree by the social structure of the institution, within which the staff work. Some situations foster competence in interpersonal relations, others hinder it. Needed is a social structure that nurtures the kind of climate that frees staff and also patients from unnecessary frustration, increases constructive ideas and energy, and produces better coordination of effort including easier interpersonal relations. Hence, one of the principal tasks of administration is to reduce inflexibility in the social structure

---

[1] Expert Committee on Mental Health, *Third Report.* World Health Organization, Technical Report Series no. 73, Geneva, 1953, pp. 17–18.

sufficiently to permit personnel to escape from the claustrophobia induced by finding themselves in little cells, occupation-wise and status-wise; to establish new media of communication whereby ideas, suggestions, and requests can flow more freely and quickly in both directions; to search for talents and creative capacities not generally associated with the roles prescribed; and to hold to an equalitarian philosophy regarding the potential of various categories of personnel to assert a wholesome influence on patients.

6. We come now to that most important subject, the patient and his role in helping himself and other patients. Because hospitals generally have been operated on the principle that the physician, nurse, nutritionist, or social worker knows better than does the patient what are his needs and capacities, it is not surprising that hospitals for psychiatric patients have fallen into the same error. Consequently, there is little organized knowledge of what patients can do to advance their own therapy, or what degree of responsibility they can take at various phases of their illness either for themselves or for others. Such experience as is available in bringing the patient into more of a partnership in the process of social treatment, in expecting him to assume responsibility on a progressively higher level for his own behavior and for sharing in group decisions regarding changes in the hospital environment, leads to the conclusion that his capacity may be far greater than is generally supposed.

Boston Psychopathic Hospital notes in a memorandum to the authors: "In the endeavor of improving details of the patient's life personnel, nurses and attendants particularly, have been the leaders. But it is surprising how eager the patients are to help and even to take over responsibility once goals are made clear, expectations stated, accountability defined, tangible results demonstrated, and satisfactions felt." Recently, Dr. Derek H. Miller has reported on an experiment with long-hospitalized and predominantly schizophrenic, women patients on an open ward.[1] Through changes designed to make the mores of the

---

[1] "The Rehabilitation of Chronic Open-Ward Neuropsychiatric Patients," *Psychiatry*, vol. 17, November, 1954, pp. 347–358.

hospital unit more nearly approximate those of everyday living, and through individual prescription of a succession of new tasks and experiences each of which required ability by the patient to assume greater responsibility, a considerable proportion of these women were not only able to leave the hospital but to be productively occupied. Such results suggest the desirability of intensive and varied studies of what can and should be expected of patients as participants in their own therapy and as contributors to the life of the hospital community. In such studies may well lie important therapeutic potentials as yet little understood or utilized.

7. Because so much remains to be done in the refinement and application of all these directions, particularly the one dealing with social structure, experiments or action-oriented research need to be made the fulcrum for advancing social therapy. Although less study has been given to effectively changing patterns of hospital organization than to altering interpersonal relations, concepts and techniques are now available for making some assessment of the strengths and weaknesses in an existing social structure, and experiments can be constructed for discovering the degree to which changes in situations alter behavior patterns. Similarly, to use other examples, it is possible to design experiments for testing the extent to which application of the theory of expectation, or of recasting roles of personnel and patients, can be used to raise staff motivation, patient responsibility, and level of ward care.

For such experiments, hospitals need the collaboration of persons trained in research in the behavior sciences. Their services will have to be obtained in the same way and for the same purpose that medical schools and hospitals have obtained the services of physical scientists. It should not be assumed that clinical psychiatrists or other categories of therapists have the time necessary to acquaint themselves sufficiently with the behavior sciences and the techniques of social research to make effective use of their potentialities. What can be expected is that administrators will increasingly recognize the importance of social science experimentation, give it support, and utilize its results.

THE ROAD AHEAD

The prognosis for the future of psychiatric hospitals is hopeful—more hopeful than would have been believed possible two decades ago. With prompt and intensive treatment provided through the somatic therapies including chemotherapy, individual and group psychotherapy, and the therapeutic use of the social environment, a large proportion of patients admitted to psychiatric hospitals can return to the community within a relatively brief period. In those institutions best prepared to use all available forms of treatment, both the percentage and rapidity of discharges are indeed impressive. It may be assumed, therefore, that as therapeutic means are still further improved and as society learns the desirability of early treatment of psychotic conditions, discharges will continue to rise. Outpatient departments and the treatment of some psychotic patients in private offices, moreover, are beginning to make it possible for many persons to receive care without having to enter hospitals, and to permit others to leave sooner, knowing that therapy can be continued elsewhere.

As the result of present trends we would seem to be approaching the time when it should no longer be necessary to expect that so large a proportion of patients would have to be transferred from intensive to continued treatment wards. But for those who are transferred, we commence to see that such wards can be transformed from places primarily of custody, as the term generally implies, into truly *continued* treatment units where emphasis is placed predominantly on social therapy. As realization grows that mental regression is often the result of impoverished hospital life as well as of sickness, and as greater skill is achieved in the use of psychological and sociological techniques of resocialization, it may be hoped that a much larger ratio of patients on continued treatment wards can be returned to the community and that others can be kept from that progressive deterioration that has hitherto landed such persons finally on the back wards.

The same social therapy that is believed useful in keeping patients from moving in the direction of the most regressed wards can also be utilized, with modification in techniques, to upgrade present conditions on such wards. The success of the program instituted in Building Seven at Bedford V.A. Hospital alone indicates how much can be done to improve patient behavior among those whose condition is longest chronic. Each such advance means generally more satisfactory living for the patient, less penalizing situations in which to expect personnel to work, more self-respect and optimism for the hospital as a whole, and equally more self-respect and hope for the public.

Patient discharge rates understandably tend to be viewed by therapists and the community at large as the criterion of a hospital's success, and, if high, can often be successfully used for eliciting greater interest and larger appropriations from public bodies. Significant as is this criterion, however, it is not the only one. Statistics indicate that nearly one person in every ten will become a patient in a psychiatric hospital during his lifetime. To be able to demonstrate to relatives who constitute no small sector of the population, and to all those members of the community who directly and indirectly influence the operation of our psychiatric institutions, that the mentally ill can be cared for in comfortable and friendly surroundings is also an important indication of success. It is one that would do much to remove that opaque curtain of pessimism and guilt that continues to hang between the mental institution and society, and that keeps so much of the American public from looking in the direction of the psychiatric hospital more often than is absolutely necessary.

Improvement of conditions on the chronic wards, moreover, might prove to be the decisive factor in the determination of future policy about the care of various categories of patients. As noted in the Introduction, this book has been centered around persons admitted to mental institutions who could profit from therapy. It is generally known, of course, that many, especially among the elderly, suffer from irreversible diseases, whether the result of brain damage or other fixed pathology. For them psychiatric treatment provides no answer, and even social treatment may achieve only limited gains. It is highly probable that another kind of social environment, completely outside the hospital, could be devised better suited to their needs. Thus far, however, because of the implicit assumption that most patients assigned to the chronic services were not likely to improve sufficiently to be discharged, these services have been chiefly custodial both in fact and in psychology. Such a psychology, with its attendant absence of therapeutic experimentation, has left psychiatrists with as yet insufficient knowledge of who would and would not profit from hospitalization as contrasted with other provisions for care. For the first time mental hospitals are in a position to make comparative studies of the potential for resocialization of patients on chronic wards. From such studies might well evolve decisions concerning greater differentiation of care, and the opportunity at last for the mental hospital to become a hospital in fact as well as in name.

So encouraging are the numbers of patients discharged from acute services generally and current attempts appreciably to upgrade the continued treatment services, that even those state hospitals that have been profoundly discouraged by seemingly insuperable problems may shortly be able to raise their sights. For the very reason that discouragement has caused many of them to remain relatively static, perhaps no greater immediate step could be taken than their psychological commitment to the philosophy of change. Much as they need vastly increased funds and staffs and freedom from political manipulations, they need, still more, recognition that change is a dynamic force which can open doors, especially when accompanied by carefully designed experimentation, to discovery of new ways for achieving desired goals. Change in and of itself has great value in challenging old and stagnant practices, mobilizing the adaptive reactions of personnel and patients, and releasing potential energy. No change can be produced without stress in the individual and the group, but stress, if not too severe or too prolonged, can be used as a positive means for raising patients and staff alike to a higher level of functioning.

Fortunately, psychiatric and social science theories are being increasingly evolved that can serve to focus and direct change. For example, one potentially productive formulation that has long been generally understood but rarely applied systematically is that of plotting change as a series of well-defined progressive steps, with movement from step to step as soon as necessary consolidation has been achieved. This methodological concept is applicable to a wide variety of situations in hospital administration and patient care: to the making and maintaining of closely knit teams of ward or other service personnel; to the remaking of the social structure of units of the hospital; and particularly to remotivation of patients or staff. Where it has been used even in an elementary form for the purpose of achieving ward changes, the results within a few months have often been scarcely short of remarkable. Sometimes they have been so remarkable that visitors have failed to recognize the ward as one they had seen earlier.

What is not known as yet is the farthest limit to which such a plan can be carried productively with any particular category of patients. Certain it is, however, from all that has been learned in recent years, that even long-hospitalized patients can be remotivated and resocialized sufficiently to alter the present picture of our psychiatric hospitals. The question facing us now is whether hospitals will strive to maximize the use of such physical and social resources as exist, including resources in patients, to achieve this end, and whether the American public will become a more active partner in this venture by contributing greatly increased funds, and sustained, informed interest and service. The combination of simultaneous forward movement on these two fronts could produce results of perhaps almost unbelievable proportions.

BIBLIOGRAPHY

COMPILED BY

FREDERIC L. WELLS, Ph.D.

Bibliography

THE PURPOSE OF THIS BIBLIOGRAPHY is to put the user *au courant* with advanced thinking concerning (1) the institutional care of the mentally unable, and (2) the broader social framework in which this institutional care operates. No attempt is made at an exhaustive listing of sources, although such a listing would be approximated through reference lists in the sources cited. In certain instances numerals in parentheses follow the citation. They signify the number of references appended to the source.

A total of 625 titles is assembled here. In general, sources prior to 1940 are not cited, but references are continued as nearly as practicable to the time of publication of this volume. Some preference has been given to contributions that reflected a distinctive approach, or dealt with a comparatively unexplored portion of the general field.

Citations are presented alphabetically by author, or editor, under categories given below. Citations may be made under more than one category. Acknowledgment is made of the essential usefulness to this undertaking of the publications *Psychological Abstracts* and *Sociological Abstracts*.

There is an *ad hoc* categorization of titles, the main divisions being Hospital Organization, Treatment, and Social Science. Headings within these are for the most part self-explanatory. Personnel Management obviously takes its cue from business and industry, and is intended to represent the area of hospital organization that is concerned with the functioning of personnel. Social Structure represents the pervasive hierarchical component in group functioning. For Empathy and Attitudes, particularly the latter, the references are comparatively restricted, and must not be thought of as representative of their current place in the discipline of psychology as a whole. Categories like Interpersonal Relations, Socialization, and Group Dynamics have much in common, but under Interpersonal Relations, the intention has been to include contributions oriented descriptively toward the topic. Under Socialization the intention has been to include contributions with more of a value orientation, socialization being conceived of as something of a goal. Under Group Dynamics the orientation is again descriptive, but with emphasis on groups rather than on individuals as in Interpersonal Relations. Behavior

Study again refers more especially to individual behavior, and subsumes such categories as might be denoted by Personality and Clinical Psychology, with contributions of relatively specific if not experimental orientation. Sociometrics is a term that applies chiefly to studies of social interaction that have developed under the influence of Moreno. Interdisciplinary research involves so large an element of social interaction that some attention to the organizational problems it presents appears relevant.

Topics that are essentially medical, such as Psychosurgery and Shock Therapy, receive comparatively limited documentation here, for reasons analogous to those with Attitudes and Empathy. No term seems to have been devised that well denotes the various therapies, active and passive ("participant" and "spectator"), which are included here under Occupational, and Recreational and Allied Therapies. Psychodrama, like Sociometrics, is a term and concept developed largely under Moreno's influence, with its therapeutic significance as an abreacting, "acting out" process.

Patient Government represents simply a transfer to this type of organization of a principle that the supervised are often in the best position to decide on methods and details of their supervision, and, indeed, in some part to administer them. Environmental Treatment and Rehabilitation largely represent for our society rediscoveries of concepts and procedures that were well established a century or more ago, but which receded into the far background under pressures derived from general social changes. Comparative study of other cultures is necessary to see them in perspective.

For anyone concerned with objectives of a bibliography like this one, as regards material subsequent to its limiting date, the most efficient sources are the Abstract Journals, examined for the departments within which the researcher is especially working. There is, however, a time-lag, sometimes considerable, between the appearance of a source and when it becomes practicable to cite the source in abstract. Moreover, abstract journals commonly, and not improperly, refrain from value judgments concerning the sources they list. For thoroughness there is no alternative to scrutinizing relevant journals as they appear, not alone for down-to-dateness and completeness, but for such value judgments of the researcher's own as may be involved.

Book reviews in relevant journals should also be scrutinized. From a general cultural standpoint, indeed, these can well be of greater value than the original writings.

BACKGROUND AND BASIC MATERIAL

BARNARD, CHESTER I., *The Functions of the Executive.* Harvard University Press, Cambridge, Mass., 1950.

DURKHEIM, EMILE, *Sociology and Philosophy,* translated by D. F. Pocock. The Free Press, Glencoe, Ill., 1953.

FROMM-REICHMANN, FRIEDA, *Principles of Intensive Psychotherapy.* University of Chicago Press, Chicago, 1950.

HOMANS, GEORGE C., *The Human Group.* Harcourt, Brace and Co., New York, 1950.

KLUCKHOHN, CLYDE, AND HENRY A. MURRAY, editors, with collaboration of David M. Schneider, *Personality in Nature, Society, and Culture.* Alfred A. Knopf, New York, 1954.

MANNHEIM, KARL, *Essays on Sociology and Social Psychology.* Oxford University Press, New York, 1953.

MEAD, GEORGE H., *Mind, Self, and Society, from the Standpoint of a Social Behaviorist.* University of Chicago Press, Chicago, 1934.

PARSONS, TALCOTT, *Essays in Sociological Theory, Pure, and Applied.* 2d ed. The Free Press, Glencoe, Ill., 1954. (Bibliography included.)
The Social System. The Free Press, Glencoe, Ill., 1951.

PARSONS, TALCOTT, ROBERT F. BALES, AND EDWARD SHILS, *Working Papers in the Theory of Action.* The Free Press, Glencoe, Ill., 1953.

PARSONS, TALCOTT, AND EDWARD A. SHILS, editors, *Toward a General Theory of Action.* Harvard University Press, Cambridge, Mass., 1951.

ROETHLISBERGER, FRITZ J., AND W. J. DICKSON, *Management and the Worker.* Harvard University Press, Cambridge, Mass., 1939.

STANTON, ALFRED H., AND MORRIS S. SCHWARTZ, *The Mental Hospital:* A Study of Institutional Participation in Psychiatric Illness and Treatment. Basic Books, New York, 1954.

SULLIVAN, HARRY STACK, *The Interpersonal Theory of Psychiatry,* edited by Helen S. Perry and Mary L. Gawel. W. W. Norton and Co., New York, 1953.
The Psychiatric Interview, edited by Helen S. Perry and Mary L. Gawel. W. W. Norton and Co., New York, 1954.

WEBER, MAX, *Essays in Sociology,* translated and edited by H. H. Gerth and C. Wright Mills. Oxford University Press, New York, 1946.

HOSPITAL ORGANIZATION

Attendants—Functions and Training

ANDERSON, LELA S., "Human Factors Involved in Providing Better Nursing Treatment and Care of Patients in Mental Hospitals," *American Journal of Psychiatry*, vol. 106, January, 1950, pp. 486-490.

BARRON, EMERSON M., AND H. H. DONOHUE, "Psychiatric Aide Selection Through Psychological Examinations: A Preliminary Report of the Screening of Applicants at the Arkansas State Hospital," *American Journal of Psychiatry*, vol. 107, May, 1951, pp. 859-865.

BARTEMEIER, LEO H., "Mental Hospital Care," *Bulletin of the Isaac Ray Medical Library* (Butler Hospital, Providence), vol. 2, April, 1954, pp. 41-44.

BATEMAN, J. FREMONT, *City of the Sick*. 16 mm. motion picture film, black and white, sound, approx. 750 ft., 20 min., 1950. (Available through Ohio Division of Mental Hygiene, Columbus 16, Ohio.)

BONNER, C. A., "Mental Hospital Employees: Their Importance in Future Mental Hospital Betterment," *American Journal of Psychiatry*, vol. 105, March, 1949, pp. 669-672. (11)

CRAWFORD, ANNIE L., AND VIRGINIA KILANDER, *Nursing Manual for Psychiatric Aides*. F. A. Davis, Philadelphia, 1954.

DALY, VERGIL M., "Our Indispensable Aides and Attendants," *American Journal of Nursing*, vol. 54, May, 1954, pp. 588-589.

DILLER, JULIET C., AND EARL W. FULLER, "Adjusted and Maladjusted Student Nurses," *Journal of Social Psychology*, vol. 36, August, 1952, pp. 45-52.

EDGETT, CATHERINE D., "Attendant Training in a School for the Mental Deficient," *American Journal of Mental Deficiency*, vol. 52, October, 1947, pp. 153-161.

EICHERT, ARNOLD H., "Morale and the Attendant: A Note on Personal Problems in Hospitals for the Mentally Disordered," *Mental Hygiene*, vol. 28, October, 1944, pp. 632-638.

FITZSIMMONS, LAURA W., *Textbook for Psychiatric Attendants*. Macmillan Co., New York, 1947.

FITZSIMMONS, LAURA W., AND CHARLES P. FITZPATRICK, "A Program for Training Attendants in Mental Hospitals," *American Journal of Psychiatry*, vol. 103, March, 1947, pp. 685-688.

HALL, BERNARD H., AND OTHERS, *Psychiatric Aide Education.* Grune and Stratton, New York, 1952.

HALSEY, GEORGE D., *Supervising People.* Harper and Bros., New York, 1953.

HARRIS, PAUL III, editor, *Handbook for Psychiatric Aides:* Section 2, Care of the Over-active and Disturbed Patient. National Association for Mental Health, New York, 1950.

KALDECK, RUDOLPH, "Group Psychotherapy by Nurses and Attendants," *Diseases of the Nervous System,* vol. 12, May, 1951, pp. 138-142. (6)

KLINE, NATHAN S., "Characteristics and Screening of Unsatisfactory Psychiatric Attendants and Attendant-Applicants," *American Journal of Psychiatry,* vol. 106, February, 1950, pp. 573-586.

LIKERT, RENSIS, "Motivation: The Core of Management," *American Management Association Personnel Series,* no. 155, 1953, pp. 3-21.

McKERRACHER, D. G., "A New Program in the Training and Employment of Ward Personnel," *American Journal of Psychiatry,* vol. 106, October, 1949, pp. 259-264.

MENNINGER, WILLIAM C., "Teaching Outlines for Nurses and Attendants," *Bulletin of the Menninger Clinic,* vol. 8, March, 1944, pp. 43-54.

MENTAL HEALTH FILM BOARD, *Man to Man.* 3 reels, sound, $6.00 a day. (Available through Contemporary Films, Inc., 13 East 37th St., New York 16.)

MIDDLETON, JOHN, "Prejudices and Opinions of Mental Hospital Employees Regarding Mental Illness," *American Journal of Psychiatry,* vol. 110, 1953, pp. 133-138.

MISHLER, ELLIOT G., "The Nursing Service and the Aims of a Psychiatric Hospital: Orientations of Ward Personnel to the Care and Rehabilitation of Psychiatric Patients," *American Journal of Psychiatry,* vol. 111, March, 1955, pp. 664-672. (15)

MORIMOTO, FRANCOISE R., "Favoritism in Personnel: Patient Interaction," *Nursing Research,* vol. 3, February, 1955, pp. 109-112.

"The Socializing Role of Psychiatric Ward Personnel," *American Journal of Nursing,* vol. 54, January, 1954, pp. 53-55.

NATIONAL ASSOCIATION FOR MENTAL HEALTH, *Handbook for Psychiatric Aides:* Section 1, A General Guide to Work in Mental Hospitals, edited by Frank L. Wright, Jr., 1946. Section 2, Care of the Over-active and Disturbed Patient, edited by Paul Harris III. National Association for Mental Health, New York, 1950.

Nursing

BARTON, WALTER E., "The Nurse as an Active Member of the Psychiatric Team," *American Journal of Nursing*, vol. 50, November, 1950, pp. 714-716.

BERNAYS, EDWARD L., "Social Scientists Look at the Nursing Profession," *American Journal of Nursing*, vol. 46, August, 1946, pp. 518-520.

BOMBARD, P. L., AND L. F. STEVENS, "The Role of the Nurse in Psychiatric Rehabilitation: A Survey of Means and Methods" in *Rehabilitation of the Handicapped*, edited by William H. Soden. Ronald Press Co., New York, 1949.

BROWN, ESTHER LUCILE, *Nursing for the Future*. Russell Sage Foundation, New York, 1948.

DENSFORD, KATHARINE J., "The Head Nurse as a Teacher," *American Journal of Nursing*, vol. 39, December, 1939, pp. 1350-1356.

DEVEREUX, GEORGE, AND FLORENCE R. WEINER, "The Occupational Status of Nurses," *American Sociological Review*, vol. 15, 1950, pp. 628-634.

DILLER, JULIET C., AND EARL W. FULLER, "Adjusted and Maladjusted Student Nurses," *Journal of Social Psychology*, vol. 36, August, 1952, pp. 45-52.

DIX, AGNES A., "Modern Psychiatric Nursing," *American Journal of Psychiatry*, vol. 107, March, 1951, pp. 695-700. (8)

GREENBLATT, MILTON, "The Nurse in Research," *Nursing Research*, vol. 1, February, 1953, pp. 36-40.

GREGG, DOROTHY E., "The Psychiatric Nurse's Role," *American Journal of Nursing*, vol. 54, July, 1954, pp. 848-851.

GROUP FOR THE ADVANCEMENT OF PSYCHIATRY, Committee on Psychiatric Nursing and the Committee on Hospitals, *The Psychiatric Nurse in the Mental Hospital*, Report no. 22. Topeka, Kan., May, 1952, p. 3.

HARGREAVES, ANN G., AND ALICE M. ROBINSON, "The Nurse-Leader in Group Psychotherapy," *American Journal of Nursing*, vol. 50, November, 1950, pp. 713-714.

HEARN, GORDON, "A Social-Psychological View of Nursing Service," *Nursing Outlook*, vol. 1, November, 1953, pp. 632-634.

HEIDGERKEN, LORETTA E., *The Nursing Student Evaluates Her Teachers*. J. B. Lippincott Co., Philadelphia, 1950. (Briefs in *Nursing Research*, vol. 1, October, 1952, pp. 40-41.)

HIBARGER, VICTORIA E., WILLIAM H. BLANCHARD, AND ELI GLOGOW, "Nurses Use the Group Process," *American Journal of Nursing*, vol. 55, March, 1955, pp. 334-336.

HYDE, ROBERT W., AND HARRIET M. KANDLER, "Altruism in Psychiatric Nursing," Chapter 25, *Forms and Techniques of Altruistic and Spiritual Growth:* A Symposium, edited by Pitirim A. Sorokin. Beacon Press, Boston, 1954.

INGRAM, MADELENE, *Principles of Psychiatric Nursing*. W. B. Saunders Co., Philadelphia, 1949, pp. 411-427.

KALKMAN, MARION E., *Introduction to Psychiatric Nursing*. McGraw-Hill Book Co., New York, 1950.

"What the Psychiatric Nurse Should Be Educated to Do," *Psychiatric Quarterly Supplement*, vol. 26, 1952, pp. 93-102.

KANDLER, HARRIET M., "Studying a Problem in Psychiatric Nursing," *American Journal of Nursing*, vol. 51, February, 1951, pp. 108-111.

KARNOSH, LOUIS J., AND DOROTHY MERENESS, *Psychiatry for Nurses*, 4th ed. C. V. Mosby Co., St. Louis, 1953.

MATHENEY, RUTH V., AND MARY TOPALIS, *Psychiatric Nursing*. C. V. Mosby Co., St. Louis, 1953.

MELLOW, JUNE, "Research in Psychiatric Nursing: Part 2, Nursing Therapy with Individual Patients," *American Journal of Nursing*, vol. 55, May, 1955, pp. 572-575.

NAHM, HELEN, "Psychology Instruction in Nursing Schools," *Nursing Outlook*, vol. 2, 1954, pp. 188-190.

ODLUM, DORIS, *Psychology, the Nurse and the Patient*. 2d ed. Philosophical Library, New York, 1954.

O'HARA, FRANK J., *Psychology and the Nurse*. W. B. Saunders Co., Philadelphia, 1954.

PEPLAU, HILDEGARDE E., *Interpersonal Relations in Nursing*. G. P. Putnam's Sons, New York, 1952.

PETRIE, ASENATH, AND MURIEL B. POWELL, "Personality and Nursing: An Investigation into Selection Tests for Nurses," *The Lancet*, vol. 258, February 25, 1950, pp. 363-365.

REINHARDT, JAMES M., AND PAUL MEADOWS, *Society and the Nursing*

Profession: An Introductory Sociology. W. B. Saunders Co., Philadelphia, 1953.

RENDER, HELENA W., *Nurse-Patient Relationships in Psychiatry.* McGraw-Hill Book Co., New York, 1947.

RICHMOND, WINIFRED, "Sociometric Tests in a Training School for Nurses," *Sociometry,* vol. 13, no. 1, 1950, pp. 29-38.

ROBINSON, ALICE M., *The Psychiatric Aide:* His Part in Patient Care. J. B. Lippincott Co., Philadelphia, 1954.

SANTOS, ELVIN H., AND EDWARD STAINBROOK, "A History of Psychiatric Nursing in the Nineteenth Century," Part 1, *Journal of the History of Medicine and Allied Sciences,* vol. 4, Spring, 1949, pp. 48-74.

SEWALL, LEE G., *The Psychiatric Nursing Team:* Utilization of the Practical Nurse in a Psychiatric Hospital. Master's thesis, Northwestern University, Evanston, Ill., 1954.

STEELE, KATHARINE McL., AND MARGUERITE L. MANFREDA, *Psychiatric Nursing.* 5th ed. F. A. Davis, Philadelphia, 1954.

STERN, EDITH M., in collaboration with Mary E. Corcoran, *The Attendant's Guide.* Commonwealth Fund, New York, 1945.

STEVENS, LEONARD F., AND PAULINE L. BOMBARD, "A Training Program for Psychiatric Aides," *American Journal of Nursing,* vol. 52, April, 1952, pp. 472-476.

STEWART, ISABEL M., *The Education of Nurses:* Historical Foundations and Modern Trends. Macmillan Co., New York, 1943.

TUDOR, GWEN E., "A Sociopsychiatric Nursing Approach to Intervention in a Problem of Mutual Withdrawal on a Mental Hospital Ward," *Psychiatry,* vol. 15, May, 1952, pp. 193-217.

VACCARO, JOSEPH J., "Judging the Adequacy of Psychiatric Aides," *Hospital Management,* vol. 73, February, 1952, pp. 46-48.

WEISS, MADELINE O., *Attitudes in Psychiatric Nursing Care.* G. P. Putnam's Sons, New York, 1954.

WELLS, FREDERIC L., "A Psychologist Assesses Psychiatric Aide Training," *Nursing Outlook,* vol. 3, March, 1955, pp. 158-161.

WELLS, FREDERIC L., MILTON GREENBLATT, AND ROBERT W. HYDE, "As the Psychiatric Aide Sees His Work and Problems." (In press with *Genetic Psychology Monographs.*)

WENDEL, LULU, "Institutional Service Units: A Link Between the

Mentally Ill and the World That Has Forgotten Them," *The Modern Hospital*, vol. 74, January, 1950, pp. 69-71.

WIVEL, ELIZABETH C., "Social Science in the Ward Teaching Program," *Annual Report and Proceedings* of the 43rd Annual Convention of the National League of Nursing Education, New York, 1937, pp. 112-116.

WRIGHT, DAVID G., *Internal Management of Psychiatric Hospitals:* Training of Attendant and Nursing Personnel. Privately printed, Providence, R.I., 1950.

WYATT, FREDERICK, "Guidance Problems Among Student Nurses," *American Journal of Orthopsychiatry*, vol. 17, July, 1947, pp. 416-425. (14)

Personnel Management

ANDREWS, KENNETH R., editor, *The Case Method of Teaching Human Relations and Administration:* An Interim Statement. Harvard University Press, Cambridge, Mass., 1953.

BARR, A. S., WILLIAM H. BURTON, AND LEO J. BRUECKNER, *Supervision:* Democratic Leadership in the Improvement of Learning. 2d ed. D. Appleton-Century Co., New York, 1947.

BROWN, J. A. C., *The Social Psychology of Industry*. Penguin Books, Inc., Baltimore, Md., 1954. (Bibliography included.)

CRISSY, WILLIAM J. E., "Personalities: Their Impact on Management Action," *Personnel Journal*, vol. 32, 1953, pp. 87-90.

FRENCH, JOHN R. P., "Retraining an Autocratic Leader," *Journal of Abnormal and Social Psychology*, vol. 39, April, 1944, pp. 224-237.

LIPPITT, RONALD, "An Experimental Study of the Effect of Democratic and Authoritarian Group Atmospheres," *University of Iowa Studies in Child Welfare*, vol. 16, 1940, pp. 43-195.

MAIER, NORMAN R. F., *Principles of Human Relations:* Applications to Management. John Wiley and Sons, New York, 1952. (Bibliography included.)

McGREGOR, DOUGLAS, "Conditions of Effective Leadership in the Industrial Organization" in *Readings in Social Psychology*, edited by Guy E. Swanson, Theodore M. Newcomb, and Eugene L. Hartley. Henry Holt and Co., New York, 1947, pp. 427-435.

MENNINGER, WILLIAM C., "Effective Human Relations," *Menninger Quarterly*, vol. 8, no. 2, 1954, pp. 1-8.

NELSON, ROBERTA, AND GEORGIANNA HERMAN, compilers, *Selected Annotated References on Human Relations in Industry.* Industrial Relations Center, University of Minnesota, Minn.

STALEY, JOHN D., "Institutional Administration at the Supervisory Level," *American Journal of Mental Deficiency*, vol. 59, January, 1955, pp. 383-387. (5)

Social Structure

ADLAND, MARVIN L., "Problems of Administrative Psychotherapy in Mental Hospitals," *Psychiatric Quarterly Supplement*, vol. 27, 1953, pp. 264-271.

BAIN, READ, "The Concept of Sociopathy," *Sociology and Social Research*, vol. 38, September-October, 1953, pp. 3-6.

BARNARD, RUTH, "Milieu Therapy," *Menninger Quarterly*, vol. 8, no. 2, 1954, pp. 20-24.

BARRABEE, PAUL S., *A Study of a Mental Hospital:* The Effect of Its Social Structure on Its Functions. Ph.D. thesis, Department of Social Relations, Harvard University, 1951.

BATES, SANFORD, "The Prison: Asset or Liability," *Annals of the American Academy of Political and Social Science*, vol. 293, May, 1954, pp. 1-9.

BOYD, RICHARD W., S. STEPHEN KEGELES, AND MILTON GREENBLATT, "Outbreak of Gang Destructive Behavior on a Psychiatric Ward," *Journal of Nervous and Mental Disease*, vol. 120, November-December, 1954, pp. 338-342. (7)

BROWN, G. GORDON, "Culture, Society and Personality: A Restatement," *American Journal of Psychiatry*, vol. 108, September, 1951, pp. 173-175.

BUELL, BRADLEY, "Planning Community-wide Attack on Behavior Disorders," *Annals of the American Academy of Political and Social Science*, vol. 286, March, 1953, pp. 150-157.

BULLARD, DEXTER M., "Problems of Clinical Administration," *Bulletin of the Menninger Clinic*, vol. 16, November, 1952, pp. 193-201.

CAMERON, D. EWEN, "Modern Methods of Treatment Require an Open Psychiatric Hospital," *The Modern Hospital*, vol. 74, February, 1950, pp. 84, 86, 88.

CAUDILL, WILLIAM, AND EDWARD STAINBROOK, "Some Covert Effects of Communication Difficulties in a Psychiatric Hospital," *Psychiatry*, vol. 17, February, 1954, pp. 27-40.

CUMMING, ELAINE, AND JOHN CUMMING, "The Locus of Power in a Large Mental Hospital." (In preparation for publication.)

CUMMING, ELAINE, I. L. W. CLANCEY, AND JOHN CUMMING, "Some Techniques of Making Changes in the Organization of Large Mental Hospitals." (In preparation for publication.)

DEMBO, TAMARA, AND EUGENIA HANFMANN, "The Patient's Psychological Situation upon Admission to a Mental Hospital," *American Journal of Psychology*, vol. 47, July, 1935, pp. 381-408.

DEUTSCH, ALBERT, "Recent Trends in Mental Hospital Care," *Social Work in the Current Scene:* Selected Papers. Columbia University Press, New York, 1950, pp. 143-159.

DEVEREUX, GEORGE, "The Social Structure of the Hospital as a Factor in Total Therapy," *American Journal of Orthopsychiatry*, vol. 19, July, 1949, pp. 492-500. (Bibliography included.)

"The Social Structure of a Schizophrenia Ward and Its Therapeutic Fitness," *Journal of Clinical Psychopathology*, vol. 6, October, 1944, pp. 231-265.

GILBERT, DORIS C., AND DANIEL J. LEVINSON, "Studies in Ideology: Part II, Ideology, Personality and System Membership in Mental Hospital Personnel." (Paper read at American Psychological Association, New York, September, 1954; mimeographed by Boston Psychopathic Hospital.)

HAIGH, GERARD, "Staff Conferences Make a Difference to Psychiatric Aides and Patients," *The Modern Hospital*, vol. 69, October, 1947, pp. 74-75.

HENDRICKSON, WILLARD J., ROBERT H. COFFER, JR., AND THOMAS N. CROSS, "The Initial Interview," *Archives of Neurology and Psychiatry*, vol. 71, January, 1954, pp. 24-30.

HENRY, JULES, "The Formal Social Structure of a Psychiatric Hospital," *Psychiatry*, vol. 17, May, 1954, pp. 139-151.

HYDE, ROBERT W., MILTON GREENBLATT, AND FREDERIC L. WELLS, "The Role of the Attendant in Authority and Compliance: Notes on Ten Cases." (In press with *Journal of General Psychology*.)

HYDE, ROBERT W., AND HARRY C. SOLOMON, "Clinical Management of Psychiatric Hospitals," *Connecticut State Medical Journal*, vol. 15, May, 1951, pp. 391-399.

KOLB, HARRY D., "Creating the Organizational 'Atmosphere' for Improved Communication," *Personnel,* vol. 30, May, 1954, pp. 482-487.

LEMKAU, PAUL V., "The Future Organization of Psychiatric Care," *Psychiatric Quarterly,* vol. 25, April, 1951, pp. 201-212.

LINTON, RALPH, "Status and Role" in *The Study of Man:* An Introduction. D. Appleton-Century Co., New York, 1936, pp. 113-131.

LOWRY, JAMES V., "Public Mental Health Agencies, State and National," *Annals of the American Academy of Political and Social Science,* vol. 286, March, 1953, pp. 100-106.

MENNINGER, WILLIAM C., "The Functions of the Psychiatric Hospital," *Bulletin of the Menninger Clinic,* vol. 6, July, 1942, pp. 109-116.

MISHLER, ELLIOT G., "The Nursing Service and the Aims of a Psychiatric Hospital: Orientations of Ward Personnel to the Care and Rehabilitation of Psychiatric Patients," *American Journal of Psychiatry,* vol. 111, March, 1955, pp. 664-672. (15)

MURDOCK, GEORGE P., *Social Structure.* Macmillan Co., New York, 1949.

OVERHOLSER, WINFRED, "Commitment of the Mentally Ill," *American Journal of Nursing,* vol. 54, February, 1954, pp. 190-192.

PALMER, JAMES O., "Group Discussion as a Method of Patient Orientation in a Neuropsychiatric Hospital," *Journal of Clinical Psychology,* vol. 6, 1950, pp. 369-373.

REES, T. P., AND M. M. GLATT, "The Organization of a Mental Hospital on the Basis of Group Participation," *International Journal of Group Psychotherapy,* vol. 5, April, 1955, pp. 157-161.

ROWLAND, HOWARD, "Interaction Processes in the State Mental Hospital," *Psychiatry,* vol. 1, August, 1938, pp. 323-337.

SEWALL, LEE G., JOHN GILLIN, AND FRANK M. LEBAR, "Through the Patient's Eyes: Hospital-Patient Attitudes," *Mental Hygiene,* vol. 39, April, 1955, pp. 284-292.

SHEFFEL, IRVING, "Administration—A Point-of-view for Psychiatrists," *Bulletin of the Menninger Clinic,* vol. 15, July, 1951, pp. 131-140. (8)

STANTON, ALFRED H., "Psychiatric Theory and Institutional Context: Part 2, Theoretical Symposium on Contributions of Interdisciplinary Research to Psychiatric Theory," *Psychiatry,* vol. 17, February, 1954, pp. 19-26.

STANTON, ALFRED H., AND MORRIS S. SCHWARTZ, "Medical Opinion and the Social Context in the Mental Hospital," *Psychiatry*, vol. 12, August, 1949, pp. 243-249.

WALKIEWICZ, SOPHIA T., "Convalescent Patients as Mental Hospital Employees," *Smith College Studies in Social Work*, vol. 16, June, 1946, pp. 282-294.

WEITZ, PAUL, AND CRAWFORD N. BAGANZ, "Application of Group Therapy Principles to Hospital Administration," *International Journal of Group Psychotherapy*, vol. 2, July, 1952, pp. 245-249.

WELLS, FREDERIC L., "The State School as a Social System," *Journal of Psychology*, vol. 5, January, 1938, pp. 119-124.

Psychiatrists—Selection and Training

BOWMAN, KARL M., AND MILTON ROSE, "Do Our Medical Colleagues Know What to Expect from Psychotherapy?" *American Journal of Psychiatry*, vol. 111, December, 1954, pp. 401-409.

GILL, MERTON, RICHARD NEWMAN, AND FREDERICK C. REDLICH, *The Initial Interview in Psychiatric Practice*. International Universities Press, New York, 1954.

LICHTENBERG, JOSEPH D., "A Study of the Changing Role of the Psychiatrist in the State Hospital," *Psychiatric Quarterly*, vol. 28, July, 1954, pp. 428-441.

RAINES, G. N., AND J. H. ROHRER, "The Operational Matrix of Psychiatric Practice," *American Journal of Psychiatry*, vol. 111, April, 1955, pp. 721-733.

SEGAL, HENRY A., "Iatrogenic Disease in Soldiers," *United States Armed Forces Medical Journal*, vol. 4, 1953, pp. 49-59.

WHITEHORN, JOHN C., editor, *Psychiatry and Medical Education: Report of the 1951 Conference on Psychiatric Education Held at Cornell University, June 21-27, 1951*. American Psychiatric Association, Washington, 1952.

WORDEN, FREDERIC G., AND JOHN D. PATTON, "A Hospital Program for Teaching and Supervising Administrative Psychiatry," *Psychiatric Quarterly Supplement*, vol. 28, part 1, 1954, pp. 38-53.

Public Relations

ANDREW, GWEN, "A Study of the Effectiveness of a Workshop Method for Mental-Health Education," *Mental Hygiene*, vol. 38, April, 1954, pp. 267-278.

BARTEMEIER, LEO, "Mental Hospital Care," *Bulletin of the Isaac Ray*

Medical Library, vol. 2, April, 1954, pp. 41-49. (Publication of Butler Hospital, Providence, R.I.)

BATEMAN, J. FREMONT, AND H. WARREN DUNHAM, "The State Mental Hospital as a Specialized Community Experience," *American Journal of Psychiatry*, vol. 105, December, 1948, pp. 445-448.

BIGELOW, NEWTON, "Opening the Doors of the Mental Hospital to the Public," *Mental Hygiene*, vol. 33, July, 1949, pp. 366-375.

BRUDER, ERNEST E., "Clinical Pastoral Training as a Hospital Medium in Public Relations," *Pastoral Psychology*, vol. 4, November, 1953, pp. 27-36.

DESSION, GEORGE H., "Psychiatry and Public Policy," *Psychiatry*, vol. 18, February, 1955, pp. 1-8.

EWALT, JACK R., "Mental Health Problems Affecting Social Relations," *Annals of the American Academy of Political and Social Science*, vol. 286, March, 1953, pp. 74-80.

FALICK, M. L., BEN RUBENSTEIN, AND MORTON LEVITT, "A Critical Evaluation of the Therapeutic Use of a Club in a School-Based Mental-Hygiene Program," *Mental Hygiene*, vol. 39, January, 1955, pp. 63-78.

FARNSWORTH, DANA L., "What Is Mental Health in a University?" *Mental Hygiene*, vol. 38, January, 1954, pp. 34-48.

FELIX, R. H., AND JOHN A. CLAUSEN, "The Role of Surveys in Advancing Knowledge in the Field of Mental Health," *Public Opinion Quarterly*, vol. 17, Spring, 1953, pp. 62-70.

FULLER, RAYMOND G., "A Study of Administration of State Psychiatric Services," *Mental Hygiene*, vol. 38, April, 1954, pp. 177-235.

GLUCKMAN, ROBERT M., "The Chaplain as a Member of the Diagnostic Clinical Team," *Mental Hygiene*, vol. 37, April, 1953, pp. 278-282.

HOVLAND, CARL I., IRVING L. JANIS, AND HAROLD H. KELLEY, *Communication and Persuasion:* Psychological Studies of Opinion Change. Yale University Press, New Haven, 1953. (Each chapter includes a bibliography.)

INWOOD, EUGENE R., "Therapeutic Interviewing of Hostile Relatives," *American Journal of Psychiatry*, vol. 109, December, 1952, pp. 455-458.

KAHN, SHIRLEY W., AND A. RODNEY PRESTWOOD, "Group Therapy of Parents as an Adjunct to the Treatment of Schizophrenic Patients," *Psychiatry*, vol. 17, May, 1954, pp. 177-185.

KAPLAN, ARTHUR, AND LOIS WOLF, "The Role of the Family in Relation to the Institutionalized Mental Patient," *Mental Hygiene,* vol. 38, October, 1954, pp. 634-639.

KRAPF, E. E., "Structure and Functions of the Mental Health Society," *Mental Hygiene,* vol. 39, April, 1955, pp. 225-231.

"MENTAL HYGIENE PROGRAM of the Civilian Public Service," *The Attendant,* vol. 1, nos. 1-7, 1944; and vol. 2, nos. 1-12, 1945. (This journal was continued as *The Psychiatric Aide,* vols. 3-9, 1946-1952, and published by the National Association for Mental Health.)

MYERS, JEROME K., AND LESLIE SCHAFFER, "Social Stratification and Psychiatric Practice: A Study of an Out-Patient Clinic," *American Sociological Review,* vol. 19, June, 1954, pp. 307-310.

NOVICK, RUDOLPH G., "The Relationship of Mental Health Societies to Governments," *Mental Hygiene,* vol. 39, April, 1955, pp. 232-245.

OVERHOLSER, WINFRED, "Psychiatry and the Law," *Mental Hygiene,* vol. 38, April, 1954, pp. 243-251.

RAINES, G. N., AND J. H. ROHRER, "The Operational Matrix of Psychiatric Practice," *American Journal of Psychiatry,* vol. 111, April, 1955, pp. 721-733. (11)

REDLICH, FREDERICK C., AUGUST B. HOLLINGSHEAD, AND ELIZABETH BELLIS, "Social Class Differences in Attitudes Toward Psychiatry," *American Journal of Orthopsychiatry,* vol. 25, January, 1955, pp. 60-70. (16)

RICHARDSON, HENRY B., *Patients Have Families.* Commonwealth Fund, New York, 1945.

SCHAFFER, LESLIE, AND JEROME K. MYERS, "Psychotherapy and Social Stratification: An Empirical Study of Practice in a Psychiatric Outpatient Clinic," *Psychiatry,* vol. 17, February, 1954, pp. 83-93.

SEELEY, JOHN R., "Social Values, the Mental Health Movement, and Mental Health," *Annals of the American Academy of Political and Social Science,* vol. 286, March, 1953, pp. 15-33.

STEVENSON, GEORGE S., "The Citizens Mental Health Movement," *Annals of the American Academy of Political and Social Science,* vol. 286, March, 1953, pp. 92-99.

SZUREK, S. A., "The Family and the Staff in Hospital Psychiatric Therapy of Children," *American Journal of Orthopsychiatry,* vol. 21, July, 1951, pp. 597-611. (21)

VAUGHN, FRANKLIN C., "A Community Experiment in Preventive Mental Health," *Mental Hygiene*, vol. 39, January, 1955, pp. 89-93.

WENDEL, LULU, "If I Am Ever Mentally Ill Again Perhaps the Hospitals Will Be Different," *The Modern Hospital*, vol. 66, May, 1946, pp. 49-53.

"Institutional Service Units: A Link Between the Mentally Ill and the World That Has Forgotten Them," *The Modern Hospital*, vol. 74, January, 1950, pp. 69-71.

Volunteers

EVANS, RUTH L., "Volunteers in Mental Hospitals," *Mental Hygiene*, vol. 39, January, 1955, pp. 111-117.

FRANK, MARJORIE H., "Volunteer Work with Psychiatric Patients," *Mental Hygiene*, vol. 33, July, 1949, pp. 353-365. (Reprinted by the National Association for Mental Health, New York.)

HYDE, ROBERT W., AND CATHERINE F. HURLEY, "Volunteers in Mental Hospitals," *Psychiatric Quarterly Supplement*, vol. 24, part 2, 1950, pp. 233-249.

KIMBALL, JAY, *Guide for Organization of Volunteer Service in Mental Hospitals*. Massachusetts Association for Mental Health, Boston, 1950.

KLINE, NATHAN S., "Volunteer Workers," *Occupational Therapy and Rehabilitation*, vol. 26, June, 1947, pp. 153-166. (Also included in *Rehabilitation of the Handicapped*, by William H. Soden. Ronald Press Co., New York, 1949, pp. 305-321.)

MALAMUD, IRENE T., "Volunteers in Community Mental Health Work: The Respective Roles of Laymen and Professionally-Trained Persons," *Mental Hygiene*, vol. 39, April, 1955, pp. 300-309.

McBEE, MARIAN, AND MARJORIE FRANK, *Volunteer Participation in Psychiatric Hospital Services:* Organization Manual and Program Guide. National Committee for Mental Hygiene, New York, 1950.

NILSSON, GERTRUDE L., "The Citizen Volunteers in the Cause of Mental Health," *Mental Hygiene*, vol. 35, July, 1951, pp. 373-385.

SCHILLER, MADELEINE B., "Volunteers: Asset or Anathema," *The Modern Hospital*, vol. 56, February, 1941, pp. 73-74.

STETSON, EDITH R., "The Role Played by Volunteers in a Mental Hospital," *American Journal of Occupational Therapy*, vol. 5, September-October, 1951, pp. 203-204, 206.

WILSON, A. T. M., *Hospital Nursing Auxiliaries:* Notes on a Background Survey and Job Analysis. Tavistock Publications, Ltd., London, 1950.

Social Work

ARSENIAN, J. M., AND GEORGINA HOTCHKISS, "Toward a Research Training Program in Psychiatric Social Work," *Journal of Psychiatric Social Work*, vol. 24, October, 1954, pp. 42-46.

BECH, ELIZABETH B., "Implications from the Viewpoint of Social Work Practice in Mental Hospitals," *Journal of Psychiatric Social Work*, vol. 21, December, 1951, pp. 102-106.

BROWN, ESTHER LUCILE, *Social Work as a Profession*. Russell Sage Foundation, New York, 1942.

CONNERY, M. F., "Problems in Teaching the Team Concept," *Journal of Psychiatric Social Work*, vol. 21, December, 1951, pp. 81-89.

CORIN, GENEVIEVE, *"Une Profession Feminine: L'Assistante Sociale"* (A Feminine Profession: The Social Worker), *Bulletin de l'Institute de Recherches Economiques et Sociales*, vol. 19, November, 1953, pp. 749-783.

CRUTCHER, HESTER B., "Psychiatric Social Work," *American Journal of Psychiatry*, vol. 111, January, 1955, pp. 537-539. (5)

KONOPKA, GISELA, *Group Work in the Institution:* A Modern Challenge. Whiteside, Inc., New York, 1954.

"Resistance and Hostility in Group Members," *The Group*, vol. 16, October, 1953, pp. 3-10.

MENZER, DORIS, LILLIAN S. IRVINE, AND ELVIN V. SEMRAD, "The Role of Social Worker in Group Therapy," pp. 158-166 of "An Institute on Group Dynamics," Elvin V. Semrad (leader), *Journal of Psychiatric Social Work*, vol. 20, June, 1951, pp. 136-166.

NEWCOMB, MARGARET L., "The Educational Role of the Psychiatric Social Worker in the Collaborative Process," *Journal of Psychiatric Social Work*, vol. 21, December, 1951, pp. 63-70.

TENNANT, MARION A., "Psychiatric Social Work in a Private Mental Hospital," *Journal of Psychiatric Social Work*, vol. 23, June, 1954, pp. 234-241.

TREATMENT

Psychosurgery

BOCKOVEN, J. SANBOURNE, AND ROBERT W. HYDE, "Application of a Sociometric Technique to the Study of Lobotomized Patients," *Journal of Nervous and Mental Disease*, vol. 114, August, 1951, pp. 95-105.

FREEMAN, WALTER, "Psychosurgery," *American Journal of Psychiatry*, vol. 111, January, 1955, pp. 518-520. (16)

GREENBLATT, MILTON, ROBERT ARNOT, AND HARRY C. SOLOMON, *Studies in Lobotomy*. Grune and Stratton, New York, 1950.

GREENBLATT, MILTON, EMILY ROBERTSON, AND HARRY C. SOLOMON, "Five-year Follow-up of One Hundred Cases of Bilateral Prefrontal Lobotomy," *Journal of the American Medical Association*, vol. 151, January 17, 1953, pp. 200-202.

GREENBLATT, MILTON, AND PAUL MYERSON, "Psychosurgery," Chapter 17, *Contributions Toward Medical Psychology*, edited by Arthur Weider. Ronald Press Co., New York, 1953, vol. 1, pp. 410-437.

GREENBLATT, MILTON, AND HARRY C. SOLOMON, "Lobotomy in Mental Disease: Indications and Results," *The Medical Clinics of North America*, vol. 38, September, 1954, pp. 1379-1391.

"Survey of Nine Years of Lobotomy Investigations," *American Journal of Psychiatry*, vol. 109, October, 1952, pp. 262-265.

GREENBLATT, MILTON, AND HARRY C. SOLOMON, editors, *Frontal Lobes and Schizophrenia*. Springer Publishing Co., New York, 1953.

HYDE, ROBERT W., AND ANNE C. WOOD, "Occupational Therapy for Lobotomy Patients," *Occupational Therapy and Rehabilitation*, vol. 28, April, 1949, pp. 109-124.

SCHERER, I. W., AND OTHERS, "Psychological Changes During the First Year Following Prefrontal Lobotomy," *Psychological Monographs*, vol. 67, no. 357, 1953. (38)

Physiotherapy

BLACK, GRACE A., "Physical Recreation and the Schizophrenic," *Physiotherapy Review*, vol. 24, March-April, 1944, pp. 57-60.

CAYLEY, CAMILLE K., "Psychiatric Aspects of Rehabilitation of the Physically Handicapped," *American Journal of Psychotherapy*, vol. 8, 1954, pp. 518-539.

DAVIS, JOHN E., "Corrective Physical Rehabilitation for Neuropsychiatric Patients," *Archives of Physical Medicine,* vol. 29, June, 1948, pp. 345-353.

KAMM, ALFRED, "Swimming as an Activity Therapy," *Mental Hygiene,* vol. 33, July, 1949, pp. 417-423.

KNUDSON, A. B. C., AND JOHN E. DAVIS, "Medically Prescribed Exercises for Neuropsychiatric Patients," *Journal of the American Medical Association,* vol. 140, July 30, 1949, pp. 1090-1095.

ROLAND, PAUL E., "An Exploratory Training Technique for the Reeducation of Catatonics," *American Journal of Psychiatry,* vol. 105, November, 1948, pp. 353-356.

Recreational and Allied Therapies

BLACKMAN, NATHAN, "Experiences with a Literary Club in the Group Treatment of Schizophrenia," *Occupational Therapy,* vol. 19, October, 1940, pp. 293-305.

BOMBARD, P. L., AND L. F. STEVENS, "The Role of the Nurse in Psychiatric Rehabilitation: A Survey of Means and Methods" in *Rehabilitation of the Handicapped,* edited by William H. Soden. Ronald Press Co., New York, 1949.

BROWNE, HERMINA E., "The Use of Music as Therapy," *Mental Hygiene,* vol. 36, January, 1952, pp. 90-103.

CALLBECK, HELEN, "The Use of Social and Non-Equipment Games in Occupational Therapy," *Occupational Therapy,* vol. 26, April, 1947, pp. 69-74.

CHACE, MARIAN, "Dance as an Adjunctive Therapy with Hospitalized Mental Patients," *Bulletin of the Menninger Clinic,* vol. 17, November, 1953, pp. 219-225.

COX, F. N., "Sociometric Status and Individual Adjustment Before and After Play Therapy," *Journal of Abnormal and Social Psychology,* vol. 48, no. 3, 1953, pp. 354-356.

DAVIS, JOHN E., *Clinical Applications of Recreational Therapy.* C. C. Thomas, Springfield, Ill., 1952.

"Recreational Therapy" in *Occupational Therapy,* edited by William R. Dunton and S. H. Licht. C. C. Thomas, Springfield, Ill., 1950.

FINEGAN, RUSSELL, AND KENNETH FINEGAN, "Mixed Groups in Recreation," *Psychiatric Quarterly Supplement,* vol. 25, part 2, 1951, pp. 206-213.

HUNTOON, MARY, "The Creative Arts as Therapy," *Bulletin of the Menninger Clinic,* vol. 13, November, 1949, pp. 198-203.

HYDE, ROBERT W., RICHARD H. YORK, AND ANNE C. WOOD, "Effectiveness of Games in a Mental Hospital," *Occupational Therapy and Rehabilitation*, vol. 27, August, 1948, pp. 304-308.

MCKENDREE, O. J., "Bowling as a Psychiatric Adjunct," *Psychiatric Quarterly Supplement*, vol. 24, part 2, 1950, pp. 303-307.

MCSORLEY, MAUREEN, "The Day-Evening Socio-Recreational Program for a Mental Hospital: Actual Practice at Rockland State Hospital," *Psychiatric Quarterly Supplement*, vol. 25, part 1, 1951, pp. 99-107.

MENNINGER CLINIC, STAFF OF, "Recreation and Morale: A Subjective Symposium," *Bulletin of the Menninger Clinic*, vol. 6, May, 1942, pp. 65-102.

MENNINGER, WILLIAM C., AND ISABELLE MCCOLL, "Recreational Therapy as Applied in a Modern Psychiatric Hospital," *Occupational Therapy and Rehabilitation*, vol. 16, February, 1937, pp. 15-23.

MESSNER, ANN G., "Artistic Self Expression of Psychotic Patients," *American Journal of Occupational Therapy*, vol. 5, November-December, 1951, pp. 235-240.

MITCHELL, S. D., AND A. ZANKER, "The Use of Music in Group Therapy," *Journal of Mental Science*, vol. 94, October, 1948, pp. 737-748. (14)

PODOLSKY, EDWARD, editor, *A Handbook of Music Therapy*. Philosophical Library, New York, 1954.

PRESTON, MARY JANE, "The Organization of a Music Program as a Rehabilitation Measure for the Mentally Ill," *Psychiatric Quarterly Supplement*, vol. 24, part 1, 1950, pp. 119-127.

RIESMAN, DAVID, "Recreation and the Recreationist," *Marriage and Family Living*, vol. 16, February, 1954, pp. 21-26.

VAN DE WALL, WILLEM, *Music in Hospitals*. Russell Sage Foundation, New York, 1946.

Occupational Therapy

BARTON, W. E., "Occupational Therapy for Psychiatric Disorders" in *Occupational Therapy*, edited by William R. Dunton and S. H. Licht. C. C. Thomas, Springfield, Ill., 1950.

BEALS, RONALD G., "Measurable Factors in Psychiatric Occupational Therapy," *American Journal of Occupational Therapy*, vol. 3, November-December, 1949, pp. 297-301.

BENNETT, A. E., AND BERNICE ENGLE, "Psychiatric Nursing and Occupational Therapy" in *Progress in Neurology and Psychiatry: An Annual Review*, edited by Ernst A. Spiegel, vol. 4, 1949, pp. 549-556.

CLARK, BEATRICE F., "Adventures in Salvage," *Psychiatric Quarterly Supplement*, vol. 28, 1954, pp. 1-9.

FIDLER, GAIL S., AND JAY W. FIDLER, *Introduction to Psychiatric Occupational Therapy*. Macmillan Co., New York, 1954.

FIDLER, J. W., JR., "The Patient's View of Occupational Therapy," *American Journal of Occupational Therapy*, vol. 3, July-August, 1949, pp. 170-177.

HYDE, ROBERT W., "Some Recent Trends in Neuropsychiatric Occupational Therapy," *Bulletin of the Massachusetts Association of Occupational Therapy*, February, 1949.

"The Twenty-Five Books That Our Occupational Therapy Department Has Found Most Useful," *American Journal of Occupational Therapy*, vol. 6, July-August, 1952, pp. 146-150.

HYDE, ROBERT W., AND CHARLES R. ATWELL, "Evaluating the Effectiveness of a Psychiatric Occupational Therapy Program," *American Journal of Occupational Therapy*, vol. 2, November-December, 1948, pp. 332-349.

HYDE, ROBERT W., AND ANNE C. WOOD, "Occupational Therapy for Lobotomy Patients," *Occupational Therapy and Rehabilitation*, vol. 28, April, 1949, pp. 109-124.

HYDE, ROBERT W., B. SCOTT, AND C. HURLEY, "Postlobotomy Changes in Social Behavior: The Occupational Therapy Laboratory," Chapter 21, *Frontal Lobes and Schizophrenia*, edited by Milton Greenblatt and Harry C. Solomon. Springer Publishing Co., New York, 1954, pp. 256-273.

McMILLEN, LOUISE, "Occupational Therapy: A Definitely Prescribed Treatment for the Neuropsychiatric Patient," *American Journal of Occupational Therapy*, vol. 3, January-February, 1949, pp. 3-9.

NICOLAOU, G. T., "Evaluation of Ward Occupational Therapy with Regressed Patients," *Psychiatric Quarterly Supplement*, vol. 25, part 2, 1951, pp. 202-205.

NISWANDER, P. D., AND ROBERT W. HYDE, "The Value of Crafts in Psychiatric Occupational Therapy," *American Journal of Occupational Therapy*, vol. 8, May-June, 1954, pp. 104-106.

OCCUPATIONAL THERAPY AND RELATED DEPARTMENTS of Boston Psychopathic Hospital, "Overall Occupational Therapy Program of a Mental Hospital," *American Journal of Occupational Therapy,* vol. 2, July-August, 1948, pp. 191-205.

WILLARD, HELEN S., AND CLARE S. SPACKMAN, editors, *Principles of Occupational Therapy.* 2d ed. J. B. Lippincott Co., Philadelphia, 1954.

WITTKOWER, E. D., AND JOHN D. LA TENDRESSE, "Rehabilitation of Chronic Schizophrenics by a New Method of Occupational Therapy," *British Journal of Medical Psychology,* vol. 28, part 1, 1955, pp. 42-47. (A digest of this article appears in *Digest of Neurology and Psychiatry,* Series 23, May, 1955, p. 217.)

WOOD, A. C., AND ROBERT W. HYDE, "Studies of Technique and Effectiveness of Ward Occupational Therapy," *American Journal of Occupational Therapy,* vol. 2, June, 1948, pp. 149-157.

WOOLLEY, LAWRENCE F., "Occupational Therapy," *American Journal of Psychiatry,* vol. 111, January, 1955, pp. 536-537. (21)

ZIERER, EDITH, "The Function of Occupational Therapy in a Psychiatric Hospital," *Journal of Hillside Hospital,* vol. 2, July, 1953, pp. 152-163.

Psychodrama

ALLERHAND, MELVIN E., "A Comparison of Two Approaches to Group Psychotherapy and Psychodrama," *Group Psychotherapy,* vol. 5, March, 1953, pp. 199-204.

ENNEIS, JAMES M., "Establishing a Psychodrama Program," *Group Psychotherapy,* vol. 5, April-November, 1952, pp. 111-119.

HAGAN, MARGARET, AND MARION KENWORTHY, "The Use of Psychodrama as a Training Device for Professional Groups Working in the Field of Human Relations," *Group Psychotherapy,* vol. 4, April-August, 1951, pp. 23-37.

HERRIOTT, FRANCES, "Some Uses of Psychodrama at St. Elizabeths Hospital," *Sociometry,* vol. 8, August-November, 1945, pp. 292-295.

HOLLISTER, WILLIAM GRAY, AND GRANT W. HUSBAND, "Two Rôle-Playing Methods of Using Mental-Health Films and Plays," *Mental Hygiene,* vol. 39, April, 1955, pp. 277-283.

LIPPITT, RONALD, "The Psychodrama in Leadership Training," *Sociometry,* vol. 6, August, 1943, pp. 286-292.

MAIER, NORMAN R. F., "Dramatized Case Material as a Springboard for Role Playing," *Group Psychotherapy*, vol. 6, 1953, pp. 30-42.

MOORE, WILLIAM E., "Introduction of New Patients into Individual-Centered Psychodrama Within a Group-Setting," *Group Psychotherapy*, vol. 6, 1954, pp. 174-182.

MORENO, JACOB L., *Psychodrama*. Beacon House, Inc., Beacon, N.Y., vol. 1, 1946.

MORENO, JACOB L., AND MORRIS SCHWARTZ, "Psychodrama Combined with Insulin in the Treatment of Psychoses," *Psychiatric Quarterly*, vol. 22, October, 1948, pp. 621-633.

STARR, ADELINE, AND IRVING CHELNEK, "Psychodrama at Veterans Administration Hospital, Downey, Illinois," *Group Psychotherapy*, vol. 8, April, 1955, pp. 20-24.

ZANDER, ALVIN F., "Role Playing: A Technique for Training the Necessarily Dominating Leader," *Sociatry* (later *Group Psychotherapy*), vol. 1, June, 1947, pp. 225-235.

Group Psychotherapy

BACH, GEORGE R., *Intensive Group Psychotherapy*. Ronald Press Co., New York, 1954.

BAEHR, GEORGE O., "The Comparative Effectiveness of Individual Psychotherapy, Group Psychotherapy, and a Combination of These Methods," *Journal of Consulting Psychology*, vol. 18, June, 1954, pp. 179-183.

BAKER, A. A., "A Community Method of Psychotherapy," *British Journal of Medical Psychology*, vol. 26, parts 3 and 4, 1953, pp. 222-244.

BELL, JOSEPH L., AND GORDON J. BARNETT, "Intensive Insulin Sub-Coma Treatments Combined with Group Therapy in a Mental Hygiene Clinic," *Diseases of the Nervous System*, vol. 16, March, 1955, pp. 80-85.

BETTELHEIM, BRUNO, AND EMMY SYLVESTER, "A Therapeutic Milieu," *American Journal of Orthopsychiatry*, vol. 18, April, 1948, pp. 191-206.

BIERER, JOSHUA, "Modern Social and Group Therapy" in *Modern Trends in Psychological Medicine*, edited by Noel G. Harris. Paul B. Hoeber, New York, 1948.

BLAIR, DONALD A. S., "The Therapeutic Social Club: An Important Measure of Social Rehabilitation in the Treatment of Psychiatric Cases," *Mental Hygiene*, vol. 39, January, 1955, pp. 54-62.

BLAU, DAVID, AND JOAN J. ZILBACH, "The Use of Group Psychotherapy in Posthospitalization Treatment: A Clinical Report," *American Journal of Psychiatry*, vol. 111, October, 1954, pp. 244-247.

BURCHARD, EDWARD M. L., JOSEPH J. MICHAELS, AND BENJAMIN KOTKOV, "Criteria for the Evaluation of Group Therapy," *Psychosomatic Medicine*, vol. 10, September-October, 1948, pp. 257-274.

CAHN, C. H., "The Effect of Drugs on Group Therapy: An Experiment," *Journal of Nervous and Mental Disease*, vol. 118, December, 1953, pp. 516-526.

CARMICHAEL, DONALD M., "Potential of Group Practices in Mental Hospitals," *International Journal of Group Psychotherapy*, vol. 3, July, 1953, pp. 309-314.

CORSINI, RAYMOND J., "Group Psychotherapy with a Hostile Group," *Group Psychotherapy*, vol. 6, 1954, pp. 168-173.

EVSEEFF, GEORGE S., "Group Psychotherapy in the State Hospital," *Diseases of the Nervous System*, vol. 9, July, 1948, pp. 214-218.

FRANK, JEROME D., "Group Psychotherapy with Chronic Hospitalized Schizophrenics" in *Psychotherapy with Schizophrenics*, edited by E. B. Brody and F. C. Redlich. International Universities Press, New York, 1952.

FRENCH, R. P., "Role-Playing as a Method in Training Foremen" in *Group Psychotherapy: A Symposium*, edited by Jacob L. Moreno. Beacon House, Inc., Beacon, N.Y., 1945. (Also in *Sociometry*, vol. 8, nos. 3-4, 1945.)

GALIONI, ELMER F., AND OTHERS, "Group Techniques in Rehabilitating 'Back-Ward' Patients," *American Journal of Nursing*, vol. 54, August, 1954, pp. 977-979.

GELLER, JOSEPH J., "A Program of Group Psychotherapy in the Treatment of Chronic Mental Illness," *Psychiatric Quarterly*, vol. 23, July, 1949, pp. 425-438. (Bibliography included.)

GOODRICH, D. WELLS, "Research in Psychiatric Occupational Therapy," *American Journal of Occupational Therapy*, vol. 6, January-February, 1952, pp. 1-3, 31-32.

HALLE, LOUIS, AND ARTHUR LANDY, "The Integration of Group Activity and Group Therapy," *Occupational Therapy*, vol. 27, August, 1948, pp. 286-298.

HARGREAVES, ANN G., AND ALICE M. ROBINSON, "The Nurse-Leader in Group Psychotherapy," *American Journal of Nursing,* vol. 50, November, 1950, pp. 713-716.

HEMPHILL, JOHN K., AND CHARLES M. WESTIE, "The Measurement of Group Dimensions," *Journal of Psychology,* vol. 29, April, 1950, pp. 325-342.

HYDE, ROBERT W., "Communication of Feelings in Group Psychotherapy," *Journal of Pastoral Care,* vol. 6, no. 3, 1952, pp. 26-33.

HYDE, ROBERT W., AND ROBERT C. LESLIE, "Introduction to Group Therapy for Graduate Theological Students," *Journal of Pastoral Care,* vol. 6, no. 2, 1952, pp. 19-27.

JONES, MAXWELL, "The Treatment of Character Disorder in a Therapeutic Community," *Bulletin of World Federation of Mental Health,* vol. 6, no. 2, 1954, pp. 66-71.

KAHN, SHIRLEY W., AND A. RODNEY PRESTWOOD, "Group Therapy of Parents as an Adjunct to the Treatment of Schizophrenic Patients," *Psychiatry,* vol. 17, May, 1954, pp. 177-185.

KALDECK, RUDOLPH, "Group Psychotherapy by Nurses and Attendants," *Diseases of the Nervous System,* vol. 12, May, 1951, pp. 138-142. (Bibliography included.)

KAPLAN, ARTHUR, AND LOIS WOLF, "The Role of the Family in Relation to the Institutionalized Mental Patient," *Mental Hygiene,* vol. 38, October, 1954, pp. 634-639.

KELMAN, HERBERT C., AND HARRY H. LERNER, "Group Therapy, Group Work, and Adult Education: The Need for Clarification," *Journal of Social Issues,* vol. 8, no. 2, 1952, pp. 3-10.

KLAPMAN, J. W., "Group Psychotherapy: Social Activities as an Adjunct to Treatment," *Group Psychotherapy,* vol. 3, March, 1951, pp. 322-338.

LEARY, TIMOTHY, AND HUBERT S. COFFEY, "The Prediction of Interpersonal Behavior in Group Psychotherapy," *Group Psychotherapy,* vol. 7, May, 1954, pp. 7-51. (15)

LESLIE, ROBERT C., "Growth Through Group Interaction," *Journal of Pastoral Care,* vol. 5, Spring, 1951, pp. 36-45.

MAIN, T. F., "The Hospital as a Therapeutic Institution," *Bulletin of the Menninger Clinic,* vol. 10, 1946, pp. 66-70.

MENZER, DORIS, LILLIAN S. IRVINE, AND ELVIN V. SEMRAD, "The Role of Social Worker in Group Therapy," pp. 158-166 of "An Institute on Group Dynamics," Elvin V. Semrad (leader), *Journal of Psychiatric Social Work,* vol. 20, June, 1951, pp. 136-166.

MORENO, JACOB L., "Group Psychotherapy, Theory and Practice," *Group Psychotherapy*, vol. 3, August-December, 1950, pp. 142-188.

MULLAN, HUGH, "Some Essentials in Group Psychotherapy," *Group Psychotherapy*, vol. 5, April-November, 1952, pp. 68-69.

PERLMAN, BERNICE, "Group Work with Psychotic Veterans," *American Journal of Orthopsychiatry*, vol. 19, January, 1949, pp. 69-76.

POLANSKY, NORMAN, "Problems of Interpersonal Relations in Research on Groups," *Human Relations*, vol. 2, July, 1949, pp. 281-291.

"The Use of Near-Sociometric Data in Research on Group Treatment Processes," *Sociometry*, vol. 13, 1950, pp. 39-62.

POWDERMAKER, FLORENCE B., AND JEROME D. FRANK, *Group Psychotherapy:* Studies in Methodology of Research and Therapy. Commonwealth Fund, Harvard University Press, Cambridge, Mass., 1953.

PRATT, JOSEPH H., AND PAUL E. JOHNSON, editors, *A Twenty Year Experiment in Group Therapy.* New England Medical Center, Boston, 1950.

ROSS, W. D., "Group Psychotherapy with Patients' Relatives," *American Journal of Psychiatry*, vol. 104, April, 1948, pp. 623-626. (Bibliography included.)

"Group Psychotherapy with Psychotic Patients and Their Relatives," *American Journal of Psychiatry*, vol. 105, November, 1948, pp. 383-386. (Bibliography included.)

SACKS, JOSEPH M., AND STANLEY BERGER, "Group Therapy Techniques with Hospitalized Chronic Schizophrenic Patients," *Journal of Consulting Psychology*, vol. 18, August, 1954, pp. 297-302.

SCHNADT, FREDERICK, "Techniques and Goals in Group Psychotherapy with Schizophrenics," *International Journal of Group Psychotherapy*, vol. 5, April, 1955, pp. 185-193.

SLAVSON, SAMUEL R., *An Introduction to Group Therapy.* Commonwealth Fund, New York, 1943.

"Criteria for Selection and Rejection of Patients for Various Types of Group Psychotherapy," *International Journal of Group Psychotherapy*, vol. 5, January, 1955, pp. 3-30.

"Remarks on Group Psychotherapy and Community Mental Health," *International Journal of Group Psychotherapy*, vol. 4, 1954, pp. 210-217.

SMITH, MARION R., JOHN E. BRYANT, AND DORIS TWITCHELL-ALLEN, "Sociometric Changes in a Group of Adult Female Psychotics Following an Intensive Socializing Program," *Group Psychotherapy*, vol. 4, December, 1951, pp. 145-155.

STANDISH, CHRISTOPHER T., "Some Difficulties in Group Psychotherapy with Psychotics," *American Journal of Psychiatry*, vol. 109, October, 1952, pp. 283-286.

STANDISH, CHRISTOPHER T., AND ELVIN V. SEMRAD, "Group Psychotherapy with Psychotics," pp. 143-150 of "An Institute on Group Dynamics," Elvin V. Semrad (leader), *Journal of Psychiatric Social Work*, vol. 20, June, 1951, pp. 136-166.

TEIRICH, H. R., "The Use of Video Methods in Group Psychotherapy," *Group Psychotherapy*, vol. 8, April, 1955, pp. 47-50. (Published under the title "Ruhebilder in der Gruppen-Psychotherapie" in *Der Psychologe*, vol. 9, 1953, pp. 347-352. Translated from the German, and abridged by Hans A. Illing, Los Angeles.)

WEITZ, PAUL, AND CRAWFORD N. BAGANZ, "Application of Group Therapy Principles to Hospital Administration," *International Journal of Group Psychotherapy*, vol. 2, July, 1952, pp. 245-249.

WENDER, LOUIS, AND AARON STEIN, "The Utilization of Group Psychotherapy in the Social Integration of Patients: An Extension of the Method of Self-Governing Patient Groups," *International Journal of Group Psychotherapy*, vol. 3, April, 1953, pp. 210-218.

WILLNER, GERDA, "Report on Further Developments in Group Psychotherapy on a Chronic Service of a Mental Hospital," *Psychiatric Quarterly Supplement*, vol. 28, part 1, 1954, pp. 54-67.

"The Problem of Anxiety in Group Psychotherapy on a Chronic Mental Hospital Service," *Psychiatric Quarterly Supplement*, vol. 27, 1953, pp. 92-104.

Patient Government

BIERER, JOSHUA, editor, *Therapeutic Social Clubs*. H. K. Lewis and Co., London, 1948.

BIERER, JOSHUA, AND F. P. HALDANE, "A Self-Governed Patients' Social Club in a Public Mental Hospital," *Journal of Mental Science*, July, 1941, pp. 419-426.

BRIDGER, H., "The Northfield Experiment," *Bulletin of the Menninger Clinic*, vol. 10, May, 1946, pp. 71-76.

Hyde, Robert W., and Harry C. Solomon, "Patient Government: A New Form of Group Therapy," *Digest of Neurology and Psychiatry*, vol. 18, April, 1950, pp. 207-218.

Shock Therapy

Alexander, George H., "Electroconvulsive Therapy: A Five-year Study of Results," *Journal of Nervous and Mental Disease*, vol. 117, March, 1953, pp. 244-250.

Cerletti, Ugo, "Electroshock Therapy," *Journal of Clinical and Experimental Psychopathology*, vol. 15, July-September, 1954, pp. 191-217. (78)

Funkenstein, Daniel H., Milton Greenblatt, and Harry C. Solomon, "Autonomic Nervous System Changes Following Electric Shock Treatment," *Journal of Nervous and Mental Disease*, vol. 108, November, 1948, pp. 409-422.

Mezer, R. R., and H. C. Solomon, "Value of Electric-Shock Treatment on Outpatients," *New England Journal of Medicine*, vol. 250, April 29, 1954, pp. 721-722.

Sakel, Manfred, "The Classical Sakel Shock Treatment: A Reappraisal," *Journal of Clinical and Experimental Psychopathology*, vol. 15, July-September, 1954, pp. 255-316.

Environmental Treatment, including Rehabilitation

Baker, Hazel B., "The Psychology of Clothing as a Treatment Aid," *Mental Hygiene*, vol. 39, January, 1955, pp. 94-98.

Banen, David M., "Suicide by Psychotics," *Bedford Research*, vol. 4, November, 1953, pp. 1-8.

Barnard, Ruth, "Milieu Therapy," *Menninger Quarterly*, vol. 8, no. 2, 1954, pp. 20-24.

Bombard, P. L., and L. F. Stevens, "The Role of the Nurse in Psychiatric Rehabilitation: A Survey of Means and Methods" in *Rehabilitation of the Handicapped*, edited by William H. Soden. Ronald Press Co., New York, 1949.

Case, Mary E., "The Forgotten Ones: An Exploratory Project in the Use of Group Activities for the Treatment of Deteriorated Psychotic Patients," *Smith College Studies in Social Work*, vol. 21, June, 1951, pp. 199-231.

Davis, John E., "Modern Dynamics of Rehabilitation for the Psychotic Patient," *Mental Hygiene*, vol. 34, July, 1950, pp. 423-437.

ENELOW, ALLEN J., "The Environmental Treatment of Psychosis," *Psychiatric Quarterly Supplement*, vol. 26, 1952, pp. 44-52.

FETTERMAN, JOSEPH L., "The Therapeutic Team: A Consideration of the Collaborative Role of Doctor, Nurse, Attendant, and Family," *Ohio State Medical Journal*, vol. 47, April, 1951, pp. 321-325.

FINK, L. J., "Aiding the Process of Reintegration," *Journal of Rehabilitation*, vol. 15, December, 1949, pp. 14-16.

FRANK, LAWRENCE K., "Psycho-Cultural Approaches to Medical Care," *Journal of Social Issues*, vol. 8, no. 4, 1952, pp. 45-54.

FREEMAN, RICHARD V., "Contaminants of Permissiveness in Hospital Care," *American Journal of Psychiatry*, vol. 111, July, 1954, pp. 52-54.

FUNKENSTEIN, D. H., AND COLLABORATORS, "Exploratory Phase of a Rehabilitation Project," *Bedford Bulletin*, vol. 2, May, 1953, pp. 27-28.

GALIONI, E. F., F. H. ADAMS, AND F. F. TALLMAN, "Intensive Treatment of Back-Ward Patients: A Controlled Pilot Study," *American Journal of Psychiatry*, vol. 109, 1953, pp. 576-583. (The Stockton Pilot Study.)

GRAYSON, MORRIS, ANN POWERS, AND JOSEPH LEVI, *Psychiatric Aspects of Rehabilitation.* Institute of Physical Medicine and Rehabilitation, New York University–Bellevue Medical Center, Rehabilitation Monograph, no. 2, 1953.

HALLORAN, ROY D., WILLIAM CORWIN, AND ELVIN SEMRAD, "Adaptation of the Total Push Treatment Principle to the State Hospital at Large," *Diseases of the Nervous System*, vol. 3, November, 1942, pp. 371-374. (5)

JONES, MAXWELL, *The Therapeutic Community: A New Treatment Method in Psychiatry.* Basic Books, New York, 1953.

KAMMAN, GORDON R., "Critical Evaluation of a Total Push Program for Regressed Schizophrenics in a State Hospital," *Psychiatric Quarterly*, vol. 28, October, 1954, pp. 650-667. (18)

KLEMES, MARVIN A., "The Therapeutic Effect of Group Morale on a Psychiatric Hospital Ward," *Bulletin of the Menninger Clinic*, vol. 15, March, 1951, pp. 58-63. (9)

KRAUS, P. STEFAN, "Considerations and Problems of Ward Care for Schizophrenic Patients: Formulation of a Total Responsibility Program," *Psychiatry*, vol. 17, August, 1954, pp. 283-292.

LACEY, MILDRED, AND J. B. KATZ, "The Hospital 'Goes to Town,'" *Menninger Quarterly*, vol. 6, January, 1952, pp. 22-29.

MAIN, T. F., "Rehabilitation and the Individual" in *Modern Trends in Psychological Medicine*, edited by N. G. Harris. Paul B. Hoeber, New York, 1948, pp. 386-441.

"The Hospital as a Therapeutic Institution," *Bulletin of the Menninger Clinic*, vol. 10, May, 1946, pp. 66-70.

MARTIN, M. G., "A Practical Treatment Program for a Mental Hospital 'Back' Ward," *American Journal of Psychiatry*, vol. 106, April, 1950, pp. 758-760.

MENNINGER, WILLIAM C., "Individualization of Psychiatric Hospital Treatment," *Wisconsin Medical Journal*, vol. 37, December, 1938, pp. 1086-1088.

MIKULICH, WALTER H., "Some Aspects of a Film Program Adjunctive to Total Psychiatric Treatment," *Journal of Psychiatric Social Work*, vol. 24, January, 1955, pp. 97-104.

MILLER, DEREK H., "The Rehabilitation of Chronic Open-Ward Neuropsychiatric Patients," *Psychiatry*, vol. 17, November, 1954, pp. 347-358.

MILLER, DEREK H., AND JOHN CLANCY, "An Approach to the Social Rehabilitation of Chronic Psychotic Patients," *Psychiatry*, vol. 15, November, 1952, pp. 435-443.

MORRIS, THAIS, AND IAN STEVENSON, "Psychiatry and Social Work in the Vocational Rehabilitation of Psychiatric Patients," *Proceedings* of National Conference of Social Work, 1953, pp. 148-158.

MURRAY, JOHN M., "Psychiatric Rehabilitation Symposium," *Occupational Therapy and Rehabilitation*, vol. 28, June, 1949, pp. 265-285.

MYERSON, ABRAHAM, "Theory and Principles of the 'Total Push' Method in the Treatment of Chronic Schizophrenia," *American Journal of Psychiatry*, vol. 95, 1939, pp. 1197-1204.

PENNINGTON, LEON A., "Rehabilitative Approaches," Chapter 24, *An Introduction to Clinical Psychology*, edited by L. A. Pennington and I. A. Berg. Ronald Press Co., New York, 1954.

PRATT, DALLAS, "Making the Environment Respond to Emotional Needs: A Challenge to the Mental Health Movement," *Psychiatry*, vol. 15, May, 1952, pp. 179-188.

ROLAND, PAUL E., "An Exploratory Training Technique for the Reeducation of Catatonics," *American Journal of Psychiatry*, vol. 105, November, 1948, pp. 353-356.

ROWLAND, HOWARD, "Friendship Patterns in the State Mental Hospital," *Psychiatry*, vol. 2, August, 1939, pp. 363-373.

SCHWARTZ, CHARLOTTE G., *Rehabilitation of Mental Hospital Patients*. Public Health Monograph, no. 17, Publication no. 297. U.S. Public Health Service, Government Printing Office, Washington, 1953. (Bibliography included.)

SCHWARTZ, CHARLOTTE G., MORRIS S. SCHWARTZ, AND ALFRED H. STANTON, "A Study of Need-Fulfillment on a Mental Hospital Ward," *Psychiatry*, vol. 14, May, 1951, pp. 223-242.

SEMRAD, ELVIN V., AND WILLIAM CORWIN, "Total Push Treatment of Chronic Schizophrenia at the Metropolitan State Hospital: Preliminary Report," *Archives of Neurology and Psychiatry*, vol. 44, July, 1940, pp. 232-233.

SYMONS, J. J., "The Nursing of the Deteriorated Patient," *Mental Health* (National Association for Mental Health, London), vol. 11, Winter, 1951, pp. 18-21.

TARNOWER, WILLIAM, "A Treatment Program for Open-ward Neuropsychiatric Patients," *Bulletin of the Menninger Clinic*, vol. 17, September, 1953, pp. 189-195.

TILLOTSON, KENNETH J., "The Practice of the Total Push Method in the Treatment of Chronic Schizophrenia," *American Journal of Psychiatry*, vol. 95, March, 1939, pp. 1205-1213.

TUDOR, GWEN E., "A Sociopsychiatric Nursing Approach to Intervention in a Problem of Mutual Withdrawal on a Mental Hospital Ward," *Psychiatry*, vol. 15, May, 1952, pp. 193-217.

Therapy—General

ALEXANDER, LEO, "The Influence of Physical Treatment Methods in Mental Disease Upon the Defensive Operations of the Ego" in *Depression*, edited by Paul E. Hoch and Joseph Zubin. Grune and Stratton, New York, 1954.

ANNAU, DÉSIRÉ, "Clinical Aspects of Combined Psychiatric Treatments," *American Journal of Psychiatry*, vol. 111, April, 1955, pp. 734-742. (23)

BOND, EARL D., "Results of Treatment in Psychoses—with a Control Series: Part 4, General Data and Summary," *American Journal of Psychiatry*, vol. 110, 1954, pp. 885-887.

BRANNON, EARL P., AND J. ARTHUR WAITES, "The Role of the Clinical Psychologist in Ward Administration: An Extension of the

Therapeutic Team Concept," *American Journal of Psychiatry,* vol. 111, January, 1955, pp. 497-501.

DEUTSCH, FELIX, AND WILLIAM F. MURPHY, *The Clinical Interview.* Vol. 1, *Diagnosis.* International Universities Press, New York, 1955.

MASSERMAN, JULES H., "Psychotherapy: A Review and an Integration," *Bulletin of the Menninger Clinic,* vol. 18, 1954, pp. 162-170.

MEISLIN, JACK, "The Psychiatric Sheltered Workshop in Rehabilitation of the Mentally Ill," *Archives of Physical Medicine,* vol. 35, April, 1954, pp. 224-227.

MILLER, JAMES G., "Criteria and Measurement of Change During Psychiatric Treatment," *Bulletin of the Menninger Clinic,* vol. 18, 1954, pp. 130-137.

ROGERS, CARL R., *Client-Centered Therapy.* Houghton Mifflin Co., Boston, 1951.

ROGERS, CARL R., AND ROSALIND F. DYMOND, *Psychotherapy and Personality Change.* University of Chicago Press, Chicago, 1954.

SCHAUER, GERHARD, "Patients as Therapeutic Agents in a Mental Hospital" in "Group Psychotherapy: A Symposium," *Sociometry,* vol. 8, August and November, 1945, pp. 394-395.

SEWALL, LEE G., JOHN GILLIN, AND FRANK M. LeBAR, "Through the Patient's Eyes: Hospital-Patient Attitudes," *Mental Hygiene,* vol. 39, April, 1955, pp. 284-292.

STANTON, ALFRED H., AND MORRIS S. SCHWARTZ, "The Management of a Type of Institutional Participation in Mental Illness," *Psychiatry,* vol. 12, February, 1949, pp. 13-26.

STRECKER, EDWARD A., "General Principles of Psychotherapy," *Veterans Administration Technical Bulletin,* TB 10-99, April 15, 1954. Veterans Administration Technical Bulletins, Series 10, vol. 7, 1954, Washington, March, 1955.

WHITE, A. A., "Special Report: Industrial Rehabilitation of Psychiatric Cases in England," *American Journal of Physical Medicine,* vol. 32, August, 1953, pp. 207-212.

SOCIAL SCIENCE

Empathy

ANIKEEFF, ALEXIS M., "Reciprocal Empathy: Mutual Understanding Among Conflict Groups," *Purdue University Studies in Higher Education,* 1951, no. 77, pp. 1-48.

AUSUBEL, DAVID P., "Sociempathy as a Function of Sociometric Status in an Adolescent Group," *Human Relations,* vol. 8, no. 1, 1955, pp. 75-84.

BELL, GRAHAM B., AND HARRY E. HALL, JR., "The Relationship Between Leadership and Empathy," *Journal of Abnormal and Social Psychology,* vol. 49, January, 1954, pp. 156-157.

DYMOND, ROSALIND F., "Personality and Empathy," *Journal of Consulting Psychology,* vol. 14, October, 1950, pp. 343-350.

KANDLER, HARRIET M., AND ROBERT W. HYDE, "Changes in Empathy in Student Nurses During the Psychiatric Affiliation," *Nursing Research,* vol. 2, June, 1953, pp. 33-36.

MCMURRY, ROBERT N., "Empathy: Management's Greatest Need," *Advanced Management,* vol. 18, July, 1953, pp. 6-11, 34.

NORMAN, RALPH D., AND PATRICIA AINSWORTH, "The Relationships Among Projection, Empathy, Reality, and Adjustment, Operationally Defined," *Journal of Consulting Psychology,* vol. 18, February, 1954, pp. 53-58.

REMMERS, H. H., "A Quantitative Index of Social-Psychological Empathy," *American Journal of Orthopsychiatry,* vol. 20, January, 1950, pp. 161-165.

WOODSON, JOSEPH F., *The Meaning and Development of Empathy.* Ph.D. thesis, Boston University, 1954.

Attitudes

ADAMS, EDWARD C., "Problems in Attitude Therapy in a Mental Hospital," *American Journal of Psychiatry,* vol. 105, December, 1948, pp. 456-461. (30)

BOGARDUS, EMORY S., "Social Distance: A Measuring Stick," *Survey,* vol. 56, May, 1926, pp. 169-170.

FIDLER, J. W., JR., "The Patient's View of Occupational Therapy," *American Journal of Occupational Therapy,* vol. 3, July-August, 1949, pp. 170-177.

FRANK, LAWRENCE K., "Individuality: A Threat and an Opportunity," *Journal of the National Association of Deans of Women,* vol. 18, January, 1955, pp. 51-56.

HOVLAND, CARL I., AND MUZAFER SHERIF, "Judgmental Phenomena and Scales of Attitude Measurement: Item Displacement in Thurstone Scales," *Journal of Abnormal and Social Psychology,* vol. 47, 1952, pp. 822-832. (21)

KINDWALL, JOSEF A., AND ELAINE F. KINDER, "Postscript on a Benign Psychosis," *Psychiatry,* vol. 3, August, 1940, pp. 527-533.

REES-THOMAS, W., "What the Patient Thinks," *Journal of Mental Science,* vol. 95, January, 1949, pp. 1-9.

SARNOFF, IRVING, AND DANIEL KATZ, "The Motivational Bases of Attitude Change," *Journal of Abnormal Social Psychology,* vol. 49, January, 1954, pp. 115-124.

THURSTONE, L. L., "The Measurement of Values," *Psychological Review,* vol. 61, 1954, pp. 47-58.

WEISS, M. OLGA, *Attitudes in Psychiatric Nursing Care.* G. P. Putnam's Sons, New York, 1954.

ZBOROWSKI, MARK, "Cultural Components in Responses to Pain," *Journal of Social Issues,* vol. 8, no. 4, 1952, pp. 16-30.

Interpersonal Relations

ADAMS, RICHARD N., "Personnel in Culture Change: A Test of a Hypothesis," *Social Forces,* vol. 30, 1951, pp. 185-189.

ARTER, RHETTA M., "The Human Relations Field Project as a Research Undertaking," *Journal of Educational Sociology,* vol. 27, February, 1954, pp. 249-254.

BALES, ROBERT F., *Interaction Process Analysis.* Rev. ed. Addison-Wesley Press, Inc., Cambridge, Mass., 1951.

BARRABEE, PAUL, "Evaluation of the Social Adjustment of Hospitalized Patients" in *Frontal Lobes and Schizophrenia,* edited by Milton Greenblatt and Harry C. Solomon. Springer Publishing Co., New York, 1953.

BARRABEE, PAUL, AND OTTO VON MERING, JR., "Ethnic Variations in Mental Stress in Families with Psychotic Children," *Social Problems,* vol. 1, October, 1953, pp. 48-53.

BEHYMER, ALICE F., "Interaction Patterns and Attitudes of Affiliate Students in a Psychiatric Hospital," *Nursing Outlook,* vol. 1, April, 1953, pp. 205-207.

BELL, GRAHAM B., AND R. L. FRENCH, "Consistency of Individual Leadership Position in Small Groups of Varying Membership," *Journal of Abnormal and Social Psychology,* vol. 45, 1950, pp. 764-767. (7)

BELLOWS, ROGER M., AND M. FRANCES ESTEP, *Employment Psychology:* The Interview. Rinehart and Co., New York, 1954.

BERKOWITZ, LEONARD, "Sharing in Small, Decision-Making Groups,"

Journal of Abnormal and Social Psychology, vol. 48, no. 2, 1953, pp. 231-238.

BORGATTA, EDGAR F., AND ROBERT F. BALES, "Interaction of Individuals in Reconstituted Groups," *Sociometry,* vol. 14, November, 1953, pp. 302-320.

"The Consistency of Subject Behavior and the Reliability of Scoring in Interaction Process Analysis," *American Sociological Review,* vol. 18, October, 1953, pp. 566-569.

BOWLBY, JOHN, "Critical Phases in the Development of Social Responses in Man and Other Animals," *New Biology,* no. 14, 1953, pp. 25-32.

BOYD, RICHARD W., T. BAKER, AND MILTON GREENBLATT, "Ward Social Behavior: An Analysis of Patient Interaction at Highest and Lowest Extremes," *Nursing Research,* vol. 3, October, 1954, pp. 77-80.

CAUDILL, WILLIAM, "Social Structure and Interaction Processes on a Psychiatric Ward," *American Journal of Orthopsychiatry,* vol. 22, April, 1952, pp. 314-334.

COHEN, JOHN, "Social Thinking," *Acta Psychologica,* vol. 9, 1953, pp. 146-158.

DI MASCIO, ALBERTO, "The Psychiatric Interview: A Sociophysiologic Study," *Diseases of the Nervous System,* vol. 16, January, 1955, pp. 4-9.

DODD, STUART D., AND JIRI NEHNEVAJSA, "Physical Dimensions of Social Distance," *Sociology and Social Research,* vol. 38, 1954, pp. 287-292.

DUNBAR, FLANDERS, *Emotions and Bodily Changes:* A Survey of Literature on Psychosomatic Inter-Relationships, 1910-1953. 4th ed. Columbia University Press, New York, 1954.

EICHORN, HERMAN, AND ROBERT W. HYDE, "Friendly and Unfriendly Interactions in the Mental Hospital," Chapter 12, *Explorations in Altruistic Love and Behavior:* A Symposium, edited by Pitirim A. Sorokin. Beacon Press, Boston, 1950, pp. 249-262.

EXPERT COMMITTEE ON MENTAL HEALTH, *Third Report.* World Health Organization, Technical Report, Series no. 73, Geneva, 1953, pp. 17-18.

FESTINGER, LEON, JANE TORREY, AND BEN WILLERMAN, "Self-Evaluation as a Function of Attraction to the Group," *Human Relations,* vol. 7, no. 2, 1954, pp. 161-174.

466 FROM CUSTODIAL TO THERAPEUTIC PATIENT CARE

FOOTE, NELSON N., AND COTTRELL, LEONARD S., JR., *Identity and Interpersonal Competence*. University of Chicago Press, Chicago, 1955. (An extensive bibliography included.)

GREENBLATT, MILTON, "Altruism in the Psychotherapeutic Relationship," Chapter 8, *Explorations in Altruistic Love and Behavior: A Symposium*, edited by Pitirim A. Sorokin. Beacon Press, Boston, 1950, pp. 188-193.

HARVEY, O. J., "An Experimental Approach to the Study of Status Relations in Informal Groups," *American Sociological Review*, vol. 18, August, 1953, pp. 357-367.

HYDE, ROBERT W., *Experiencing the Patient's Day:* A Manual for Psychiatric Hospital Personnel. G. P. Putnam's Sons, New York, 1955.

HYDE, ROBERT W., AND RICHARD H. YORK, "A Technique for Investigating Interpersonal Relations in a Mental Hospital," *Journal of Abnormal and Social Psychology*, vol. 43, July, 1948, pp. 287-299. (11)

KANDLER, HARRIET M., "A Study of Nurse-Patient Interaction in a Mental Hospital," *American Journal of Nursing*, vol. 52, September, 1952, pp. 1100-1103.

MORIMOTO, FRANCOISE R., THELMA S. BAKER, AND MILTON GREENBLATT, "Similarity of Socializing Interests as a Factor in Selection and Rejection of Psychiatric Patients," *Journal of Nervous and Mental Disease*, vol. 120, July and August, 1954, pp. 56-61.

MORIMOTO, FRANCOISE R., AND MILTON GREENBLATT, "Personnel Awareness of Patients' Socializing Capacity," *American Journal of Psychiatry*, vol. 110, December, 1953, pp. 443-447.

PARSONS, TALCOTT, AND RENÉE FOX, "Illness, Therapy, and the Modern Urban Family," *Journal of Social Issues*, vol. 8, no. 4, 1952, pp. 31-44.

POWELL, J. W., "Group Reading in Mental Hospitals," *Psychiatry*, vol. 13, May, 1950, pp. 213-226.

ROMANO, JOHN, "Patients' Attitudes and Behavior in Ward Round Teaching," *Journal of the American Medical Association*, vol. 117, August 30, 1941, pp. 664-667.

RUESCH, JURGEN, "Psychiatry and the Challenge of Communication: Part 1, Theoretical Symposium on Contributions of Interdisciplinary Research to Psychiatric Theory," *Psychiatry*, vol. 17, February, 1954, pp. 1-18.

"Social Technique, Social Status, and Social Change in Illness" in *Personality in Nature, Society, and Culture,* edited by Clyde Kluckhohn and H. A. Murray. Alfred A. Knopf, New York, 1948.

SCHWARTZ, MORRIS S., *Social Interaction on a Disturbed Ward of a Mental Hospital.* Ph.D. thesis, University of Chicago, 1951.

SCHWARTZ, MORRIS S., AND CHARLOTTE G. SCHWARTZ, "Problems in Participant Observation," *American Journal of Sociology,* vol. 60, January, 1955, pp. 343-353.

SEMRAD, ELVIN V., AND OTHERS, "A Study of the Doctor-Patient Relationship in Psychotherapy of Psychotic Patients," *Psychiatry,* vol. 15, November, 1952, pp. 377-385.

STANTON, ALFRED H., AND MORRIS S. SCHWARTZ, "Observations on Dissociation as Social Participation," *Psychiatry,* vol. 12, November, 1949, pp. 339-354.

STOUFFER, SAMUEL A., "Conflicting Roles and Leadership" in *Problems in Social Psychology,* edited by J. E. Hulett, Jr., and Ross Stagner. University of Illinois, Urbana, 1952, pp. 136-139.

SULLIVAN, HARRY STACK, *The Interpersonal Theory of Psychiatry,* edited by Helen S. Perry and Mary L. Gawel. W. W. Norton and Co., New York, 1953.

TAGIURI, RENATO, ROBERT R. BLAKE, AND JEROME S. BRUNER, "Some Determinants of the Perception of Positive and Negative Feelings in Others," *Journal of Abnormal and Social Psychology,* vol. 48, October, 1953, pp. 585-592.

THIBAUT, JOHN W., AND JOHN COULES, "The Role of Communication in the Reduction of Interpersonal Hostility," *Journal of Abnormal and Social Psychology,* vol. 47, 1952, pp. 770-777.

Socialization

BARRABEE, PAUL, "Evaluation of the Social Adjustment of Hospitalized Patients," Chapter 6, *Frontal Lobes and Schizophrenia,* edited by Milton Greenblatt and Harry C. Solomon. Springer Publishing Co., New York, 1953, pp. 78-86.

BERKOWITZ, LEONARD, "Sharing in Small, Decision-Making Groups," *Journal of Abnormal and Social Psychology,* vol. 48, no. 2, 1953, pp. 231-238.

BOCKOVEN, J. SANBOURNE, MILTON GREENBLATT, AND HARRY C. SOLOMON, "Social Behavior and Autonomic Physiology in Long-Standing Mental Illness," *Journal of Nervous and Mental Disease,* vol. 117, January, 1953, pp. 55-58.

"Treatment Results in the Major Psychoses," *New England Journal of Medicine,* vol. 244, March 8, 1951, pp. 357-361.

BOCKOVEN, J. SANBOURNE, AND HARRY C. SOLOMON, "Five Year Follow-up Study of One Hundred Patients Committed to the Boston Psychopathic Hospital," *New England Journal of Medicine,* vol. 251, July 15, 1954, pp. 81-85.

BOCKOVEN, J. SANBOURNE, ANNA R. PANDISCIO, AND HARRY C. SOLOMON, "Social Adjustment of Patients in the Community Three Years After Commitment to the Boston Psychopathic Hospital." (In preparation for publication by *Mental Hygiene.*)

DE SCHWEINITZ, KARL, JR., AND KENNETH W. THOMPSON, *Man and Modern Society: Conflict and Choice in the Industrial Era.* Henry Holt and Co., New York, 1953.

GOLDBERG, NAOMI, AND ROBERT W. HYDE, "Role-Playing in Psychiatric Training," *Journal of Social Psychology,* vol. 39, February, 1954, pp. 63-75.

KOHN, MELVIN L., AND JOHN A. CLAUSEN, "Social Isolation and Schizophrenia," *American Sociological Review,* vol. 20, June, 1955, pp. 265-273.

LESLIE, ROBERT C., "Growth Through Group Interaction," *Journal of Pastoral Care,* vol. 5, Spring, 1951, pp. 36-45.

MORIMOTO, FRANCOISE R., THELMA S. BAKER, AND MILTON GREENBLATT, "Similarity of Socializing Interests as a Factor in Selection and Rejection of Psychiatric Patients," *Journal of Nervous and Mental Disease,* vol. 120, July and August, 1954, pp. 56-61.

PARSONS, TALCOTT, "Some Comments on the State of the General Theory of Action," *American Sociological Review,* vol. 18, December, 1953, pp. 618-631.

PROEHL, ELIZABETH ANNE, "The Transition from Institutional to Social Adjustment," *American Sociological Review,* vol. 3, 1938, pp. 534-540.

RABIN, A. I., "Social Contacts of Psychiatric Patients: Some Preliminary Observations," *Psychiatric Quarterly Supplement,* vol. 19, part 2, 1945, pp. 177-183.

REDL, FRITZ, AND DAVID WINEMAN, *Children Who Hate:* The Disorganization and Breakdown of Behavior Controls. The Free Press, Glencoe, Ill., 1951.

RIESMAN, DAVID, *Individualism Reconsidered.* The Free Press, Glencoe, Ill., 1954. (Bibliography included.)

ROGERS, CARL R., *Client-Centered Therapy.* Houghton Mifflin Co., Boston, 1951.

SCHAUER, GERHARD, "Social Adjustment in a Mental Hospital Community," *Sociometry,* vol. 9, May-August, 1946, p. 144.

STEVENSON, IAN, AND THAIS MORRIS FISHER, "Techniques in the Vocational Rehabilitation of Chronically Unemployed Psychiatric Patients," *American Journal of Psychiatry,* vol. 3, October, 1954, pp. 289-300.

Group Dynamics

ADAMS, RICHARD N., "Personnel in Culture Change: A Test of a Hypothesis," *Social Forces,* vol. 30, 1951, pp. 185-189.

ARSENIAN, JOHN, AND ELVIN V. SEMRAD, "Application of Analytic Observations to Teaching of Group Dynamics," pp. 150-158 of "An Institute on Group Dynamics," Elvin V. Semrad (leader), *Journal of Psychiatric Social Work,* vol. 20, June, 1951, pp. 136-166.

BAIN, READ, "Action Research and Group Dynamics," *Social Forces,* vol. 30, October, 1951, pp. 1-10.

BENDIX, REINHARD, "Compliant Behavior and Individual Personality," *American Journal of Sociology,* vol. 58, 1952, pp. 292-303.

BENDIX, REINHARD, AND SEYMOUR M. LIPSET, editors, *Class, Status and Power: A Reader in Social Stratification.* The Free Press, Glencoe, Ill., 1953.

BENNE, KENNETH D., AND B. MUNTYAN, *Human Relations in Curriculum Change: Selected Readings with Special Emphasis on Group Development.* Dryden Press, New York, 1949.

BERKOWITZ, LEONARD, "Sharing in Small, Decision-Making Groups," *Journal of Abnormal and Social Psychology,* vol. 48, no. 2, 1953, pp. 231-238.

BINGHAM, WALTER V., "Expectancies," *Educational and Psychological Measurement,* vol. 13, 1953, pp. 47-53.

BLUM, MILTON L., "Group Dynamics in Industry," *International Journal of Group Psychotherapy,* vol. 4, 1954, pp. 172-176.

BORGATTA, EDGAR F., ROBERT F. BALES, AND ARTHUR S. COUCH, "Some Findings Relevant to the Great Man Theory of Leadership," *American Sociological Review,* vol. 19, December, 1954, pp. 755-759.

Boyd, Richard W., S. Stephen Kegeles, and Milton Greenblatt, "Outbreak of Gang Destructive Behavior on a Psychiatric Ward," *Journal of Nervous and Mental Disease*, vol. 120, November-December, 1954, pp. 338-342. (7)

Carter, L. R., "Leadership and Small-Group Behavior" in *Group Relations at the Crossroads*, edited by Muzafer Sherif and M. O. Wilson. Harper and Bros., New York, 1953.

Cohen, Oscar, "The Application of Social Research to Intergroup Relations," *Social Problems*, vol. 2, July, 1954, pp. 20-25.

Davis, Kingsley, "Mental Hygiene and the Class Structure," *Psychiatry*, vol. 1, February, 1938, pp. 55-65.

Festinger, Leon, and Harold H. Kelley, *Changing Attitudes Through Social Contact: An Experimental Study of a Housing Project*. Research Center for Group Dynamics, Institute for Social Research, Publication no. 1, University of Michigan Press, Ann Arbor, 1951.

Frank, Lawrence K., "Dilemma of Leadership," *Psychiatry*, vol. 2, August, 1939, pp. 343-361.

"'Facing Reality' in Family Life," *Mental Hygiene*, vol. 21, April, 1937, pp. 224-230.

"Freedom for the Personality," *Psychiatry*, vol. 3, August, 1940, pp. 341-349.

Greco, Marshall C., *Group Life: The Nature and Treatment of Its Specific Conflicts*. Philosophical Library, New York, 1950. (Includes bibliography prepared by Ronald Lippitt, Research Center for Group Dynamics, University of Michigan.)

Gross, Neal, William E. Martin, and John G. Darley, "Studies of Group Behavior: Leadership Structures in Small Organized Groups," *Journal of Abnormal and Social Psychology*, vol. 48, July, 1953, pp. 429-432. (7)

Grossack, Martin M., "Some Effects of Cooperation and Competition upon Small Group Behavior," *Journal of Abnormal and Social Psychology*, vol. 49, July, 1954, pp. 341-348.

Haring, Douglass G., editor, *Personal Character and Cultural Milieu: A Collection of Readings*. Syracuse University Press, Syracuse, N.Y., 1948.

Himes, Joseph S., *Social Planning in America: A Dynamic Interpretation*. Doubleday and Co., New York, 1954. (Bibliography included.)

HORWITZ, MURRAY, "The Conceptual Status of Group Dynamics," *Review of Educational Research,* vol. 23, October, 1953, pp. 309-328.

HYDE, ROBERT W., "Factors in Group Motivation in a Mental Hospital," *Journal of Nervous and Mental Disease,* vol. 117, March, 1953, pp. 212-225. (4)

JAQUES, ELLIOTT, *The Changing Culture of a Factory.* Dryden Press, New York, 1952.

JENKINS, R. L., AND FRANK J. CURRAN, "The Evolution and Persistence of Groups in a Psychiatric Observation Ward," *Journal of Social Psychology,* vol. 12, November, 1940, pp. 279-289.

LEVINSON, DANIEL J., "The Intergroup Relations Workshop: Its Psychological Aims and Effects," *Journal of Psychology,* vol. 38, July, 1954, pp. 103-126. (11)

LEWIN, KURT, "Frontiers in Group Dynamics: II, Channels of Group Life; Social Planning and Action Research," *Human Relations,* vol. 1, November, 1947, pp. 143-153.

"Group Decision and Social Change" in *Readings in Social Psychology,* edited by Guy E. Swanson, Theodore M. Newcomb, and Eugene L. Hartley. Henry Holt and Co., New York, 1947.

Resolving Social Conflicts: Selected Papers on Group Dynamics," edited by Gertrud Weiss Lewin. Harper and Bros., New York, 1948.

LIPPITT, RONALD, "Action-Research and the Value of the Social Scientist" in "Values and the Social Scientist: A Symposium," *Journal of Social Issues,* vol. 6, no. 4, 1950, pp. 50-55.

LIPPITT, RONALD, AND R. K. WHITE, "An Experimental Study of Leadership and Group Life" in *Readings in Social Psychology,* edited by Guy E. Swanson, Theodore M. Newcomb, and Eugene L. Hartley. Henry Holt and Co., New York, 1947.

MANN, JAMES, "An Analytically Oriented Study of Groups," pp. 137-143 of "An Institute on Group Dynamics," by Elvin V. Semrad (leader), *Journal of Psychiatric Social Work,* vol. 20, June, 1951, pp. 136-166. (Bibliography included.)

MOORE, WILBERT E., *Industrial Relations and the Social Order.* Macmillan Co., New York, 1949.

MURPHY, GARDNER, "Human Potentialities," *Journal of Social Issues,* vol. 7, Supplement Series, 1953, pp. 4-19.

MURRAY, JANET P., AND CLYDE E. MURRAY, *Guide Lines for Group Leaders*, Whiteside, Inc., New York, 1954. (Bibliography included.)

NATIONAL TRAINING LABORATORY IN GROUP DEVELOPMENT, *Role-Playing in Human Relations*. 16 mm. motion picture film, black and white, sound, approx. 1200 ft., 25 min., 1949. (Available through Communication Materials Center, Columbia University Press, New York.)

POLANSKY, NORMAN, RONALD LIPPITT, AND FRITZ REDL, "An Investigation of Behavioral Contagion in Groups," *Human Relations*, vol. 3, November, 1950, pp. 319-348.

SCHRAG, CLARENCE, "Leadership Among Prison Inmates," *American Sociological Review*, vol. 19, February, 1954, pp. 37-42.

SEMRAD, ELVIN V., "An Institute on Group Dynamics," *Journal of Psychiatric Social Work*, vol. 20, June, 1951, pp. 136-166.

SEMRAD, ELVIN V., AND JOHN ARSENIAN, "The Use of Group Processes in Teaching Group Dynamics," *American Journal of Psychiatry*, vol. 108, 1951-1952, pp. 358-363. (Bibliography included.)

SHERIF, MUZAFER, AND CAROLYN W. SHERIF, *Groups in Harmony and Tension:* An Integration of Studies of Intergroup Relations. Harper and Bros., New York, 1953. (Bibliography included.)

SHERIF, MUZAFER, AND M. O. WILSON, *Group Relations at the Crossroads*. Harper and Bros., New York, 1953.

SIMMONS, LEO W., "The Dynamic Psychology of the Group and the Shaping of Individual Behavior" in *Psychological Dynamics of Health Education:* Proceedings of Eastern States Health Education Conference, 1950. Columbia University Press, New York, 1951, pp. 55-68.

SLAVSON, SAMUEL R., "Remarks on Group Psychotherapy and Community Mental Health," *International Journal of Group Psychotherapy*, vol. 4, 1954, pp. 210-217.

STANDISH, CHRISTOPHER T., AND ELVIN V. SEMRAD, "Group Psychotherapy with Psychotics," pp. 143-150 of "An Institute on Group Dynamics," Elvin V. Semrad (leader), *Journal of Psychiatric Social Work*, vol. 20, June, 1951, pp. 136-166. (Bibliography included.)

THELEN, HERBERT ARNOLD, *Dynamics of Groups at Work*. University of Chicago Press, Chicago, 1954.

WHYTE, WILLIAM FOOTE, "Corner Boys: A Study of Clique Behavior," *American Journal of Sociology,* vol. 46, no. 5, 1941, pp. 647-664.

Behavior Study

BAYARD, JEAN, AND GERALD R. PASCAL, "Studies of Prognostic Criteria in the Case Records of Hospitalized Mental Patients: Affective Expression," *Journal of Consulting Psychology,* vol. 18, April, 1954, pp. 122-126. (15)

BETTELHEIM, BRUNO, AND EMMY SYLVESTER, "A Therapeutic Milieu," *American Journal of Orthopsychiatry,* vol. 18, April, 1948, pp. 191-206.

BIDDLE, W. EARL, "The Nurse and 'Spontaneous' Recovery in Schizophrenia," *American Journal of Nursing,* vol. 49, no. 6, 1949, pp. 371-372. (9)

CAMERON, WILLIAM B., AND THOMAS C. McCORMICK, "Concepts of Security and Insecurity," *American Journal of Sociology,* vol. 59, May, 1954, pp. 556-564.

CHAPPLE, ELIOT D., "The Measurement of Interpersonal Behavior," *Transactions* of the New York Academy of Sciences, Series II, vol. 4, May, 1942, pp. 222-233.

"The Standard Experimental (Stress) Interview as Used in Interaction Chronograph Investigations," *Human Organization,* vol. 12, Summer, 1953, pp. 23-32.

COTTRELL, LEONARD S., JR., "The Analysis of Situational Fields in Social Psychology," *American Sociological Review,* vol. 7, June, 1942, pp. 370-382.

DANIEL, ROBERT S., AND C. M. LOUTTIT, *Professional Problems in Psychology.* Prentice Hall, Inc., New York, 1953.

DREYER, ALBERT S., "Aspiration Behavior as Influenced by Expectation and Group Comparison," *Human Relations,* vol. 7, no. 2, 1954, pp. 175-190.

DUNBAR, FLANDERS, *Emotions and Bodily Changes: A Survey of Literature on Psychosomatic Inter-Relationships, 1910-1953.* 4th ed. Columbia University Press, New York, 1954. (Bibliography included.)

FINNEY, BEN C., "A Scale to Measure Interpersonal Relationships in Group Psychotherapy," *Group Psychotherapy,* vol. 7, May, 1954, pp. 52-66.

Fox, Renée C., *A Sociological Study of Stress:* Physician and Patient on a Research Ward. Ph.D. thesis, Radcliffe College, Cambridge, Mass., 1953.

Frank, Lawrence K., "The Promotion of Mental Health," *Annals of the American Academy of Political and Social Science,* vol. 286, March, 1953, pp. 167-174.

Goodrich, Anne T., Jules Henry, and D. Wells Goodrich, "Laughter in Psychiatric Staff Conferences: A Sociopsychiatric Analysis," *American Journal of Orthopsychiatry,* vol. 24, 1954, pp. 175-184.

Goodrich, W., J. Sanbourne Bockoven, and Robert W. Hyde, "Behavioral Characteristics of Recovery from a Psychosis," *Occupational Therapy and Rehabilitation,* vol. 30, June, 1951, pp. 147-153.

Goodstein, Leonard D., "Intellectual Rigidity and Social Attitudes," *Journal of Abnormal and Social Psychology,* vol. 48, July, 1953, pp. 345-353. (17)

Grosser, Daniel, Norman Polansky, and Ronald Lippitt, "A Laboratory Study of Behavioral Contagion," *Human Relations,* vol. 4, May, 1951, pp. 115-142. (Reprinted in *Readings in Social Group Work,* edited by Dorothea F. Sullivan, Association Press, New York, 1952, pp. 284-317.)

Hoffman, Martin L., "Some Psychodynamic Factors in Compulsive Conformity," *Journal of Abnormal and Social Psychology,* vol. 48, July, 1953, pp. 383-393.

Holt, William L., Jr., and Winifred M. Holt, "Long-term Prognosis in Mental Illness: A Thirty-Year Follow-up of 141 Mental Patients," *American Journal of Psychiatry,* vol. 108, April, 1952, pp. 735-739.

Honigmann, John J., *Culture and Personality.* Harper and Bros., New York, 1954. (Extensive bibliography included.)

Horwitz, Murray, and Dorwin Cartwright, "A Projective Method for the Diagnosis of Group Properties," *Human Relations,* vol. 6, no. 4, 1953, pp. 397-410.

Jahoda, Marie, Morton Deutsch, and Stuart W. Cook, editors, *Research Methods in Social Relations with Especial Reference to Prejudice.* 2 vols. Dryden Press, New York, 1951.

Kelley, Harold H., and Martin M. Shapiro, "An Experiment on Conformity to Group Norms Where Conformity Is Detrimental to Group Achievement," *American Sociological Review,* vol. 19, December, 1954, pp. 667-677.

LEWIN, KURT, RONALD LIPPITT, AND R. K. WHITE, "Patterns of Aggressive Behavior in Experimentally Created 'Social Climates,'" *Journal of Social Psychology,* vol. 10, 1939, pp. 271-299.

LUCERO, RUBEL J., AND BILL T. MEYER, "A Behavior Rating Scale Suitable for Use in Mental Hospitals," *Journal of Clinical Psychology,* vol. 7, July, 1951, pp. 250-254.

MAAS, HENRY S., EDITH VARON, AND DAVID ROSENTHAL, "A Technique for Studying the Social Behavior of Schizophrenics," *Journal of Abnormal and Social Psychology,* vol. 46, 1951, pp. 119-123.

MEAD, MARGARET, editor, *Cultural Patterns and Technical Change.* Columbia University Press, New York, 1954.

MEADOW, ARNOLD, "Discomfort-Relief Quotient as a Measure of Tension and Adjustment in Schizophrenia," *Journal of Abnormal and Social Psychology,* vol. 47, July, 1952, pp. 658-661.

MELBIN, MURRAY, "The Action-Interaction Chart," *Human Organization,* vol. 12, Spring, 1953, pp. 34-35.

MURPHY, GARDNER, *Personality:* A Biosocial Approach to Origins and Structure. Harper and Bros., New York, 1947.

OFFICE OF STRATEGIC SERVICES ASSESSMENT STAFF, *Assessment of Men.* Rinehart and Co., New York, 1948.

PEAR, T. H., "The Social Psychology of Everyday Life" in *Current Trends in British Psychology,* by C. A. Mace and P. E. Vernon. Methuen and Co., London, 1953, pp. 113-124.

PETERSON, DONALD R., "Predicting Hospitalization of Psychiatric Outpatients," *Journal of Abnormal and Social Psychology,* vol. 49, 1954, pp. 260-265.

SARASON, SEYMOUR B., *The Clinical Interaction:* With Special Reference to the Rorschach. Harper and Bros., New York, 1954. (Bibliography included.)

SCHWARTZ, MORRIS S., AND ALFRED H. STANTON, "A Social Psychological Study of Incontinence," *Psychiatry,* vol. 13, November, 1950, pp. 399-416.

SEIDENFELD, MORTON A., "Medical Psychology" in *Medical Progress,* by M. Fishbein. Blakiston Co., Philadelphia, 1954, pp. 299-313.

STAINBROOK, EDWARD, "A Cross-cultural Evaluation of Depressive Reactions" in *Depression,* edited by Paul E. Hoch and Joseph Zubin. Grune and Stratton, New York, 1954, pp. 39-50.

THURSTON, JOAN, "The Patients Rule Themselves," *Smith College Studies in Social Work*, vol. 22, October, 1951, pp. 27-51.

VELD-LANGVELD, H. M., "De Techniek van Participerend Waarnemen" (The Technique of Participant Observation), *Mens en Maatschappij*, vol. 29, March, 1954, pp. 96-103.

WYATT, FREDERICK, "Clinical Psychology," *American Journal of Psychiatry*, vol. 111, January, 1955, pp. 508-510. (17)
"Die Sozialen Entwicklungslinien der Klinischen Psychologie in den Vereinigten Staaten" (The Social Development of Clinical Psychology in the United States), *Soziale Welt*, vol. 4, no. 3, 1953, pp. 251-260.

ZBOROWSKI, MARK, "Cultural Components in Responses to Pain," *Journal of Social Issues*, vol. 8, no. 4, 1952, pp. 16-30.

Psychoanalysis

DEVEREUX, GEORGE, "Applied Psychoanalysis: II, Social Sciences," *The Annual Survey of Psychoanalysis*, vol. 2, 1951, pp. 493-538.

FROMM-REICHMANN, FRIEDA, "Problems of Therapeutic Management in a Psychoanalytic Hospital," *Psychoanalytic Quarterly*, vol. 16, 1947, pp. 325-356.

HALL, CALVIN S., AND GARDNER LINDZEY, "Psychoanalytic Theory and Its Applications in the Social Sciences" in *Handbook of Social Psychology*, edited by Gardner Lindzey. Addison-Wesley Publishing Co., Cambridge, Mass., 1954.

JAQUES, ELLIOTT, "On the Dynamics of Social Structure: A Contribution to the Psychoanalytical Study of Social Phenomena," *Human Relations*, vol. 6, 1953, pp. 3-24.

MENNINGER, WILLIAM C., "Psychoanalytic Principles Applied to the Treatment of Hospitalized Patients," *Bulletin of the Menninger Clinic*, vol. 1, 1937, pp. 35-43.

MUENSTERBERGER, WARNER, AND SIDNEY AXELRAD, editors, *Psychoanalysis and the Social Sciences*. International Universities Press, New York, vol. 4, 1955.

POLLAK, OTTO, AND CONTRIBUTORS, *Social Science and Psychotherapy for Children:* Contributions of the Behavior Sciences to Practice in a Psychoanalytically Oriented Child Guidance Clinic. Russell Sage Foundation, New York, 1952.

SIMMEL, E., "Psychoanalytic Treatment in a Sanatorium," *International Journal of Psychoanalysis*, vol. 10, 1929, pp. 70-89.

Psychiatric Theory

APPEL, KENNETH E., "Presidential Address: The Present Challenge of Psychiatry," *American Journal of Psychiatry*, vol. 111, July, 1954, pp. 1-12.

BURGESS, ERNEST W., "Social Relations, Activities and Personal Adjustment," *American Journal of Sociology*, vol. 59, January, 1954, pp. 352-360.

CABOT, RICHARD C., AND RUSSELL L. DICKS, *The Art of Ministering to the Sick*. Macmillan Co., New York, 1949.

CAUDILL, WILLIAM, "Applied Anthropology in Medicine" in *Anthropology Today: An Encyclopedic Inventory*, edited by Alfred L. Kroeber. University of Chicago Press, Chicago, 1953.

DERSHIMER, F. W., "Review of Psychiatric Progress, 1953: Psychiatry in Industry," *American Journal of Psychiatry*, vol. 110, 1954, pp. 527-528.

DUNHAM, H. WARREN, "Social Psychiatry," *American Sociological Review*, vol. 13, April, 1948, pp. 183-197.

FRANK, LAWRENCE K., "Social Order and Psychiatry," *American Journal of Orthopsychiatry*, vol. 11, October, 1941, pp. 620-627.

"Society as the Patient," *American Journal of Sociology*, vol. 42, November, 1936, pp. 335-344.

GILBERT, DORIS C., *Ideologies Concerning Mental Illness:* A Sociopsychological Study of Mental Hospital Personnel. Ph.D. thesis, Radcliffe College, Cambridge, Mass., 1954.

GOLDHAMER, HERBERT, AND ANDREW MARSHALL, *Psychosis and Civilization:* Studies in the Frequency of Mental Disease. The Free Press, Glencoe, Ill., 1953.

GORDON, JOHN E., "The Biological and Social Sciences in an Epidemiology of Mental Disorder," *American Journal of the Medical Sciences*, vol. 223, 1952, pp. 316-343.

HARRIS, NOEL G., editor, *Modern Trends in Psychological Medicine*. Paul B. Hoeber, New York, 1948.

HENRY, NELSON B., editor, *Mass Media and Education:* Part II of the 53rd Yearbook of the National Society for the Study of Education. University of Chicago Press, Chicago, 1954.

HOLLINGSHEAD, AUGUST B., R. ELLIS, AND E. KIRBY, "Social Mobility and Mental Illness," *American Sociological Review*, vol. 19, October, 1954, pp. 577-584.

HOLLINGSHEAD, AUGUST B., AND FREDERICK C. REDLICH, "Social Stratification and Schizophrenia," *American Sociological Review,* vol. 19, June, 1954, pp. 302-306.

HUSTON, P. E., "The Relations of Psychiatry and Psychology," *American Journal of Psychiatry,* vol. 110, 1954, pp. 814-816.

JACO, E. GARTLY, "The Social Isolation Hypothesis and Schizophrenia," *American Sociological Review,* vol. 19, October, 1954, pp. 567-577.

JAHODA, MARIE, "Toward a Social Psychology of Mental Health" in *Problems of Infancy and Childhood:* Transactions of the Fourth Conference, Supplement II, Josiah Macy, Jr. Foundation, New York, 1950.

JOHNSON, CHARLES S., "The Influence of Social Science on Psychiatry" in *Mid-Century Psychiatry:* An Overview, edited by Roy R. Grinker. C. C. Thomas, Springfield, Ill., 1953, pp. 144-156.

LEMERT, EDWIN M., *Social Pathology:* A Systematic Approach to the Theory of Sociopathic Behavior. McGraw-Hill Book Co., New York, 1951.

MYERS, JEROME K., AND LESLIE SCHAFFER, "Social Stratification and Psychiatric Practice: A Study of an Out-Patient Clinic," *American Sociological Review,* vol. 19, June, 1954, pp. 307-310.

RAINES, G. N., AND J. H. ROHRER, "The Operational Matrix of Psychiatric Practice," *American Journal of Psychiatry,* vol. 111, April, 1955, pp. 721-733.

ROSS, MATHEW, "Some Psychiatric Aspects of Senescence: A Review of the Literature," *Psychiatric Quarterly,* vol. 28, January, 1954, pp. 93-112. (Bibliography included.)

RUESCH, JURGEN, AND GREGORY BATESON, *Communication:* The Social Matrix of Psychiatry. W. W. Norton and Co., New York, 1951.

SEIDENFELD, MORTON A., *Psychological Aspects of Medical Care.* C. C. Thomas, Springfield, Ill., 1949.

SIMMONS, LEO W., AND HAROLD G. WOLFF, *Social Science in Medicine.* Russell Sage Foundation, New York, 1954. (Bibliography included.)

STANTON, ALFRED H., "Psychiatric Theory and Institutional Context: Part II, Theoretical Symposium on Contributions of Interdisciplinary Research to Psychiatric Theory," *Psychiatry,* vol. 17, February, 1954, pp. 19-26.

SULLIVAN, HARRY STACK, *Conceptions of Modern Psychiatry.* William Alanson White Psychiatric Foundation, Washington, 1947.

Historical and Theoretical

BOWMAN, KARL M., "Legal and Welfare Aspects of Psychiatric Care," *Proceedings* of the Fourth International Congress on Mental Health, 1951, pp. 153-164.

CABOT, HUGH, JOSEPH A. KAHL, in association with Joseph C. Bailey and others, *Human Relations, Concepts and Cases in Concrete Social Science.* Harvard University Press, Cambridge, Mass., 1953.

CAMERON, WILLIAM B., AND THOMAS C. McCORMICK, "Concepts of Security and Insecurity," *American Journal of Sociology,* vol. 59, May, 1954, pp. 556-564.

CHAPPLE, ELIOT D., AND CARLETON S. COON, *Principles of Anthropology.* Henry Holt and Co., New York, 1942, pp. 3-69.

CLAUSEN, JOHN A., AND MELVIN L. KOHN, "The Ecological Approach in Social Psychiatry," *American Journal of Sociology,* vol. 60, September, 1954, pp. 140-151.

CURTI, MERLE E., *Changing Concepts of Leadership in the Past Forty Years* (Nursing Education Bulletin). Teachers College, Columbia University, Bureau of Publications, New York, February, 1940.

DURKHEIM, EMILE, *The Division of Labor in Society.* The Free Press, Glencoe, Ill., 1947.

KROEBER, A. L., editor, *Anthropology Today:* An Encyclopedic Inventory. University of Chicago Press, Chicago, 1953.

LAZARSFELD, PAUL F., AND MORRIS ROSENBERG, editors, *The Language of Social Research:* A Reader in the Methodology of the Social Sciences. The Free Press, Glencoe, Ill., 1955.

LEMKAU, PAUL V., "The Epidemiological Study of Mental Illnesses and Mental Health," *American Journal of Psychiatry,* vol. 111, May, 1955, pp. 801-809. (41)

LEVINSON, DANIEL J., AND DORIS C. GILBERT, "Studies in Ideology: Part I, 'Custodial' Mental Illness Ideology and Its Relation to Personality." (Paper read at American Psychological Association, New York, September, 1954; mimeographed by Boston Psychopathic Hospital.)

MacKay, Roland P., editor, *The Year Book of Neurology, Psychiatry, and Neurosurgery, 1953-1954*. The Year Book Publishers, Inc., Chicago, 1954.

McKinney, John C., "Methodological Convergence of Mead, Lundberg, and Parsons," *American Journal of Sociology*, vol. 59, May, 1954, pp. 565-574.

Merton, Robert K., *Social Theory and Social Structure:* Toward the Codification of Theory and Research. The Free Press, Glencoe, Ill., 1949.

Mihanovich, Clement S., editor, *Social Theorists*. Bruce Publishing Co., Milwaukee, 1953. (Each chapter includes a bibliography, and the appendix, "Who's Who in Social Theory," gives accounts of 80 significant men in history of social theory.)

Moreno, Jacob L., "Interpersonal Therapy, Group Psychotherapy and the Function of the Unconscious," *Group Psychotherapy*, vol. 7, December, 1954, pp. 191-204.

Myrdal, Gunnar, "The Relation Between Social Theory and Social Policy," *British Journal of Sociology*, vol. 4, 1953, pp. 210-242.

Newcomb, Theodore M., *Social Psychology*. Dryden Press, New York, 1950.

Opler, Marvin K., "Cultural Perspectives in Mental Health Research," *American Journal of Orthopsychiatry*, vol. 25, January, 1955, pp. 51-59. (24)

Parsons, Talcott, *The Structure of Social Action:* A Study in Social Theory with Special Reference to a Group of Recent European Writers. 2d ed. The Free Press, Glencoe, Ill., 1949.

Podolsky, Edward, "John Conolly and the Introduction of Nonrestraint in Psychiatric Treatment," *American Journal of Psychiatry*, vol. 108, May, 1952, pp. 857-858.

Potter, David Morris, *People of Plenty:* Economic Abundance and the American Character. University of Chicago Press, Chicago, 1954.

Robinson, George Canby, *The Patient as a Person:* A Study of the Social Aspects of Illness. Commonwealth Fund, New York, 1939.

Russell, Bertrand, *The Impact of Science on Society*. Simon and Schuster, New York, 1953.

Santos, Elvin H., and Edward Stainbrook, "A History of Psychiatric Nursing in the Nineteenth Century," Part 1, *Journal of the*

History of Medicine and Allied Sciences, vol. 4, Spring, 1949, pp. 48-74.

SAPIR, EDWARD, *Selected Writings in Language, Culture, and Personality,* edited by David G. Mandelbaum. University of California Press, Berkeley and Los Angeles, 1949.

SPIEGEL, E. E., editor, *Progress in Neurology and Psychiatry.* Grune and Stratton, New York, 1953.

SWANSON, GUY E., THEODORE M. NEWCOMB, AND EUGENE L. HARTLEY, editors, *Readings in Social Psychology.* Henry Holt and Co., New York, 1947.

THOMAS, WILLIAM I., AND FLORIAN ZNANIECKI, "Methodological Note" in *A Polish Peasant in Europe and America:* Monograph of an Immigrant Group. University of Chicago Press, Chicago, 1918.

VALENTINE, ALAN C., *The Age of Conformity.* Henry Regnery Co., Chicago, 1954.

VOLKART, EDMUND H., editor, *William Isaac Thomas:* His Contributions to Theory and Social Research. Social Science Research Council, New York, 1951.

WALK, ALEXANDER, "Some Aspects of the 'Moral Treatment' of the Insane up to 1854," *Journal of Mental Science,* vol. 100, October, 1954, pp. 807-837.

WILMER, HARRY A., AND RICHARD E. SCAMMON, "Neuropsychiatric Patients Reported Cured at St. Bartholomew's Hospital in the Twelfth Century," *Journal of Nervous and Mental Disease,* vol. 119, 1954, pp. 1-22.

WILSON, LOGAN, AND WILLIAM L. KOLB, *Sociological Analysis.* Harcourt, Brace and Co., New York, 1949.

WOODWARD, JULIAN L., "Changing Ideas on Mental Illness and Its Treatment," *American Sociological Review,* vol. 16, 1951, pp. 443-454.

ZILBOORG, GREGORY, "The Changing Concept of Man in Present-Day Psychiatry," *American Journal of Psychiatry,* vol. 111, December, 1954, pp. 445-448.

Sociometrics

AUSUBEL, DAVID P., "Sociempathy as a Function of Sociometric Status in an Adolescent Group," *Human Relations,* vol. 8, no. 1, 1955, pp. 75-84.

BORGATTA, EDGAR F., "Analysis of Social Interaction and Sociometric Perception," *Sociometry*, vol. 17, 1954, pp. 7-32. (31)

GEE, WILSON, *Social Science Research Methods*. Appleton-Century-Crofts Co., New York, 1950.

HEINICKE, CHRISTOPH, AND ROBERT F. BALES, "Developmental Trends in the Structure of Small Groups," *Sociometry*, vol. 16, 1953, pp. 7-38.

HYDE, ROBERT W., J. SANBOURNE BOCKOVEN, AND PAUL BARRABEE, "Methods and Procedures Used in Sociometric Investigation," Chapter 5, *Frontal Lobes and Schizophrenia*, edited by Milton Greenblatt and Harry C. Solomon. Springer Publishing Co., New York, 1954.

KANDLER, HARRIET M., AND ROBERT W. HYDE, "A Socialization Activity Index for a Mental Hospital," *The Nursing World*, vol. 125, August, 1951, pp. 343-345.

KEGELES, S. STEPHEN, ROBERT W. HYDE, AND MILTON GREENBLATT, "Sociometric Network on an Acute Psychiatric Ward," *Group Psychotherapy*, vol. 5, April-November, 1952, pp. 91-110.

MILLER, DELBERT C., "A Role Playing Workshop for Business and Government Administrators: Its Research Implications," *Group Psychotherapy*, vol. 6, 1953, pp. 50-62.

MORENO, JACOB L., *Sociometry, Experimental Method and the Science of Society:* An Approach to a New Political Orientation. Beacon House, Inc., Beacon, N.Y., 1951.

Who Shall Survive: Foundations of Sociometry, Group Psychotherapy and Sociodrama. Beacon House, Inc., Beacon, N.Y., 1935. (Bibliography included.)

POLANSKY, NORMAN, AND OTHERS, "The Use of Near-Sociometric Data in Research on Group Treatment Processes," *Sociometry*, vol. 13, no. 1, 1950, pp. 39-62.

RICHMOND, WINIFRED, "Sociometric Tests in a Training School for Nurses," *Sociometry*, vol. 13, no. 1, 1950, pp. 29-38.

SMITH, MARION R., JOHN E. BRYANT, AND DORIS TWITCHELL-ALLEN, "Sociometric Changes in a Group of Adult Female Psychotics Following an Intensive Socializing Program," *Group Psychotherapy*, vol. 4, no. 3, 1951, pp. 145-155.

SULLIVAN, HARRY STACK, "Socio-Psychiatric Research: Its Implications for the Schizophrenia Problem and for Mental Hygiene,"

American Journal of Psychiatry, vol. 10, May, 1931, pp. 977-991.

Research Organization

ACKOFF, RUSSELL L., *The Design of Social Research*. University of Chicago Press, Chicago, 1953. (Bibliography included.)

BERG, IRWIN A., "The Use of Human Subjects in Psychological Research," *American Psychologist*, vol. 9, March, 1954, pp. 108-111.

BORDIN, EDWARD S., "Measurement Problems in Process Research on Psychotherapy," *Journal of Consulting Psychology*, vol. 18, April, 1954, pp. 79-82.

BROSIN, HENRY W., "On Discovery and Experiment in Psychiatry," *American Journal of Psychiatry*, vol. 111, February, 1955, pp. 561-575. (Bibliography included.)

CLANCY, JOHN, AND OTHERS, "Design and Planning in Psychiatric Research as Illustrated by the Weyburn Chronic Nucleotide Project," *Bulletin of the Menninger Clinic*, vol. 18, 1954, pp. 147-153.

DODDS, HAROLD W., "The Dangers of Project Research," *Social Problems*, vol. 1, January, 1954, pp. 90-93.

FESTINGER, LEON, AND DANIEL KATZ, editors, *Research Methods in the Behavioral Sciences*. Dryden Press, New York, 1953. (Each chapter includes a bibliography.)

FOX, HARLAND, "Leadership and Executive Development: A Bibliography," *University of Minnesota Industrial Relations Center Bulletin*, no. 14, 1954.

GLOVER, EDWARD, "Team-Research on Delinquency: A Psychoanalytical Commentary," *British Journal of Delinquency*, vol. 4, January, 1954, pp. 173-188.

GOTTSCHALK, L. R., CLYDE KLUCKHOHN, AND ROBERT ANGELL, *The Use of Personal Documents in History, Anthropology, and Sociology*. Social Science Research Council, New York, 1947.

HYDE, ROBERT W., "The Twenty-Five Books That Our Occupational Therapy Department Has Found Most Useful," *American Journal of Occupational Therapy*, vol. 6, July-August, 1952, pp. 146-150.

KAPLAN, LOUIS, *Research Materials in the Social Sciences: An Annotated Guide for Graduate Students*. University of Wisconsin Press, Madison, 1939.

MARKS, MORTON, AND LEE B. GREENE, "Rehabilitation" in *Progress in Neurology and Psychiatry,* edited by E. A. Spiegel. Grune and Stratton, New York, 1953, vol. 8, pp. 568-575.

SPINDLER, GEORGE, AND WALTER GOLDSCHMIDT, "Experimental Design in the Study of Culture Change," *Southwestern Journal of Anthropology,* vol. 8, 1952, pp. 68-83.

STOUFFER, SAMUEL A., "Measurement in Sociology," *American Sociological Review,* vol. 18, December, 1953, pp. 591-604.

STRODTBECK, FRED L., AND A. PAUL HARE, "Bibliography of Small Group Research," *Sociometry,* vol. 17, May, 1954, pp. 107-178.

WHYTE, WILLIAM FOOTE, "Observational Field-Work Methods," Chapter 14, *Research Methods in Social Relations,* Part 2, edited by Marie Jahoda, Morton Deutsch, and Stuart W. Cook. Dryden Press, New York, 1951.

WORMSER, MARGOT H., AND CLAIRE SELLTIZ, "Community Self-Surveys: Principles and Procedures," Chapter 19, *Research Methods in Social Relations* (cited above).

INDEX

Index

NOTE. Boston Psychopathic Hospital offers the central theme of pages 37–245; Bedford Veterans Administration Hospital, of pages 249–346; Metropolitan State Hospital, of pages 349–403. Index citations within these page numbers may normally be understood as having special reference to these respective institutions.